Edexcel IGCSE
Chemistry

Student Book

Jim Clark

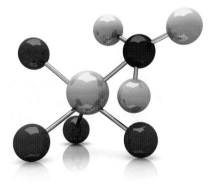

A PEARSON COMPANY

Published by Pearson Education Limited, a company incorporated in England and Wales, having its registered office at Edinburgh Gate, Harlow, Essex, CM20 2JE. Registered company number: 872828

www.heinemann.co.uk

Edexcel is a registered trade mark of Edexcel Limited

Text © Jim Clark, 2009

This edition first published 2009

12 11 10

10 9 8 7 6 5

British Library Cataloguing in Publication Data
A catalogue record for this book is available from the British Library.

ISBN 978 0 435966 89 8

Designed by Richard Ponsford

Typeset by HL Studios

Cover design by Creative Monkey

Cover photo/illustration © Digital Vision

Printed in China (SWTC/05)

Acknowledgements
My thanks to Pete Seymour and the other members of the Truro School Chemistry Department for their help in producing my lab-based photographs.

The author and publisher would like to thank the following individuals and organisations for permission to reproduce photographs:

l = left, r = right, c = centre, t = top, b = bottom

3tb Gustoimages/Science Photo Library; 6bl NASA; 6br Corbis; 8 Bettmann/Corbis; 20 Paul A Souders/Corbis; 23tl Baron Wolman/Stone/Getty Images; 23bl William Whitehurst/The Stock Market; 23br Bernhard Edmaier/Science Photo Library; 24 HP Merten/ The Stock Market; 26 Charles D. Winters/Science Photo Library; 29 David Guyon, the BOC Group PLC/Science Photo Library; 41tl Firefly Productions/The Stock Market; 41br Hans Stroud/Stone/Getty Images; 44 John Durham/Science Photo Library; 46 Thomas Eisner and Daniel Aneshansley, Cornell University; 50 Ace Photo Agency; 54l George Steinmetz/Science Photo Library; 54r Photodisc. Photolink. T O'Keefe; 55 Andrew Lambert Photography/Science Photo Library; 56 Andrew Lambert Photography/Science Photo Library; 57tl Photodisc. Photolink. Kent Knudson; 57tr Simon Fraser/Science Photo Library; 57br Digital Vision; 58 Cordelia Molloy/Science Photo Library; 60l Alvey & Towers; 60r © Archivo

Iconigrafico SA/Corbis; 63t Andrew Lambert/Leslie Garland Picture Library; 66 Charles D. Winters/Science Photo Library; 70tl Sandro Vannini/Corbis; 73tr © Bettmann/Corbis; 74 Pascal Goetcheluck/ Science Photo Library; 89tl Andy Crump/TDR/WHO/Science Photo Library; 89tr Andrew Lambert Photography/Science Photo Library; 93tr Andrew Lambert Photography; 93br Andrew Lambert Photography; 100tl Pasieka/Science Photo Library; 100bl Gary Retherford/Science Photo Library; 105br Claude Nuridsany and Marie Perennou/Science Photo Library; 120tl NASA; 120tr Ronald Toms/Ace Photo Agency; 120bl *Diver Magazine* www.divernet.com; 122t Andrew Lambert Photography/Science Photo Library; 122b Dirk Wiersma/Science Photo Library; 129 Charles D. Winters/ Science Photo Library; 133l Martin Bond/Science Photo Library; 133r Tim Graham/Getty; 134 David Aubrey/Science Photo Library; 139c Sinclair Stammers/Science Photo Library; 139r Geoscience Features; 140t Leslie Garland/Leslie Garland Picture Library; 140b James L Amos/Corbis; 141t Paul A Souders/Corbis; 141c1 Maria Platt-Evans/Science Photo Library; 141c2 Aluminium Federation; 141b Alan Kearney/Telegraph Colour Library/Getty Images; 142 Heine Schnebeeli/Science Photo Library; 143bl Maximilian Stock Ltd/Science Photo Library; 156 ER Degginger/Science Photo Library; 157 A.J Photo/Science Photo Library; 159b Ulrike Welsche/Science Photo Library; 161 David R. Frazier/Science Photo Library; 163t Mike Taylor/Leslie Garland Picture Library; 163b Staton R. Winter/Newsmakers/Camera Press Digital; 165t Alvey & Towers; 165b Alvey & Towers; 166t Steve Dunwell Photography/Image Bank/Getty Images; 166b Alvey & Towers; 171 Maximilian Stock Ltd./Science Photo Library; 173t Charles D. Winters/Science Photo Library; 173b Margaret Durrance/Science Photo Library; 176 Craig Aurness/Corbis; 179t Arnold Fisher/Science Photo Library; 179b Roger Wood/Corbis; 182 Martin Bond/Science Photo Library; 183 Arnold Fisher/Science Photo Library; 187 Andrew Lambert Photography/Science Photo Library; 188 Stock Photo: 7800884; 192 Martin Bond/Science Photo Library; 193 Andrew Lambert Photography/Science Photo Library; 210 Paul Deakin.

All remaining photography: Jim Clark.

Every effort has been made to contact copyright holders of material reproduced in this book. Any omissions will be rectified in subsequent printings if notice is given to the publishers.

Websites
The websites used in this book were correct and up to date at the time of publication. It is essential for tutors to preview each website before using it in class so as to ensure that the URL is still accurate, relevant and appropriate. We suggest that tutors bookmark useful websites and consider enabling students to access them through the school/college intranet.

Disclaimer
This Edexcel publication offers high-quality support for the delivery of Edexcel qualifications.

Edexcel endorsement does not mean that this material is essential to achieve any Edexcel qualification, nor does it mean that this is the only suitable material available to support any Edexcel qualification. No endorsed material will be used verbatim in setting any Edexcel examination/assessment and any resource lists produced by Edexcel shall include this and other appropriate texts.

Copies of official specifications for all Edexcel qualifications may be found on the Edexcel website, www.edexcel.com

Contents

Section D:
Organic Chemistry

Section E:
Chemistry
Calculations

Appendices

About this book

This book has several features to help you with IGCSE Chemistry.

Introduction
Each chapter has a short introduction to help you start thinking about the topic and let you know what is in the chapter.

End of chapter checklists
These lists summarise the material in the chapter. They could also help you to make revision notes because they form a list of things that you need to revise. (You need to check your specification to find out exactly what you need to know.)

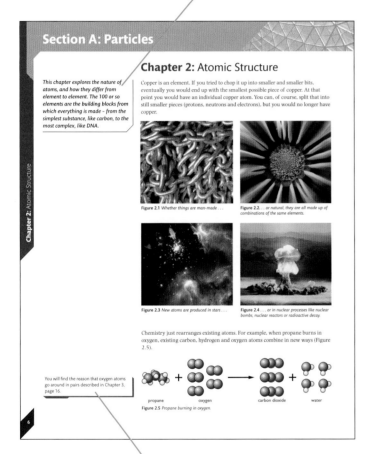

Section A: Particles

Chapter 2: Atomic Structure

This chapter explores the nature of atoms, and how they differ from element to element. The 100 or so elements are the building blocks from which everything is made – from the simplest substance, like carbon, to the most complex, like DNA.

Copper is an element. If you tried to chop it up into smaller and smaller bits, eventually you would end up with the smallest possible piece of copper. At that point you would have an individual copper atom. You can, of course, split that into still smaller pieces (protons, neutrons and electrons), but you would no longer have copper.

Figure 2.1 *Whether things are man-made . . .*

Figure 2.2 *. . . or natural, they are all made up of combinations of the same elements.*

Figure 2.3 *New atoms are produced in stars . . .*

Figure 2.4 *. . . or in nuclear processes like nuclear bombs, nuclear reactors or radioactive decay.*

Chemistry just rearranges existing atoms. For example, when propane burns in oxygen, existing carbon, hydrogen and oxygen atoms combine in new ways (Figure 2.5).

You will find the reason that oxygen atoms go around in pairs described in Chapter 3, page 16.

propane   oxygen   carbon dioxide   water
Figure 2.5 *Propane burning in oxygen.*

6

End of Chapter Checklist

You should now be able to:

✓ state the relative masses and charges of protons, neutrons and electrons

✓ understand what is meant by *atomic (proton) number* and *mass number*

✓ explain the existence of isotopes

✓ know that the nucleus contains protons and neutrons, and that the electrons are found in a series of energy levels

✓ work out the arrangement of the electrons in the first 20 elements in the Periodic Table

✓ know that for elements in groups 1–7, the number of electrons in the outer level is the same as the group number

✓ know that noble gases have full (or temporarily full) outer levels.

Questions

You will need to use the Periodic Table on page 226.

1 Fluorine atoms have a mass number of 19.
   a) Use the Periodic Table to find the atomic number of fluorine.
   b) Explain what *mass number* means.
   c) Write down the number of protons, neutrons and electrons in a fluorine atom.
   d) Draw a diagram to show the arrangement of electrons in the fluorine atom.

2 Work out the numbers of protons, neutrons and electrons in each of the following atoms:
   a) $^{56}_{26}Fe$ b) $^{93}_{41}Nb$ c) $^{235}_{92}U$

3 Chlorine has two isotopes, chlorine-35 and chlorine-37.
   a) What are isotopes?
   b) Write down the numbers of protons, neutrons and electrons in the two isotopes.
   c) Write down the arrangement of the electrons in each of the two isotopes.

4 Draw diagrams to show the arrangement of the electrons in a) sodium, b) silicon, c) sulfur.

5 Find each of the following elements in the Periodic Table, and write down the number of electrons in their outer energy level: a) arsenic, As; b) bromine, Br; c) tin, Sn; d) xenon, Xe.

6 The questions refer to the electronic structures below. Don't worry if some of these are unfamiliar to you. All of these are the electronic structures of neutral atoms.
   A   2, 4
   B   2, 8, 8
   C   2, 8, 18, 18, 7
   D   2, 8,18, 18, 8
   E   2, 8, 8, 2
   F   2, 8, 18, 32, 18, 4
   a) Which of these atoms are in group 4 of the Periodic Table?
   b) Which of these structures represents carbon?
   c) Which of these structures represents an element in group 7 of the Periodic Table?
   d) Which of these structures represent noble gases?
   e) Name element E.
   f) How many protons does element F have? Name the element.
   g) Element G has one more electron than element B. Draw a diagram to show how the electrons are arranged in an atom of G.

12

Margin boxes
The boxes in the margin give you extra help or information. They might explain something in a little more detail or guide you to linked topics in other parts of the book.

Questions
There are short questions at the end of each chapter. These help you to test your understanding of the material from the chapter. Some of them may also be research questions – you will need to use the Internet and other books to answer these.

There are also questions at the end of each section. The end-of-section questions are written in an exam style and cover topics from all the chapters in the section.

Chapter 1: Kinetic Theory and Diffusion

Figure 1.1 *Everything you look at is a solid, liquid or gas . . .*

Figure 1.2 *. . . metals, concrete, water, air, clouds – everything!*

Everything around you is made of particles so small that you can't see them. This chapter looks at the arrangement of particles in solids, liquids and gases, and the ways in which the particles can move around. The nature of the different sorts of particles will be explored in Chapters 2–4.

Solids, liquids and gases

The arrangement of the particles

Think about these facts:

- You can't walk through a brick wall, but you can move (with some resistance) through water. Moving through air is easy.

- When you melt most solids, their volume increases slightly. Most liquids are less dense than the solid they come from.

- If you boil about 5 cm³ of water, the steam will fill an average bucket.

The arrangement of the particles in solids, liquids and gases explains these facts.

> Water is very unusual in that solid water (ice) is less dense than the liquid, and so ice floats on water. For almost everything else, the solid will sink in the liquid.

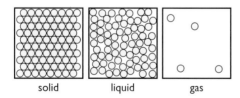

solid   liquid   gas

Figure 1.3 *The arrangement of particles in different states of matter.*

> The particles are drawn as spheres, but they might be any shape. The packing in the solid might be completely different – what is important is that the particles are close together and, in most cases, regularly packed. When you draw a gas, keep the particles well separated. A typical gas will have particles about 10 molecular diameters away from each other.

In a solid, the particles are closely, and often regularly, packed. The only movement the particles have is vibration. You can't walk through a brick wall because the particles have strong forces of attraction between them, and they can't move out of your way.

In a liquid, the particles are still mainly touching, but some gaps have appeared. Liquids are usually less dense than the solid because of this. The forces between the particles are less effective, and the particles can move. You can swim through water because you can push the particles aside.

In a gas, the particles are much further apart and there are almost no forces of attraction between them. It is easy to move through a gas because of all the spaces between the particles.

Changes of state

Solids, liquids and gases are known as the three states of matter.

Changing state between solid and liquid

If you heat a solid, the energy makes the particles in it vibrate faster and faster. Eventually, they vibrate fast enough that the forces of attraction between the particles are no longer strong enough to hold them together. The solid melts to a liquid. The temperature needed to melt the solid is obviously its melting point.

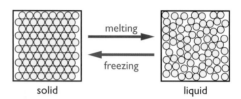

Figure 1.4 *Melting to become a liquid – and freezing to become a solid.*

If the liquid is cooled again, the liquid particles will move around more and more slowly. Eventually, they are moving slowly enough that the forces of attraction between them will hold them into a solid. The liquid freezes. The temperature needed for this is obviously the freezing point.

Although they are called different things depending on which way you are going, melting point and freezing point are exactly the same temperature.

Changing state between liquid and gas

There are two different ways this can happen – evaporation and boiling.

Boiling happens when the liquid is heated so strongly that the particles are moving fast enough to break all the forces of attraction in the liquid. The liquid boils. Bubbles of gaseous particles are formed throughout the whole liquid and rise to the surface, forming a gas. If the gas is cooled, the particles eventually move slowly enough that attractions between them hold them as a liquid. The gas condenses.

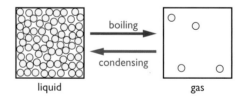

Figure 1.5 *Boiling to become a gas – and condensing to become a liquid.*

Evaporation is different. In any liquid or gas, the average speed of the particles varies with the temperature. But at each temperature, some particles will be moving faster, others more slowly, than the average.

Some very fast particles on the surface of the liquid will have enough energy to break away to form a gas – that's evaporation. You don't see any bubbling; liquid just slowly disappears if the liquid is open to the air. If it is in a closed container, particles in the gas will also be sticking back to the liquid surface again. The particles breaking away and those rejoining the surface end up in balance. There will be a roughly constant number of particles of gas over the top of a liquid in a closed container.

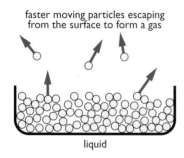

faster moving particles escaping from the surface to form a gas

liquid

Figure 1.6 *Evaporation.*

Changing state between solid and gas – sublimation

A small number of substances have the ability to change directly from solid to gas, or vice versa, without involving any liquid on the way. This is known as sublimation.

Heating ammonium chloride crystals in a test tube is a simple example in the lab. The white crystals gradually disappear from the bottom of the test tube and reappear further up, where the tube is cooler. There is a chemical reason for this, which you will find described on page 125.

Another example is carbon dioxide. At ordinary pressures, there is no such thing as liquid carbon dioxide. It turns straight from a solid to a gas at −78 °C. Solid carbon dioxide is known as dry ice.

In the photograph, notice the white solid carbon dioxide in the beaker. The white cloud appears because the carbon dioxide gas produced is so cold that it causes water vapour in the air to condense. Carbon dioxide gas itself is invisible.

Diffusion

Diffusion in gases

Suppose someone accidentally releases some smelly gas in the lab – ammonia, perhaps. Within a minute or so, everybody in the lab will be able to smell it. That isn't surprising – particles in the gas are free to move around. What does need explaining, though, is why it takes so long.

At room temperature, ammonia particles travel at speeds of about 600 m/s. In the time that it takes for the smell to reach all corners of the lab, each ammonia particle may have travelled 30 or more kilometres! Each particle is bouncing off endless air particles on its way.

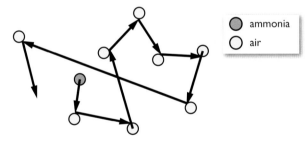

| ● | ammonia |
| ○ | air |

Figure 1.9 An ammonia particle bouncing off air particles.

The spreading out of particles in a gas or liquid is known as diffusion. You can say that ammonia particles diffuse through the air.

You can show diffusion in gases very easily using the apparatus in Figure 1.10. The lower gas jar contains bromine gas; the top one contains air. If the lids are removed, the brown colour of the bromine diffuses upwards until both gas jars are uniformly brown. The bromine particles and air particles bounce around at random to give an even mixture.

You can do the same thing with hydrogen and air, except that you have to put a lighted splint in at the end to find out where the gases have gone. People often expect that the very light hydrogen will all end up in the top gas jar. In fact, you will get identical explosions from both jars.

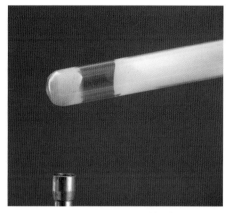

Figure 1.7 Heating ammonium chloride.

Figure 1.8 Dry ice subliming.

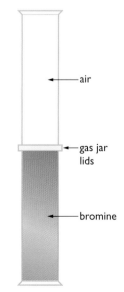

air

gas jar lids

bromine

Figure 1.10 Demonstrating diffusion in gases.

Don't worry if you don't know how to write symbol equations. It's included here so that you can refer back to it in later revision.

Showing that particles in different gases travel at different speeds

This experiment relies on the reaction between ammonia and hydrogen chloride gases to give white solid ammonium chloride:

$$NH_3(g) + HCl(g) \rightarrow NH_4Cl(s)$$

Bits of cotton wool are soaked in concentrated ammonia solution (as a source of ammonia gas) and concentrated hydrochloric acid (as a source of hydrogen chloride gas). These are placed in the ends of a long glass tube with rubber bungs to stop the poisonous gases escaping.

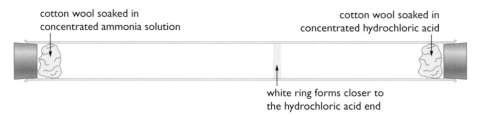

cotton wool soaked in
concentrated ammonia solution

cotton wool soaked in
concentrated hydrochloric acid

white ring forms closer to
the hydrochloric acid end

Figure 1.11 *Demonstrating that particles in ammonia and hydrogen chloride travel at different speeds.*

The white ring of ammonium chloride takes a little time to form (depending on the length and diameter of the tube), and appears closer to the hydrochloric acid end. In the time it takes for the ring to form, the ammonia particles have travelled further. That's because their speed is higher.

Ammonia particles are lighter than hydrogen chloride particles. *Light particles are faster than heavier ones.*

Diffusion in liquids

Diffusion through a liquid is very slow if the liquid is totally still. For example, if a small jar of strongly coloured solution (such as potassium manganate(VII) solution) is left to stand in a gas jar of water, it can take days for the colour to diffuse throughout the whole of the water. This is because there are only small gaps between the liquid particles for other particles to diffuse into.

Showing that the particles are very small

Suppose you dissolve 0.1 g of potassium manganate(VII) in 10 cm³ of water to give a deep purple solution. Assume that the smallest drop you can see is 1/1000 cm³. The whole solution will be made up of 10,000 drops. So each drop will contain 0.00001 g of potassium manganate(VII).

Suppose you dilute this down 10 times by taking 1 cm³ of the solution and making it up to 10 cm³ with more water. Now continue doing this until the colour is too faint to see. Perhaps you can still see some colour after you have diluted the solution a total of five times, but not after the sixth dilution.

By the time of the fifth dilution, each drop will only contain a billionth of a gram of potassium manganate(VII). If you only needed one 'particle' of potassium manganate(VII) per drop in order to see the colour, the 'particle' can't weigh more than a billionth of a gram (0.000000001 g).

Is this a good answer? Nowhere near it! A potassium manganate(VII) 'particle' actually weighs about 0.0000000000000000000026 g ! In reality, you need huge numbers of particles in each drop in order to see the colour.

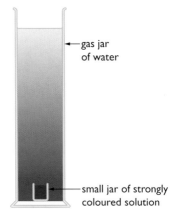

gas jar
of water

small jar of strongly
coloured solution

Figure 1.12 *Demonstrating diffusion in liquids.*

Why the inverted commas around 'particle'? Potassium manganate(VII) is an ionic compound and contains more than one sort of particle. You will find out more about ionic compounds in Chapters 3 and 4.

You should now be able to:

✓ draw simple diagrams to show the arrangement of the particles in solids, liquids and gases

✓ understand that heating a substance makes the particles vibrate (solid) or move (liquid or gas) faster

✓ explain what happens in terms of the particles when a solid is heated until it becomes a gas

✓ understand what is meant by melting, freezing, boiling, condensing and subliming, in terms of the particles present

✓ understand the difference between evaporation and boiling

✓ understand what is meant by diffusion, and describe an experiment to show that light particles diffuse faster than heavy ones

✓ explain why diffusion in liquids is slower than in gases

✓ describe a simple dilution experiment to show that the particles are very small.

Questions

1 What name is given to each of the following changes of state?

    a) solid to liquid; *b)* liquid to solid; *c)* solid to gas; *d)* gas to solid.

2 *a)* Draw simple diagrams to show the arrangement of the particles in a solid, a liquid and a gas.

    b) Describe the difference between the movement of the particles in a solid and a liquid.

    c) The change of state from a liquid to a gas can be either evaporation or boiling. Explain the difference between evaporation and boiling.

    d) Some liquids are stored in sealed bottles for a very long time – decades or more. Explain why they don't evaporate.

3 The questions refer to the substances in the table below.

	Melting point (°C)	Boiling point (°C)
A	−259	−253
B	0	100
C	3700 (sublimes)	
D	−116	34.5
E	801	1413

    a) Write down the physical states of each substance at 20 °C.

    b) Which substance has the strongest attractions between its particles? Explain your answer.

    c) Which substance has the weakest attractions between its particles? Explain your answer.

    d) Which substance has the greatest distance between its particles at 20 °C? Explain your answer.

    e) Why is no boiling point given for substance C?

    f) Which liquid substance would evaporate most quickly in the open air at 20 °C? Explain your answer.

4 Refer to Figure 1.11, which shows the diffusion experiment.

    a) Explain why the ring takes a little time to form.

    b) If you heat a gas, what effect will this have on the movement of the particles?

    c) In the light of your answer to *(b)*, what difference would you find if you did this experiment outside on a day when the temperature was 2 °C instead of in a warm lab at 25 °C? Explain your answer.

    d) Explain why the ring was formed nearer the hydrochloric acid end of the tube.

    Suppose you replaced the concentrated hydrochloric acid by concentrated hydrobromic acid. This releases the gas hydrogen bromide. Hydrogen bromide also reacts with ammonia to form a white ring.

    e) Suggest a name for the white ring in this case.

    f) Hydrogen bromide particles are about twice as heavy as hydrogen chloride particles. What effects do you think this would have on the experiment?

5 Design a simple experiment, giving full practical details, which would let you compare the rates at which two strongly coloured solutions diffused through water. At each stage, think about exactly what problems might arise in carrying out the experiment, and say clearly how you would overcome them.

Section A: Particles

Chapter 2: Atomic Structure

This chapter explores the nature of atoms, and how they differ from element to element. The 100 or so elements are the building blocks from which everything is made – from the simplest substance, like carbon, to the most complex, like DNA.

Copper is an element. If you tried to chop it up into smaller and smaller bits, eventually you would end up with the smallest possible piece of copper. At that point you would have an individual copper atom. You can, of course, split that into still smaller pieces (protons, neutrons and electrons), but you would no longer have copper.

Figure 2.1 *Whether things are man-made . . .*

Figure 2.2. *. . . or natural, they are all made up of combinations of the same elements.*

Figure 2.3 *New atoms are produced in stars . . .*

Figure 2.4 *. . . or in nuclear processes like nuclear bombs, nuclear reactors or radioactive decay.*

Chemistry just rearranges existing atoms. For example, when propane burns in oxygen, existing carbon, hydrogen and oxygen atoms combine in new ways (Figure 2.5).

You will find the reason that oxygen atoms go around in pairs described in Chapter 3, page 16.

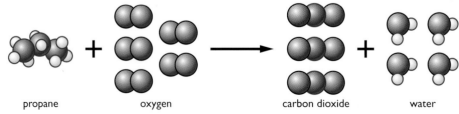

propane   oxygen   carbon dioxide   water

Figure 2.5 *Propane burning in oxygen.*

The structure of the atom

Atoms are made of protons, neutrons and electrons.

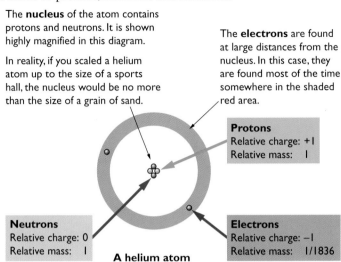

The **nucleus** of the atom contains protons and neutrons. It is shown highly magnified in this diagram.

In reality, if you scaled a helium atom up to the size of a sports hall, the nucleus would be no more than the size of a grain of sand.

The **electrons** are found at large distances from the nucleus. In this case, they are found most of the time somewhere in the shaded red area.

Protons
Relative charge: +1
Relative mass: 1

Neutrons
Relative charge: 0
Relative mass: 1

A helium atom

Electrons
Relative charge: −1
Relative mass: 1/1836

Figure 2.6 *The structure of an atom.*

You may have come across diagrams of the atom in which the electrons are drawn orbiting the nucleus, rather like planets around the Sun. This is misleading. It is impossible to know exactly how the electrons are moving in an atom. All you can tell is that they have a particular energy, and that they are likely to be found in a certain region of space at some particular distance from the nucleus. Electrons with different energies are found at different distances from the nucleus.

Virtually all the mass of the atom is concentrated in the nucleus, because the electrons weigh hardly anything.

The masses and charges are measured relative to each other because the actual values are incredibly small. For example, it would take about 600,000,000,000,000,000,000,000,000 protons to weigh 1 g.

Atomic number and mass number

The number of protons in an atom is called its **atomic number** or **proton number**. Each of the 100 or so different elements has a different number of protons. For example, if an atom has eight protons, it must be an oxygen atom.

> Atomic number = number of protons

The **mass number** (sometimes known as the **nucleon number**) counts the total numbers of protons and neutrons in the nucleus of the atom.

> Mass number = number of protons + number of neutrons

For any particular atom, this information can be shown simply as, for example:

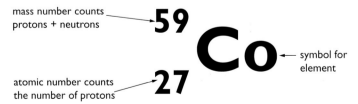

mass number counts protons + neutrons

atomic number counts the number of protons

symbol for element

Be careful! When you are writing symbols with two letters in them, the first is a capital letter, and the second *must* be lower case. If you write 'CO', you are talking about carbon monoxide, not cobalt.

This particular atom of cobalt contains 27 protons. To make the total number of protons and neutrons up to 59, there must also be 32 neutrons.

Isotopes

The number of neutrons in an atom can vary slightly. For example, there are three kinds of carbon atom, called carbon-12, carbon-13 and carbon-14. They all have the same number of protons (because all carbon atoms have 6 protons – its atomic number), but the number of neutrons varies. These different atoms of carbon are called **isotopes**.

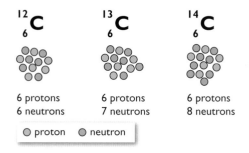

Figure 2.7 *The nuclei of the three isotopes of carbon.*

Isotopes are atoms that have the same atomic number, but different mass numbers. They have the same number of protons, but different numbers of neutrons.

The fact that they have varying numbers of neutrons makes no difference whatsoever to their chemical reactions. The chemical properties are governed by the number and arrangement of the electrons and, as you will see shortly, that is identical for all three isotopes.

A radioactive isotope

Carbon-14 is **radioactive**. Its nucleus is unstable and radiation is released as it reorganises into a more stable form. The radiation given off by carbon-14 is used in carbon dating. The nuclei of the carbon-12 and carbon-13 isotopes are perfectly stable, and so these aren't radioactive.

If you are interested you could do an internet search on 'turin shroud' to find out how carbon dating was used to determine its age, and why there is still controversy about it.

The electrons

Counting the number of electrons in an atom

Atoms are electrically neutral, and the positiveness of the protons is balanced by the negativeness of the electrons. In a neutral atom, it follows that:

Number of electrons = number of protons

So, if an oxygen atom (atomic number = 8) has 8 protons, it must also have 8 electrons; if a chlorine atom (atomic number = 17) has 17 protons, it must also have 17 electrons.

You will see that the key feature in this is knowing the atomic number. You can find that from the Periodic Table.

Figure 2.8 *Despite carbon dating, there is still considerable controversy about the age of the Turin shroud.*

Remember that the number of protons is the same as the atomic number of the element.

Atomic number and the Periodic Table

Atoms are arranged in the Periodic Table in order of increasing atomic number. You will find a full version of the Periodic Table on page 226. Most Periodic Tables have two numbers against each symbol – be careful to choose the right one. *The atomic number will always be the smaller number*. The other number will be either the mass number of the most common isotope of the element, or the relative atomic mass of the element. The Table will tell you which.

You use a Periodic Table to find out the atomic number of an element and therefore how many protons and electrons there are in its atoms.

Chapter 12 (page 99) deals in detail with what you need to know about the Periodic Table for GCSE purposes.
Relative atomic mass is explained in Chapter 22 on page 176.

The arrangement of the electrons

The electrons are found at considerable distances from the nucleus in a series of levels called **energy levels** or **shells**. Each energy level can only hold a certain number of electrons. Low energy levels are always filled before higher ones.

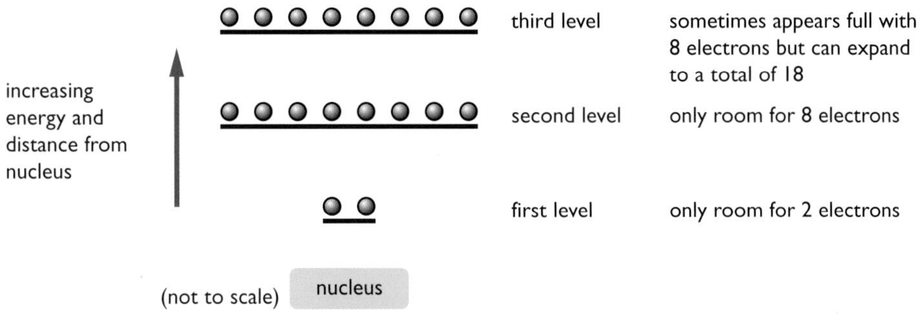

increasing energy and distance from nucleus

⬆

○ ○ ○ ○ ○ ○ ○ ○   third level   sometimes appears full with 8 electrons but can expand to a total of 18

○ ○ ○ ○ ○ ○ ○ ○   second level   only room for 8 electrons

○ ○   first level   only room for 2 electrons

(not to scale)   nucleus

Figure 2.9 *The different energy levels of electrons.*

The diagram shows the maximum number of electrons that each energy level can hold. The third level can expand to hold a total of 18 electrons, but this is a problem beyond GCSE.

How to work out the arrangement of the electrons

We will use chlorine as an example.

● Look up the atomic number in the Periodic Table. (If you have a choice, make sure you don't use the wrong number. The atomic number will always be the smaller one.)

The Periodic Table tells you that chlorine's atomic number is 17.

● This tells you the number of protons, and hence the number of electrons. The number of electrons is equal to the number of protons

There are 17 protons, and so 17 electrons in a neutral chlorine atom.

● Arrange the electrons in levels, always filling up an inner (lower energy) level before you go to an outer one. Remember that the first level can take 2 electrons, the second one can take 8, and the third one (for the simple cases you will meet) also takes 8.

*These will be arranged 2 in the first level, 8 in the second level and 7 in the third level. This is written as **2**, **8**, **7**. When you have finished, always check to make sure that the electrons add up to the right number – in this case, 17.*

Don't just accept Figure 2.10! Use the Periodic Table on page 226 and work out each of these electronic structures for yourself (preferably in a random order to make it more difficult). Check your answers when you have finished.

The first 20 elements in the Periodic Table

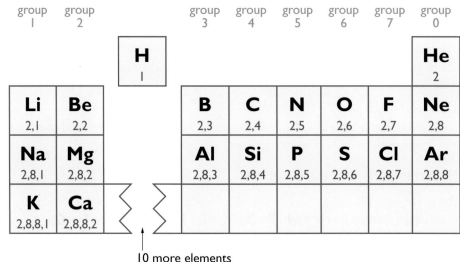

Figure 2.10 *The electronic arrangements of the first 20 elements in the Periodic Table.*

Vertical columns in the Periodic Table are called **groups**. Groups contain elements with similar properties. Their similarity depends on the fact that (apart from helium) elements in the same group have the same number of electrons in their outer levels. These are the electrons which normally get involved when the elements bond to other things.

There are two important generalisations you can make:

● The number of electrons in the outer level is the same as the group number for groups 1–7.

This pattern extends right down the Periodic Table for these groups.

So if you know that barium is in group 2, you know it has 2 electrons in its outer level. Iodine (group 7) has 7 electrons in its outer level. Lead (group 4) has 4 electrons in its outer level. Working out what is in the inner levels is much more difficult. The simple patterns we have described don't work beyond calcium.

● The elements in group 0 have 8 electrons in their outer levels (apart from helium, which has 2).

This idea of 'full' levels is best avoided. If you carry it through to a higher level of chemistry, you will give yourself real problems.

These are often thought of as being 'full' levels. This is true for helium and neon, but not for the elements from argon downwards. For example, the third energy level will eventually contain 18 electrons.

The group 0 elements are known as the **noble gases** because they are almost completely unreactive – in fact the three at the top of the group from helium to argon don't react with anything. This lack of reactivity is associated with their electronic structures – often described as **noble gas structures**.

Drawing diagrams of electronic arrangements

The electrons in their various energy levels can be shown by drawing circles with dots or crosses on them showing the electrons. It doesn't matter whether you draw dots or crosses.

Hydrogen has one electron and helium has two in the first level.

Figure 2.11 *Electronic arrangements of hydrogen and helium.*

The helium electrons are sometimes shown as a pair (as here), and sometimes as two separate electrons on opposite sides of the circle. Either form is acceptable.

The next four atoms are drawn like this:

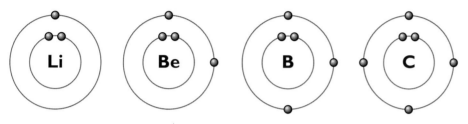

Figure 2.12 *Electronic arrangements of lithium, beryllium, boron and carbon.*

Drawing circles like this *does not* imply that the electrons are orbiting the nucleus along the circles.

The circles represent energy levels. The further the level is from the nucleus, the higher its energy.

For theoretical reasons, it is impossible to work out exactly how an electron is moving in that energy level.

The electrons in the second energy level are drawn singly up to a maximum of 4. After that, pair them up as necessary. It makes them much easier to count. More importantly, it gives a much better picture of the availability of the electrons in the atom for bonding purposes. This is explored in Chapter 3.

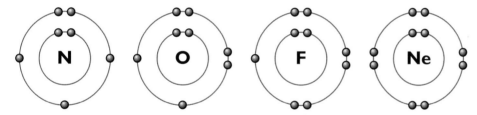

Figure 2.13 *Electronic arrangements of nitrogen, oxygen, fluorine and neon.*

The atoms in the Periodic Table from sodium to argon fill the third level in exactly the same way, and potassium and calcium start to fill the fourth level.

Potassium and calcium will look like Figure 2.14.

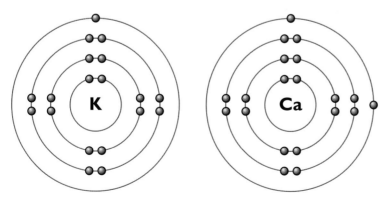

Figure 2.14 *Electronic arrangements of potassium and calcium.*

End of Chapter Checklist

You should now be able to:

✓ state the relative masses and charges of protons, neutrons and electrons

✓ understand what is meant by *atomic (proton) number* and *mass number*

✓ explain the existence of isotopes

✓ know that the nucleus contains protons and neutrons, and that the electrons are found in a series of energy levels

✓ work out the arrangement of the electrons in the first 20 elements in the Periodic Table

✓ know that for elements in groups 1–7, the number of electrons in the outer level is the same as the group number

✓ know that noble gases have full (or temporarily full) outer levels.

Questions

You will need to use the Periodic Table on page 226.

1 Fluorine atoms have a mass number of 19.

   a) Use the Periodic Table to find the atomic number of fluorine.

   b) Explain what *mass number* means.

   c) Write down the number of protons, neutrons and electrons in a fluorine atom.

   d) Draw a diagram to show the arrangement of electrons in the fluorine atom.

2 Work out the numbers of protons, neutrons and electrons in each of the following atoms:

   a) $^{56}_{26}Fe$ *b)* $^{93}_{41}Nb$ *c)* $^{235}_{92}U$

3 Chlorine has two isotopes, chlorine-35 and chlorine-37.

   a) What are isotopes?

   b) Write down the numbers of protons, neutrons and electrons in the two isotopes.

   c) Write down the arrangement of the electrons in each of the two isotopes.

4 Draw diagrams to show the arrangement of the electrons in *a)* sodium, *b)* silicon, *c)* sulfur.

5 Find each of the following elements in the Periodic Table, and write down the number of electrons in their outer energy level: *a)* arsenic, As; *b)* bromine, Br; *c)* tin, Sn; *d)* xenon, Xe.

6 The questions refer to the electronic structures below. Don't worry if some of these are unfamiliar to you. All of these are the electronic structures of neutral atoms.

A 2, 4
B 2, 8, 8
C 2, 8, 18, 18, 7
D 2, 8,18, 18, 8
E 2, 8, 8, 2
F 2, 8, 18, 32, 18, 4

   a) Which of these atoms are in group 4 of the Periodic Table?

   b) Which of these structures represents carbon?

   c) Which of these structures represents an element in group 7 of the Periodic Table?

   d) Which of these structures represent noble gases?

   e) Name element E.

   f) How many protons does element F have? Name the element.

   g) Element G has one more electron than element B. Draw a diagram to show how the electrons are arranged in an atom of G.

Chapter 3: Bonding

Figure 3.1 *The elements sodium and chlorine are dangerous; the compound sodium chloride (salt) isn't.*

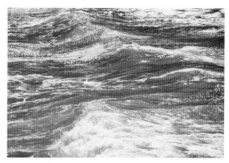

Figure 3.2 *Water has completely different properties from its elements, hydrogen and oxygen.*

> *This chapter looks at what happens when atoms combine together – whether into small groups or into very large ones.*

Sodium is a dangerously reactive metal. It is stored under oil to prevent it reacting with air or water. Chlorine is a very poisonous, reactive gas.

But salt, sodium chloride, is safe to eat in small quantities. Combining the elements to make salt obviously changes them significantly.

A mixture of hydrogen and oxygen gas would explode violently if you held a lighted match to it. Dropping a lighted match into water (a compound of hydrogen and oxygen) doesn't cause a literally Earth-shattering explosion.

Reacting the elements to make a compound has again made a huge difference to them.

Covalent bonding

What is a covalent bond?

In any bond, particles are held together by electrical attractions between something positively charged and something negatively charged. In a covalent bond, a pair of electrons is shared between two atoms. Each of the positively charged nuclei is attracted to the same negatively charged pair of electrons.

A and B in Figure 3.3 are held together by this shared attraction.

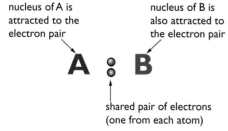

nucleus of A is attracted to the electron pair

nucleus of B is also attracted to the electron pair

shared pair of electrons (one from each atom)

Figure 3.3 *A covalent bond.*

> In most of the simple examples you will meet at GCSE, each atom in a covalent bond supplies one electron to the shared pair of electrons. That doesn't have to be the case. Both electrons may come from the same atom.

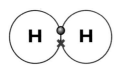

Figure 3.4 *A dots-and-crosses diagram for hydrogen.*

Covalent bonding in a hydrogen molecule

Covalent bonds are often shown using 'dots-and-crosses' diagrams. Although the electrons are drawn as dots or as crosses, there is absolutely no difference between them in reality. The dot and the cross simply show that the electrons have come from two different atoms. You could equally well use two different coloured dots, or two different coloured crosses.

Both hydrogen nuclei in Figure 3.4 are strongly attracted to the shared pair of electrons.

The covalent bond between two hydrogen atoms is very strong. Hydrogen atoms therefore go around in pairs called a hydrogen **molecule**, with the symbol H_2.

Molecules contain a certain fixed number of atoms, which are joined together by covalent bonds. Hydrogen molecules are said to be **diatomic** because they contain two atoms. Other sorts of molecule may have as many as thousands of atoms joined together.

Why does hydrogen form molecules?

Whenever a bond is formed (of whatever kind), energy is released, and that makes the things involved more stable than they were before. The more bonds an atom can form, the more energy is released and the more stable the system becomes.

In the case of hydrogen, each hydrogen atom has only one electron to share, so it can only form one covalent bond. The H_2 molecule is still much more stable than two separate hydrogen atoms.

Covalent bonding in a hydrogen chloride molecule

The chlorine atom has one unpaired electron in its outer level, which it can share with the hydrogen atom to produce a covalent bond.

Notice in Figure 3.5 that only the electrons in the outer energy level of the chlorine are used in bonding. In the examples you will meet at GCSE, the inner electrons never get used. In fact, the inner electrons are often left out of bonding diagrams. But be careful! In an exam, only leave out the inner electrons if the question tells you to.

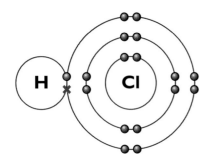

Figure 3.5 *Covalent bonding in hydrogen chloride.*

The significance of noble gas structures in covalent bonding

If you look at the arrangement of electrons around the chlorine atom in the covalently bonded molecule of HCl (Figure 3.5), you will see that its structure is now 2,8,8. That is the same as an argon atom. Similarly, the hydrogen now has 2 electrons in its outer level – the same as helium.

Does that mean that the hydrogen has turned into helium, and the chlorine has turned into argon? No – the number of protons in each nucleus hasn't changed, and it is the number of protons that defines what an atom is.

At GCSE, formation of covalent bonds producing noble gas structures is quite common. When atoms bond covalently, they often produce outer electronic structures the same as noble gases – in other words with four pairs of electrons (or one pair in the case of hydrogen). There are, however, a lot of examples where different numbers of pairs are formed, producing structures that are quite unlike noble gases.

Warning! At GCSE people frequently talk about atoms 'wanting' to form noble gas structures. This is nonsense! Avoid thinking about it in this way.

Covalent bonding in a chlorine molecule

Each chlorine has one unpaired electron in its outer energy level. These are shared between the two to give a chlorine molecule, Cl_2.

Covalent bonding in methane, ammonia and water

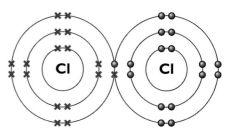

Figure 3.6 *Covalent bonding in chlorine.*

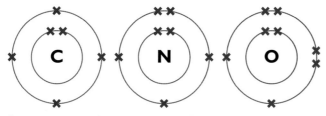

Figure 3.7 *The electronic structures of carbon, nitrogen and oxygen atoms.*

In methane, the carbon atom has four unpaired electrons. Each of these forms a covalent bond by sharing with the electron from a hydrogen atom. Methane has the formula CH_4.

In ammonia, the nitrogen only has three unpaired electrons and so can only form bonds with three hydrogen atoms to give NH_3.

In water, there are two unpaired electrons on the oxygen atom which can bond with hydrogen atoms to give H_2O.

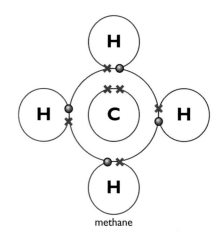

methane

Figure 3.8 *Methane.*

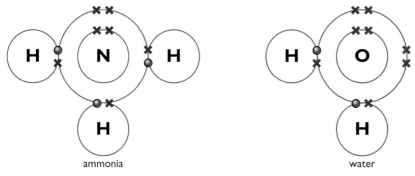

ammonia

water

Figure 3.9 *Ammonia.*   **Figure 3.10** *Water.*

Covalent bonding in a slightly more complicated molecule – ethane

Ethane has the formula C_2H_6. The bonding is similar to methane (Figure 3.8), except that there is a carbon–carbon covalent bond as well as the carbon–hydrogen bonds.

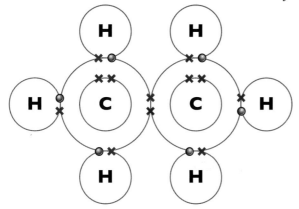

Figure 3.11 *Ethane.*

Multiple covalent bonding

Covalent bonding in an oxygen molecule – double bonding

When atoms bond covalently, they tend to do so in a way that forms the maximum number of bonds. That makes the final molecule more stable.

Figure 3.12a shows that forming a single covalent bond between the two oxygen atoms still leaves unpaired electrons. If these are shared as well (as in Figure 3.12b), a more stable molecule is formed.

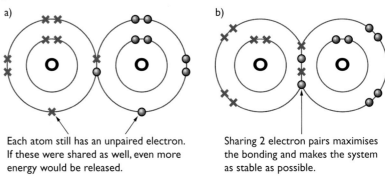

a)

Each atom still has an unpaired electron. If these were shared as well, even more energy would be released.

b)

Sharing 2 electron pairs maximises the bonding and makes the system as stable as possible.

Figure 3.12 *Oxygen atoms with (a) a single covalent bond and (b) two shared electron pairs.*

Covalent double bonding in carbon dioxide, CO_2

Two double bonds are formed between the carbon and the two oxygens (Figure 3.13). This uses up all the unpaired electrons.

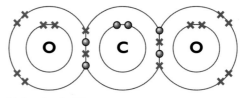

Figure 3.13 *Covalent double bonding in CO_2.*

The double bond in ethene, C_2H_4

Ethene is rather like ethane on page 15, except that it only has two hydrogen atoms attached to each carbon atom.

Ethane and ethene are organic compounds, and you will find out more about them in Section D of this book. You have to look at their names very carefully – even one different letter in the name can matter. Here, for example, ethane and ethene are completely different compounds.

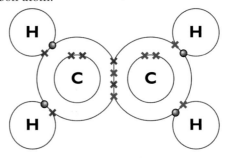

Figure 3.14 *Ethene.*

The triple bond in a nitrogen molecule

The triple bond from the sharing of three pairs of electrons between the two nitrogen atoms is very strong and needs a lot of energy to break. Nitrogen gas consists of nitrogen molecules bonded like this. That is why it is relatively unreactive.

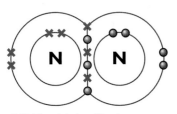

Figure 3.15 *The triple bond in nitrogen.*

Ways of representing covalent bonds

Apart from full dots-and-crosses diagrams, covalent molecules can also be shown in other ways. In models, each link between the atoms represents a covalent bond – a pair of shared electrons.

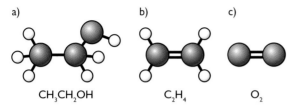

Figure 3.16 *Models of (a) ethanol, (b) ethene and (c) oxygen.*

On paper, we often simplify dots-and-crosses diagrams by leaving out the inner electrons. You might leave out the circles as well, and show only the electrons in the outer energy levels.

Or you might draw each covalent bond as a straight line joining the atoms. Each line means a pair of shared electrons. In diagrams of this sort, sometimes you draw the non-bonding pairs of electrons in the outer level (called **lone pairs**); sometimes you leave them out.

All the diagrams in Figure 3.17 show the covalent bonding in ammonia, NH_3.

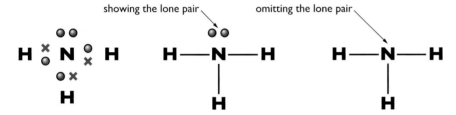

Figure 3.17 *Covalent bonding in ammonia.*

Ionic (electrovalent) bonding

In a covalent bond, the electrons are shared between two atoms. Both nuclei are attracted to the same electron pair.

But sometimes it happens that one of the atoms is attracted to the electron pair much more strongly than the other one. The electron pair is then pulled very close to that atom, and away from the other one.

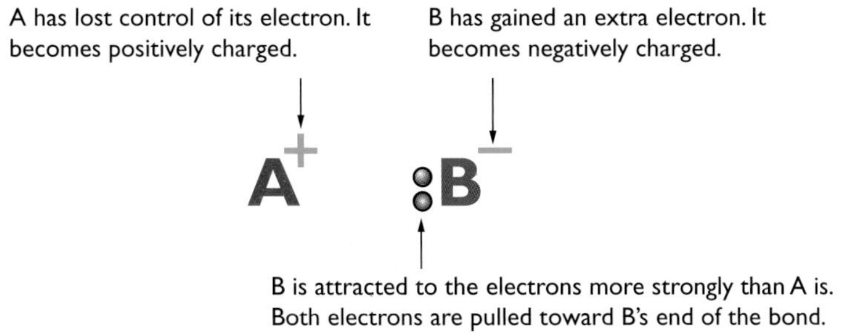

A has lost control of its electron. It becomes positively charged.

B has gained an extra electron. It becomes negatively charged.

$$A^+ \quad \overset{\bullet}{\underset{\bullet}{}}B^-$$

B is attracted to the electrons more strongly than A is. Both electrons are pulled toward B's end of the bond.

Figure 3.19 *Positive and negative charges.*

In Figure 3.19, atom A has, in effect, given its electron to atom B.

If you find this a bit confusing, don't worry about it too much for now. The important thing at the moment is that you can draw dots-and-crosses diagrams for the molecules we have been looking at. Also remember that, in a diagram, any line you draw between two atoms represents a pair of shared electrons – a covalent bond. You may come across the other variations now and then during your course, but they will always be explained at the time.

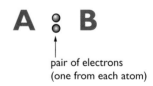

pair of electrons
(one from each atom)

Figure 3.18 *A covalent bond.*

In Figure 3.19, A has become positively charged because it has effectively lost an electron. It still has the same number of positively charged protons, but now has one less electron to balance them.
B is negatively charged because it has gained an extra negative electron.

The electrically charged particles are called **ions**. An ion is an atom (or group of atoms) which carries an electrical charge, either positive or negative.

- A positive ion is called a **cation**.

- A negative ion is called an **anion**.

Ionic bonding is bonding in which there has been a transfer of electrons from one atom to another to produce ions. The substance is held together by strong electrical attractions between positive and negative ions.

Ionic bonding in sodium chloride

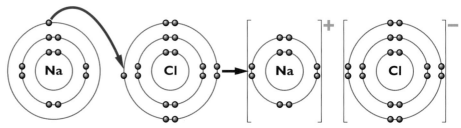

Figure 3.20 *Ionic bonding in sodium chloride.*

The single electron in the outer energy level of the sodium has been transferred to the chlorine. The sodium chloride is held together by the strong attraction between the sodium ion and the chloride ion. (Notice that it is called a **chloride** ion, not a chlorine ion.)

Overall, a lot of energy is given out when this process happens – mainly due to the energy released when the strong bonding between the ions is set up.

You can draw dots-and-crosses diagrams to show ionic bonding, but it is much quicker, and takes up much less space, to write electronic structures in the form 2,8,1 or 2,8,7.

Na   2,8,1   →   Na⁺ [2,8]⁺
Cl   2,8,7   →   Cl⁻ [2,8,8]⁻

Figure 3.21 *Another way of expressing ionic bonding in sodium chloride.*

Ionic bonding in magnesium oxide

Mg   2,8,2   →   Mg²⁺ [2,8]²⁺
O   2,6   →   O²⁻ [2,8]²⁻

Figure 3.22 *Ionic bonding in magnesium oxide.*

In this case, two electrons are transferred from the magnesium to the oxygen.

The two electrons in the outer energy level of the magnesium are relatively easy to remove, and the oxygen has enough space in its outer level to receive them. More energy is given out this time, mainly due to the very, very strong attractions between the 2+ and 2− ions – the higher the number of charges, the stronger the attractions.

This is a simplification! In reality, you don't react sodium with chlorine *atoms*, but with chlorine *molecules*, Cl_2. Before the electron transfer can happen, energy has to be supplied to break the chlorine molecules into individual atoms. You do, in fact, have to heat sodium in chlorine to get it to start to react.

The significance of noble gas structures in ionic bonding

If you look at the structures of the ions formed in Figures 3.21 and 3.22, each of them has a noble gas structure: 2,8 (the neon structure), or 2,8,8 (the argon structure). You might therefore say that atoms lose or gain electrons so that they achieve a noble gas structure. This is true of the elements in Groups 1 and 2 of the Periodic Table (forming 1+ and 2+ ions), and for those in Groups 6 and 7 when they form 2– and 1– ions, as in all these examples.

But there are a lot of common ions that don't have noble gas structures. Fe^{2+}, Fe^{3+}, Cu^{2+}, Zn^{2+}, Ag^+ and Pb^{2+} are all ions that you will come across during a GCSE course – although you won't have to write their electronic structures. Not one of them has a noble gas structure.

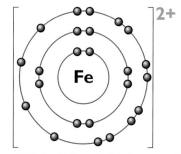

Figure 3.23 *An Fe^{2+} ion – definitely not a noble gas structure!*

Other examples of ionic bonding

Ionic bonds are usually formed only if small numbers of electrons need to be transferred – typically 1 or 2, but occasionally 3. In cases where the ions produced would have, say, a 3+ charge, the situation is rarely as simple as it might appear at first sight.

Lithium fluoride

$$Li \quad 2,1 \qquad Li^+ \quad [2]^+$$
$$F \quad 2,7 \qquad F^- \quad [2,8]^-$$

Figure 3.24 *Ionic bonding in lithium fluoride.*

The lithium atom has one electron in its outer energy level that is easily lost, and the fluorine has space to receive one. Lithium fluoride is held together by the strong attractions between lithium and fluoride ions.

Calcium chloride

$$Cl \quad 2,8,7 \qquad Cl^- \quad [2,8,8]^-$$
$$Ca \quad 2,8,8,2 \longrightarrow Ca^{2+} \quad [2,8,8]^{2+}$$
$$Cl \quad 2,8,7 \qquad Cl^- \quad [2,8,8]^-$$

Figure 3.25 *Ionic bonding in calcium chloride.*

The calcium has two electrons in its outer energy level that are relatively easy to give away, but each chlorine atom only has room in its outer level to take one of them. You need two chlorines for every one calcium. The formula for calcium chloride is therefore $CaCl_2$. There will be very strong attractions holding the ions together because of the 2+ charge on the calcium ions.

Potassium oxide

$$K \quad 2,8,8,1 \qquad K^+ \quad [2,8,8]^+$$
$$O \quad 2,6 \longrightarrow O^{2-} \quad [2,8]^{2-}$$
$$K \quad 2,8,8,1 \qquad K^+ \quad [2,8,8]^+$$

Figure 3.26 *Ionic bonding in potassium oxide.*

This time, the oxygen has room for two electrons in its outer level, but each potassium can only supply one. Potassium oxide's formula is therefore K_2O.

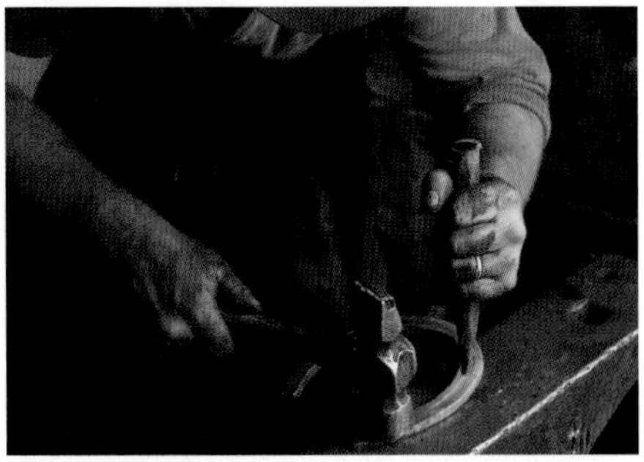

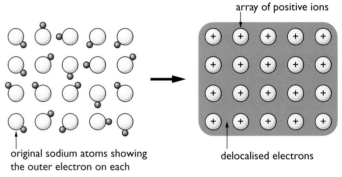

Figure 3.27 *Metals are hard and have high melting points.*

Metallic bonding

Most metals are hard and have high melting points. This suggests that the forces holding the particles in the metal together are very strong.

Figure 3.28 shows what happens when sodium atoms bond together to form the solid metal. The outer electron on each sodium atom becomes free to move throughout the whole structure. The electrons are said to be **delocalised**. These electrons are no longer attached to particular atoms or pairs of atoms. Instead, you can think of them as flowing around throughout the whole metal.

If a sodium atom loses its outer electron, that leaves behind a sodium ion. The attraction of each positive ion to the delocalised electrons holds the structure together.

Metallic bonding is sometimes described as an array of positive ions in a '**sea of electrons**'.

array of positive ions

original sodium atoms showing
the outer electron on each

delocalised electrons

Figure 3.28 *Sodium atoms bonding together to form the metal.*

Warning! When they come to write the symbol for a metal such as sodium in equations, students who know about metallic bonding sometimes worry whether they should write it as Na or Na$^+$. You write it as *atoms* – as Na. Thinking about the structure *as a whole*, the number of electrons exactly balances the number of positive charges. The metal *as a whole* carries no charge.

In the case of sodium, only one electron per atom is delocalised, leaving ions with only one positive charge on them. The ions don't pack very efficiently either. The effect of all this is that the bonding in sodium is quite weak, as metals go, which is why sodium is fairly soft, with a low melting point for a metal.

By contrast, magnesium has two outer electrons, both of which are delocalised into the 'sea', leaving behind ions that carry a charge of 2+. It also packs more efficiently. There is a much stronger attraction between the more negative 'sea' and the doubly charged ions, and so the bonding is stronger and the melting point is greater.

Metals such as iron have even more outer electrons to delocalise, so the bonding is stronger still.

You can find out more about metallic structures in Chapter 4.

Intermolecular forces

You will remember that water, H_2O, is a molecule with strong covalent bonds between the hydrogen and oxygen. In liquid water, or in ice, there must also be attractions between one molecule and its neighbours – otherwise they wouldn't stick together to make a liquid or a solid.

These forces of attraction between separate molecules are called **intermolecular forces** or **intermolecular attractions**. They are a lot weaker than covalent or ionic bonds, and vary in strength from substance to substance.

For example, the intermolecular forces between hydrogen molecules, H_2, are very, very weak. You have to cool hydrogen to $-253\,°C$ before the molecules are travelling slowly enough for the intermolecular attractions to be able to hold them together as a liquid.

By contrast, sugar (also a covalent compound) is a solid that doesn't melt until $185\,°C$. The intermolecular forces between sugar molecules must be quite strong.

Intermolecular forces arise from slight electrical distortions in molecules.

In Figure 3.30, δ is read as 'delta'. So δ+ is read as 'delta plus'. δ is used to mean 'slightly', so δ+ means slightly positive.

You can see that the slightly positive end of one molecule attracts the slightly negative end of a neighbouring molecule. Heating will supply enough energy to break these intermolecular attractions and cause the substance to either melt or boil.

Figure 3.29 *Breaking the intermolecular attractions in water to produce steam.*

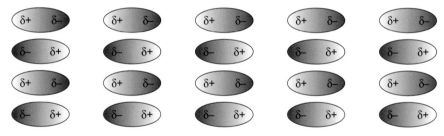

Figure 3.30 *Intermolecular forces.*

A hint at how these distortions arise in water molecules is given in Chapter 4 on page 26.

In melting, some but not all of the intermolecular forces are broken. In boiling, the attractions are totally disrupted and the molecules become free to move around as a gas.

It is very important that you realise that melting or boiling a substance made of molecules breaks intermolecular forces – *not* covalent bonds. When you boil water, you get steam – not a mixture of hydrogen and oxygen atoms. The weak attractions between one molecule and its neighbours are broken, but not the covalent bonds within the molecule.

If you boil a teaspoonful of water (about $5\,cm^3$) in the bottom of an average bucket, enough steam will be produced to fill the bucket. That shows how spread out the water molecules become once you have broken the intermolecular attractions.

End of Chapter Checklist

You should now be able to:

✓ explain what is meant by a covalent bond and a molecule

✓ draw dots-and-crosses diagrams for simple covalent molecules

✓ explain what is meant by an ionic bond

✓ explain the formation of simple ionic compounds

✓ describe how atoms are bound together in a metal

✓ explain what is meant by intermolecular forces.

Questions

You will need to use the Periodic Table on page 226.

1 a) What is meant by a *covalent bond*? How does this bond hold two atoms together?

b) Draw dots-and-crosses diagrams to show the covalent bonding in: **(i)** methane, CH_4; **(ii)** hydrogen sulphide, H_2S; **(iii)** phosphine, PH_3; **(iv)** silicon tetrachloride, $SiCl_4$.

2 Draw dots-and-crosses diagrams to show the covalent bonding in **a)** ethane, C_2H_6; **b)** ethene, C_2H_4; **c)** ethanol, CH_3CH_2OH. You will find models of ethene and ethanol on page 17, which might help you.

3 a) What is meant by (i) an ion; (ii) an ionic bond?

b) In each of the following cases, write down the electronic structures of the original atoms and then explain (in words or diagrams) what happens when:

   (i) sodium bonds with chlorine to make sodium chloride;

   (ii) lithium bonds with oxygen to make lithium oxide;

   (iii) magnesium bonds with fluorine to make magnesium fluoride.

4 a) A solid metal is often described as having 'an array of positive ions in a sea of electrons'. Write down the electronic structure of a magnesium atom and use it to explain what this phrase means.

b) Metallic bonds are not fully broken until the metal has first melted and then boiled. The boiling points of sodium, magnesium and aluminium are 890 °C, 1110 °C and 2470 °C, respectively. What does this suggest about the strengths of the metallic bonds in these three elements?

c) Find these three metals in the Periodic Table, and suggest why the boiling points show this pattern.

d) Assuming that an electric current is simply a flow of electrons, suggest why all these elements are good conductors of electricity.

5 The table below gives details of the boiling temperatures of some substances made up of covalent molecules. Arrange these substances in increasing order of the strength of their intermolecular attractions.

	Boiling point (°C)
ammonia	−33
ethanamide	221
ethanol	78.5
hydrogen	−253
phosphorus trifluoride	−101
water	100

(Don't panic if you don't recognise some of the names. The substances could just as well have been labelled A, B, C, D, E and F.)

6 Boron and aluminium are both in Group 3 of the Periodic Table. Both form compounds with fluorine (BF_3 and AlF_3). Unusually for elements found in the same group of the Periodic Table, their compounds are bonded differently. BF_3 is covalent, whereas AlF_3 is a straightforward ionic compound.

a) Draw a diagram to show the covalent bonding in BF_3.

b) Explain, using diagrams or otherwise, the origin of the ionic bonding in AlF_3.

c) BF_3 is described as an *electron-deficient* compound. What do you think that might mean?

Chapter 4: Structure

The photographs show some substances with quite different physical properties – including hardness, melting point and solubility. This chapter explores some of the reasons for these differences, based on the bonding in the substances. It assumes that you are already familiar with the topic of bonding in Chapter 3.

Figure 4.1 *Metals are strong and easily shaped.*

Figure 4.2 *Many substances form brittle crystals that dissolve easily in water.*

Figure 4.3 *Diamond (a form of carbon) is obviously crystalline, and is the hardest naturally occurring substance.*

Figure 4.4 *Ice is also crystalline, but melts easily to form water.*

Giant structures

You can divide substances into two quite different types – giant structures and molecular structures.

You will remember that molecules are made up of *fixed* numbers of atoms, joined together by covalent bonds. The number of atoms per molecule is usually fairly small, but can run into thousands in the case of big molecules such as plastics or proteins or DNA.

By contrast, giant structures contain huge numbers of either atoms or ions arranged in some regular way, but the number of particles *isn't fixed*.

Examples will make this clear.

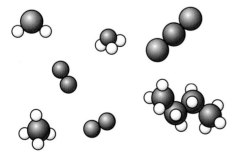

Figure 4.5 *Some simple molecules.*

Chapter 4: Structure

Giant metallic structures

If you aren't sure about this, read page 20 in Chapter 3 before you go on.

Remember that metals consist of a regular array of positive ions in a 'sea of electrons'. The metal is held together by the attractions between the positive ions and the delocalised electrons.

The simple physical properties of metals

Metals tend to be strong, with high melting and boiling points, because of the powerful attractions involved.

Metals conduct electricity. This is because the delocalised electrons are free to move throughout the structure. Imagine what happens if a piece of metal is attached to an electrical power source.

If you compare Figure 4.6 with a similar picture of metallic bonding in Chapter 3 (page 20), you will find that the ions are arranged differently. Figure 4.6 shows the staggered rows typical of efficiently packed metals.

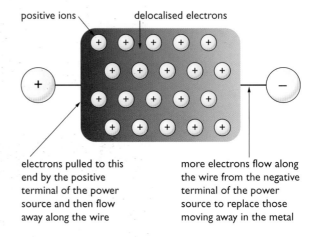

positive ions   delocalised electrons

electrons pulled to this end by the positive terminal of the power source and then flow away along the wire

more electrons flow along the wire from the negative terminal of the power source to replace those moving away in the metal

Figure 4.6 *How metals conduct electricity.*

Metals are good conductors of heat. This is again due to the mobile, delocalised electrons. If you heat one end of a piece of metal, the energy is picked up by the electrons. As the electrons move around in the metal, the heat energy is transferred throughout the structure.

The workability of metals

If a metal is subjected to just a small force, it will stretch and then return to its original shape when the force is released. The metal is described as being **elastic**.

But if a large force is applied, the particles slide over each other and stay in their new positions.

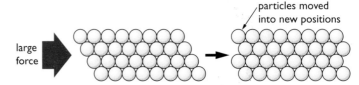

large force

particles moved into new positions

Figure 4.7 *A large force applied to a metal.*

Figure 4.8 *Steel being rolled into strips.*

Metals are usually easy to shape because their regular packing makes it simple for the atoms to slide over each other. Metals are said to be **malleable** and **ductile**. Malleable means that it is easily beaten into shape. Ductile means that it is easily pulled out into wires.

Alloys

Metals can be made harder by **alloying** them with other metals. An alloy is a mixture of metals – for example, **brass** is a mixture of copper and zinc.

In an alloy, the different metals have slightly differently sized atoms. This breaks up the regular arrangement and makes it more difficult for the layers to slide.

Figure 4.9 *Atoms in an alloy.*

The diagram shows how mixing atoms of only slightly different sizes disrupts the regular packing, and makes it much more difficult for particles to slide over each other when a force is applied. This tends to make alloys harder than the individual metals that make them up.

In some cases, alloys have unexpected properties. For example, solder – an alloy of tin and lead – melts at a lower temperature than either of the metals individually. Its low melting point, and the fact that it is a good conductor of electricity, make it useful for joining components in electrical circuits.

Other common alloys include bronze (a mixture of copper and tin), stainless steel (an alloy of iron with chromium and nickel), and the mixture of copper and nickel (cupronickel) which is used to make 'silver' coins.

You can read more about alloys in Chapter 17.

Giant ionic structures

An ion is an atom or group of atoms that carries an electrical charge – either positive or negative. If you aren't sure about ionic bonding, you should read pages 17–19 in Chapter 3 before you go on.

All ionic compounds consist of huge lattices of positive and negative ions packed together in a regular way. A **lattice** is a regular array of particles. The lattice is held together by the strong attractions between the positively and negatively charged ions.

The structure of sodium chloride

In a diagram, the ions are usually drawn in an 'exploded' view. Figure 4.11 shows how they actually occupy the space.

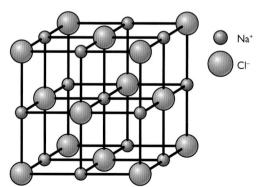

Na⁺
Cl⁻

Figure 4.12 *An 'exploded' view of sodium chloride.*

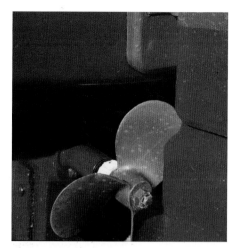

Figure 4.10 *A brass propeller.*

Figure 4.11 *A model of a small part of a sodium chloride crystal.*

Warning! The lines in this diagram are **not** covalent bonds. There are just there to help show the arrangement of the ions. Those ions joined by lines are touching each other. Compare the diagram with the model in Figure 4.11.

Only ions joined by lines in Figure 4.12 are actually touching. Each sodium ion is touched by 6 chloride ions. In turn, each chloride ion is touched by 6 sodium ions.

You have to remember that this structure repeats itself over vast numbers of ions.

The structure of magnesium oxide

Magnesium oxide, MgO, contains magnesium ions, Mg^{2+}, and oxide ions, O^{2-}. It has exactly the same structure as sodium chloride.

The only difference is that the magnesium oxide lattice is held together by stronger forces of attraction. This is because in magnesium oxide, 2+ ions are attracting 2– ions. In sodium chloride, the attractions are weaker because they are only between 1+ and 1– ions.

The simple physical properties of ionic substances

Ionic compounds have high melting points and boiling points because of the strong forces holding the lattices together. Magnesium oxide has much higher melting and boiling points than sodium chloride because the attractive forces are much stronger.

Ionic compounds tend to be crystalline. This reflects the regular arrangement of ions in the lattice. Sometimes the crystals are too small to be seen except under powerful microscopes. Magnesium oxide, for example, is always seen as a white powder because the individual crystals are too small to be seen with the naked eye.

Ionic crystals tend to be brittle. This is because any small distortion of a crystal will bring ions with the same charge alongside each other. Like charges repel and so the crystal splits itself apart.

Figure 4.13 *The shape of the sodium chloride crystal reflects the arrangement of the ions.*

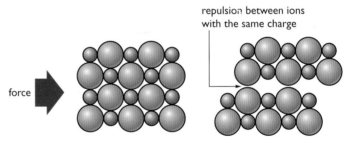

Figure 4.14 *Ionic crystals tend to be brittle.*

Ionic substances tend to be soluble in water. Although water is a covalent molecule, the electrons in the bonds are attracted towards the oxygen end of the bond. This makes the oxygen slightly negative. It leaves the hydrogen slightly short of electrons, and therefore slightly positive.

For the use of the symbol δ, see page 21 in Chapter 3.

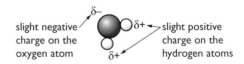

Figure 4.15 *Electrical distortion in a water molecule.*

Because of this electrical distortion, water is described as a **polar** molecule.

There are quite strong attractions between the polar water molecules and the ions in the lattice.

The slightly positive hydrogens in the water molecules cluster around the negative ions, and the slightly negative oxygens are attracted to the positive ions.

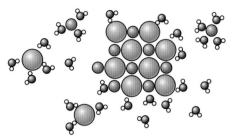

Figure 4.16 *Water molecules, which are polar, pull the crystal apart.*

The water molecules then literally pull the sodium chloride crystal apart.

Magnesium oxide isn't soluble in water because the attractions between the water molecules and the ions aren't strong enough to break the very powerful ionic bonds between magnesium and oxide ions.

Ionic compounds tend to be insoluble in organic solvents. Organic solvents contain molecules which have much less electrical distortion than there is in water – their molecules are less polar. There isn't enough attraction between these molecules and the ions in the crystal to break the strong forces holding the lattice together.

Organic solvents include alcohol (ethanol) and hydrocarbons, such as those found in petrol. If you are interested in these, you could explore the organic chemistry section of this book (Section D).

The electrical behaviour of ionic substances

Ionic compounds don't conduct electricity when they are solid, because they don't contain any mobile electrons. They do, however, conduct electricity when they melt, or if they are dissolved in water. This happens because the ions then become free to move around. How this enables the compound to conduct electricity is explained in Chapter 13.

Giant covalent structures

Diamond

Diamond is a form of pure carbon.

Each carbon atom has four unpaired electrons in its outer energy level (shell), and it uses these to form four covalent bonds. In diamond, each carbon bonds strongly to four other carbon atoms in a **tetrahedral** arrangement. Figure 4.17 shows enough of the structure to see what it is happening.

A tetrahedron is a triangular-based pyramid. In a tetrahedral arrangement, one atom is at the centre of the tetrahedron, and the ones it is attached to are at the four corners. Look carefully at the top five atoms in Figure 4.17 to see what this looks like. You will find other similar arrangements in this diagram.

In Figure 4.17, some carbon atoms seem to be forming only two bonds (or even one bond), but that's not really the case. We are only showing a small bit of the whole structure. The structure continues in three dimensions, and each of the atoms drawn here will be attached to four others. Each of the lines in this diagram represents a covalent bond.

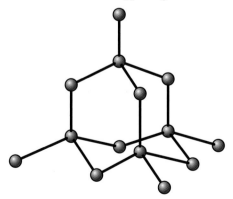

Figure 4.17 *The structure of diamond.*

This is a giant covalent structure – it continues on and on in three dimensions. It is *not* a molecule, because the number of atoms joined up in a real diamond is completely variable – depending on the size of the crystal. Molecules always contain *fixed numbers* of atoms joined by covalent bonds.

Draw this structure in stages, as shown in Figure 4.18.

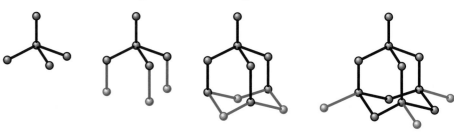

Figure 4.18 *How to draw the structure of diamond.*

> This is a very easy structure to draw as long as you practise it. You should be able to produce a reasonable sketch in 30 seconds.

Diamond is very hard, with a very high melting and boiling point. This is because of the very strong carbon–carbon covalent bonds, which extend throughout the whole crystal in three dimensions. Saw blades can be tipped with diamonds in high-speed cutting tools used on stone and concrete.

Diamond doesn't conduct electricity. All the electrons in the outer levels of the carbon atoms are tightly held in covalent bonds between the atoms. None are free to move around.

Diamond doesn't dissolve in water or in any other solvent. This is again because of the powerful covalent bonds between the carbon atoms. If the diamond dissolved, these bonds would have to be broken.

Graphite

Graphite is also a form of carbon, but the atoms are arranged differently – although still as a giant structure. Graphite has a layer structure, rather like a pack of cards. In a pack of cards, each card is strong but the individual cards are easily separated. The same is true in graphite.

> It is difficult to find a way of drawing more than one layer of graphite in a way that can be done quickly and accurately in an exam. It is much easier to avoid the problem by drawing a top view of a layer and then the stacking of the layers separately. Label any diagram carefully to explain what you are doing, and show the gaps between the layers at about 2.5 times the distance between the atoms in your layer.

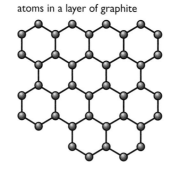

atoms in a layer of graphite   edge-on view of the layers

The gaps between the layers are much bigger than the distances between the atoms in the layers

Figure 4.20 *How to draw the structure of graphite.*

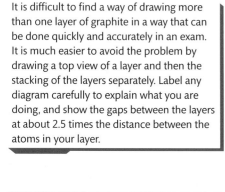

Figure 4.19 *Rubbing layers of graphite off on paper.*

Graphite is a soft material with a slimy feel. Although the forces holding the atoms together in each layer are very strong, the attractions between the layers are much weaker. Layers can easily be flaked off.

Graphite (mixed with clay to make it harder) is used in pencils. When you write with a pencil, you are leaving a trail of graphite layers behind on the paper. Pure graphite is so slippery that it is used as a dry lubricant – for example, powdered graphite is used to lubricate locks.

Graphite has a high melting and boiling point and is insoluble in any solvents. To melt or dissolve graphite, you don't just have to break the layers apart – you have to break up the whole structure, including the covalent bonds. That needs very large amounts of energy because the bonds are so strong.

Graphite is less dense than diamond because the layers in graphite are relatively far apart. The distance between the graphite layers is more than twice the distance between atoms in each layer. In a sense, a graphite crystal contains a lot of wasted space, which isn't there in a diamond crystal.

Graphite conducts electricity. If you look back at Figure 4.20, you will see that each carbon atom is joined to only three others.

Each carbon atom uses three of its electrons to form these simple covalent bonds. The fourth electron in the outer layer of each atom is free to move around throughout the whole of the layer. The movement of these electrons allows the graphite to conduct electricity.

Figure 4.21 *Three graphite electrodes glow red hot after their removal from an electric arc furnace used to produce steel.*

Simple molecular structures

Remember that molecules contain fixed numbers of atoms joined by strong covalent bonds. The forces of attraction between one molecule and its neighbours (intermolecular forces) are much weaker than the covalent bonds, and vary in strength from compound to compound, as shown in Figure 4.22.

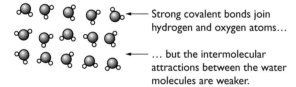

Strong covalent bonds join hydrogen and oxygen atoms…

… but the intermolecular attractions between the water molecules are weaker.

Figure 4.22 *A simple molecular compound.*

It doesn't take very much heat energy to break the relatively weak intermolecular attractions, and so *simple molecular compounds tend to be gases, liquids or solids with a low melting point.*

Molecular substances tend to be insoluble in water unless they react with it.

For their size, water molecules have stronger intermolecular attractions between them than you might expect. In order for a substance to dissolve, these attractions between water molecules have to be broken so that the dissolving molecules can fit between them. Any new attractions between water molecules and the covalent molecules are not usually big enough to make up for this.

On the other hand, *molecular substances are often soluble in organic solvents.* In this case, the intermolecular attractions between the two different types of molecule are much the same as in the pure substances.

Molecular substances don't conduct electricity, because the molecules don't have any overall electrical charge and there are no electrons mobile enough to move from molecule to molecule.

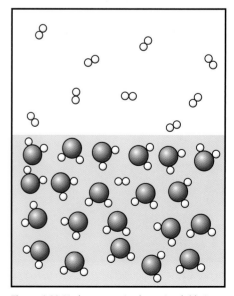

Figure 4.23 *Hydrogen gas is almost insoluble in water.*

Elements, compounds and mixtures

Elements

It isn't quite true to say that elements consist of only one type of atom. Most elements consist of mixtures of isotopes – with the same atomic number, but different numbers of neutrons. When we draw diagrams or make models, we aren't usually interested in the differences between the isotopes.

Elements are substances that can't be split into anything more simple by chemical means. All the atoms in an element have the same atomic number. You can recognise them in models or diagrams because they consist of atoms of a single colour or size.

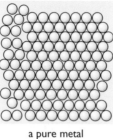
a pure metal

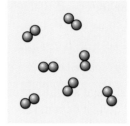
diatomic molecular gas like oxygen

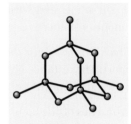
giant structure in diamond

Figure 4.24 *Some elements.*

The substances in Figure 4.24 are all elements because they consist of only one sort of atom.

Compounds

All compounds are made from combinations of two or more elements in fixed proportions, joined by strong bonds. It doesn't matter whether the compound is molecular, giant covalent or giant ionic.

water – a molecular compound

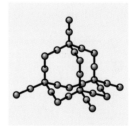
silicon dioxide – a giant covalent compound

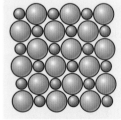
sodium chloride – a giant ionic structure

Figure 4.25 *Some compounds.*

Mixtures

In a mixture, the various components can be in any proportions. An alloy is a mixture rather than a compound because of the totally variable proportions.

Figure 4.26 *A compound, water, flowing through a metal sculpture. Is the metal a pure element? No – it is stainless steel, an alloy, and therefore a mixture of elements.*

mixture of elements – nitrogen and oxygen

mixture of compounds – CO_2 and H_2O

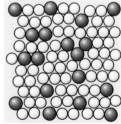
mixture of elements – metals in an alloy

Figure 4.27 *Some mixtures.*

Simple differences between mixtures and compounds

Proportions

In water (a compound), every single water molecule has two hydrogen atoms combined with one oxygen atom. It never varies. In a mixture of hydrogen and oxygen gases, the two could be mixed in any proportions.

If you had some silvery zinc metal and some yellow sulfur, you could mix them in any proportions you wanted to. In zinc sulfide (ZnS, a white powder), the proportions of zinc to sulfur are always exactly the same.

Properties

In a mixture of elements, each element still has its own properties, but the properties of the compound are quite different. For example, in a mixture of iron and sulfur, the iron is grey and the sulfur is yellow. The iron reacts with dilute acids such as hydrochloric acid to produce hydrogen; the sulfur doesn't react with the acid. However, the compound iron sulfide (FeS) reacts quite differently with acids to produce poisonous hydrogen sulfide gas, smelling of bad eggs.

You can find out about the reactions of metals with dilute acids on page 71. The reaction between iron sulfide and acids isn't needed for exam purposes at GCSE.

A mixture of hydrogen and oxygen is a colourless gas which explodes when you put a flame to it. The compound, water, is a colourless liquid which just puts out a flame.

Ease of separation

Mixtures can be separated by physical means. 'Physical means' are things like changing the temperature, or dissolving part of the mixture in a solvent like water – things that don't involve any chemical reactions.

For example, a mixture of iron and sulfur is quite easy to separate into the two elements using a magnet. The iron sticks to the magnet, and the sulfur doesn't. To separate the iron and sulfur from iron sulfide would need quite a lot of chemistry to convert it into separate samples of iron and sulfur.

You can just cool a mixture of hydrogen and oxygen gases to separate it by a physical process. Oxygen condenses into a liquid at a much higher temperature than hydrogen does (−183 °C as opposed to −253 °C). This would leave you with liquid oxygen and hydrogen gas, which would be easy to separate. But to separate water into hydrogen and oxygen, you have to change it chemically using electrolysis.

Electrolysis is explained in Chapter 13, and the use of electrolysis to find the formula for water is explained in Chapter 23. If you are just starting on this course, ignore that reference for now.

Energy changes

If you mix some hydrogen and oxygen gas together, there isn't any temperature change. On the other hand, if you combine hydrogen and oxygen together to make water, a huge amount of energy is released. You see and hear that as an explosion.

This is typical. Assuming there isn't any reaction on simple mixing, when you mix things together there is either a small energy change, or none at all. When you make a compound, energy changes are much greater.

End of Chapter Checklist

You should now be able to:

✓ understand what is meant by giant metallic structure, giant ionic structure, giant covalent structure and molecular structure

✓ relate the simple physical properties of a substance (melting and boiling temperatures, conduction of heat and electricity, workability/hardness, solubility) to its structure

✓ recognise and draw structures for the compounds you have met

✓ understand the differences between the words element, compound and mixture in terms of the way the particles are arranged, and describe some simple differences between a compound and a mixture.

Questions

1 a) Draw simple diagrams to show the structures of diamond and graphite.

b) Choose any one physical property where diamond and graphite have similar characteristics, and any two physical properties where they are different. Use your diagrams to explain the similarity and the differences.

2 a) Most metals are malleable and ductile. Explain what happens to the particles in a metal when it is subjected to a large stress.

b) State any other physical property of metals, and explain how it arises from the metallic structure.

c) Alloys are mixtures of metals. Explain why an alloy is usually harder than the individual metals that make it up.

3 Explain why sodium chloride **a)** has a high melting point; **b)** has brittle crystals; **c)** is soluble in water.

4 Decide what sort of structure each of the following substances is most likely to have. You can choose between: giant metallic structure, giant covalent structure, giant ionic structure, molecular structure.

a) Substance A melts at 2300 °C. It doesn't conduct electricity even when it is molten. It is insoluble in water.

b) Substance B is a colourless gas.

c) Substance C is a yellow solid with a low melting point of 113 °C. It doesn't conduct electricity and is insoluble in water.

d) Substance D forms brittle orange crystals which melt at 398 °C. D dissolves freely in water to give an orange solution.

e) Substance E is a pinkish-brown flexible solid. It conducts electricity.

f) Substance F is a liquid with a boiling point of 80 °C. It is insoluble in water.

g) Substance G is a silvery solid which melts at 660 °C. It is used in overhead power cables.

h) Substance H is a glassy solid which melts at 450 °C and boils at 1860 °C. It doesn't conduct electricity even when molten, but reacts very slowly with water.

5 Look back at the structure of silicon dioxide, SiO_2, on page 30. Silicon–oxygen bonds are strong.

a) Would you expect silicon dioxide to be a solid, liquid or gas? Explain your answer.

b) Would you expect silicon dioxide to be hard or soft? Explain your answer.

c) Silicon dioxide doesn't *react* with water, but would you expect silicon dioxide to *dissolve* in water? Explain your answer.

d) By doing an internet or book search, find out where silicon dioxide occurs in nature. Are your answers to **(a–c)** consistent with what you have found out? Explain why.

Chapter 5: Formulae and Equations

Writing formulae

Formulae for covalent substances

Common everyday examples

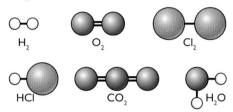

Figure 5.1 *Some common covalent substances.*

Learning how to understand and write chemical formulae and equations isn't one of the most exciting parts of Chemistry, but once you have the skill to do it, you will find that the subject suddenly becomes much clearer and easier to follow. Don't worry if it sometimes seems to take a long time to work out a formula or write an equation in the early stages. It does take a long time to start with – you just need patience and lots of practice.

Remember that each line represents a covalent bond – a pair of shared electrons. All these examples are described in detail on pages 14–16.

The formula simply counts the number of atoms combined to make the compound. You won't usually have to work out the formula of a covalent compound – most of the ones you will meet at GCSE are so simple and so common that you just remember them.

Suppose you had to work one out

Suppose you had to find the formula for phosphine – a simple compound of phosphorus and hydrogen.

Find phosphorus in the Periodic Table. Its atomic number is 15, so the atom has 15 protons and 15 electrons. The electrons would be arranged 2,8,5. All you are interested in are the electrons in the outer level.

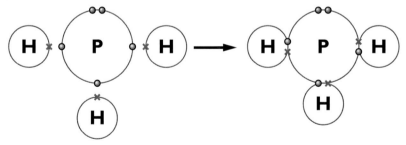

If you aren't happy about this, then you should read the beginning of Chapter 3 on covalent bonding (page 13).

Figure 5.2 *Phosphine.*

The phosphorus can create three covalent bonds by sharing the single electrons with three hydrogen atoms. That means the formula for phosphine must be PH_3.

Formulae for ionic compounds

There are so many different ionic compounds that you might come across at GCSE, that it would be impossible to learn all their formulae. You need a simple way to work them out. You could work out a few from first principles, using their electronic structures, but that would take ages. Others would be too difficult. You need a simple, short-cut method.

Before you go on, it would be a good idea to remind yourself about ionic bonding by reading pages 17–19.

The need for equal numbers of pluses and minuses

Ions are atoms, or groups of atoms, that carry an electrical charge, either positive or negative. Compounds are electrically neutral. Therefore in an ionic compound there must be the right number of each sort of ion, so that the total positive charge exactly cancels out the total negative charge. Obviously, then, if you are going to work out a formula, you need to know the charges on the ions.

Cases where you can work out the number of charges on an ion

Any element in Group 2 has two outer electrons, which it will lose to form a 2+ ion. Any element in Group 6 has six outer electrons, and it has room to gain two more. This leads to a 2− ion. Similar arguments apply in the other Groups shown in Table 5.1.

> You will always have a copy of the Periodic Table – even in an exam. That means that you can always find out which group an element is in. Elements in Groups 4 and 5 form few simple ions. Where they do, the pattern isn't always easily predictable. You won't need to worry about this at GCSE. The only one you might come across at this level is nitrogen, which sometimes forms a 3− nitride ion, N^{3-}.

Element in Periodic Table Group	Charge on ion
1	+1
2	+2
3	+3
(5)	(−3)
6	−2
7	−1

Table 5.1: *The number of charges on an ion in Groups 1–7.*

Cases where the name tells you the charge

All metals form positive ions. Names such as lead(II) oxide, iron(III) chloride or copper(II) sulfate tell you directly about the charge on the metal ion. The number after the metal tells you the number of charges. So . . .

> This is really important. Remember that all metals form positive ions.

- lead(II) oxide contains a Pb^{2+} ion

- iron(III) chloride contains an Fe^{3+} ion

- copper(II) sulfate contains a Cu^{2+} ion.

Find the symbols for the metals from a Periodic Table if you need to.

Ions that need to be learnt are shown in Table 5.2.

Charge	Substance	Ion
Positive	zinc	Zn^{2+}
	silver	Ag^+
	hydrogen	H^+
	ammonium	NH_4^+
Negative	nitrate	NO_3^-
	hydroxide	OH^-
	hydrogencarbonate	HCO_3^-
	carbonate	CO_3^{2-}
	sulfate	SO_4^{2-}

Table 5.2: *Ions that you should learn.*

You will come across other ions during the course, but these are the important ones for now. The ions in this list are the tricky ones – be sure to learn both the formula and the charge for each ion.

Confusing endings!

Don't confuse ions such as sulf**ate** and sulf**ide**. A name like copper(II) sulf**ide** means that it contains copper and sulfur **only**. Any '**ide**' ending means that there isn't anything complicated there. Sodium chloride, for example, is just sodium and chlorine combined together.

Once you have an '**ate**' ending, it means that there is something else there as well – often, but not always, oxygen. So, for example, copper(II) sulfate contains copper, sulfur and oxygen.

Not looking carefully at word endings is one of the commonest mistakes students make when they start to write formulae.

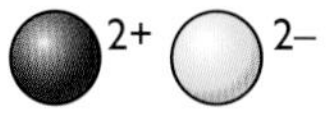

Working out the formula for an ionic compound

Example 1: To find the formula for sodium oxide

Sodium is in Group 1, so the ion is Na^+.

Oxygen is in Group 6, so the ion is O^{2-}.

To have equal numbers of positive and negative charges, you would need two sodium ions to provide the two positive charges to cancel the two negative charges on one oxide ion. In other words, you need:

Na^+ Na^+ O^{2-}
The formula is therefore **Na_2O**.

Example 2: To find the formula for barium nitrate

Barium is in Group 2, so the ion is Ba^{2+}.

Nitrate ions are NO_3^-. You will have to remember this.

To have equal numbers of positive and negative charges, you would need two nitrate ions for each barium ion.

The formula is **$Ba(NO_3)_2$**.

Notice the brackets around the nitrate group. *Brackets must be written if you have more than one of these complex ions* (ions containing more than one type of atom). In any other situation, they are completely unnecessary.

Example 3: To find the formula for iron(III) sulfate

Iron(III) tells you that the metal ion is Fe^{3+}.

Sulfate ions are SO_4^{2-}. You will have to remember this.

To have equal numbers of positive and negative charges, you would need two iron(III) ions for every three sulfate ions – to give 6+ and 6− in total.

The formula is **$Fe_2(SO_4)_3$**.

Why aren't ion charges shown in formulae?

Actually, they can be shown. For example, the formula for sodium chloride is NaCl. It is sometimes written Na^+Cl^- if you are trying to make a particular point, but for most purposes the charges are left out. In an ionic compound, the charges are there – whether you write them or not.

copper(II) sulfide

Figure 5.3 *Copper(II) sulfide.*

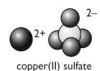

copper(II) sulfate

Figure 5.4 *Copper(II) sulfate.*

If you didn't write the brackets, the formula would look like this: $BaNO_{32}$.
That would read as 1 barium, 1 nitrogen and 32 oxygens. That's not what you mean!

Writing equations

What all the numbers mean

When you write equations, it is important to be able to count up how many of each sort of atom you have. In particular, you must understand the difference between big numbers written in front of formulae, such as the **2** in **2**HCl, and the smaller, subscript (slightly lower on the line) numbers such as the **4** in CH_4.

What, for example, is the difference between **2Cl** and **Cl$_2$**? It shows whether or not the atoms are joined together.

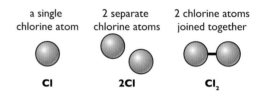

Figure 5.5 *The difference between 2Cl and Cl$_2$.*

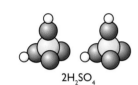

$2H_2SO_4$

Figure 5.6 *$2H_2SO_4$.*

Look at the way the numbers work in $2H_2SO_4$. The big number in front tells you that you have 2 sulfuric acid molecules. The subscript 4, for example, tells you that you have 4 oxygen atoms in each molecule. A small subscript number in a formula applies only to the atom immediately before it in the formula.

If you count the atoms in $2H_2SO_4$, you will find 4 hydrogens, 2 sulfurs and 8 oxygens.

If you have brackets in a formula, a small number refers to everything inside the brackets. For example, in the formula $Ca(OH)_2$, the **2** applies to both the oxygen and the hydrogen. The formula shows 1 calcium, 2 oxygens and 2 hydrogens.

Balancing equations

Chemical reactions involve taking elements or compounds and shuffling their atoms around into new combinations. It follows that you must always end up with the same number of atoms that you started with.

Suppose you had to write an equation for the reaction between methane, CH_4, and oxygen, O_2. Methane burns in oxygen to form carbon dioxide and water. Think of this in terms of rearranging the atoms in some models.

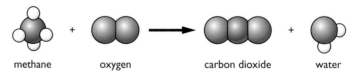

methane   oxygen   carbon dioxide   water

Figure 5.7 *Rearranging the atoms in methane and oxygen.*

This can't be right! During the rearrangement you seem to have gained an oxygen atom and lost two hydrogens. The reaction must be more complicated than this. Since the substances are all correct, the proportions must be wrong.

Try again:

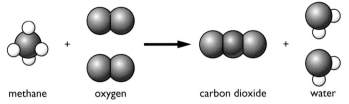

methane   oxygen   carbon dioxide   water

Figure 5.8 *A balanced equation for the reaction between methane and oxygen.*

There are now the same number of each sort of atom before and after. This is called **balancing the equation**.

In symbols, this equation would be:

$$CH_4 + 2O_2 \rightarrow CO_2 + 2H_2O$$

Think of each symbol (C or H or O) as representing one atom of that element. Count them up in the equation, and check that there are the same number on both sides.

How to balance equations

Balancing equations isn't a hit-and-miss affair. If you are patient and work systematically, the equations you will meet at GCSE almost balance themselves.

● Work across the equation from left to right, checking one element after another, except if an element appears in several places in the equation. In that case, leave it until the end – you will often find that it has sorted itself out.

● If you have a group of atoms (like a sulfate group, for example), which is unchanged from one side of the equation to the other, there is no reason why you can't just count that up as a whole group, rather than counting individual sulfurs and oxygens. It saves time.

● Check everything at the end to make sure you haven't changed something that you have already counted.

Example 1: zinc + hydrochloric acid → zinc chloride + hydrogen

Balance the equation: $Zn + HCl \rightarrow ZnCl_2 + H_2$

Work from left to right. Count the zinc atoms. 1 on each side – no problem!

Count the hydrogen atoms. 1 on the left; 2 on the right. If you end up with 2, you must have started with 2. The only way of achieving this is to have 2HCl. (You *must not* change the formula to H_2Cl – there's no such substance.)

This is really important! You must *never, never* change a formula in balancing an equation. All you are allowed to do is to write big numbers in front of the formula.

$$Zn + 2HCl \rightarrow ZnCl_2 + H_2$$

Now count the chlorines. There are 2 on each side. Good! Finally check everything again to make sure – and that's it.

Example 2: silver nitrate solution and calcium chloride solution to give calcium nitrate solution and solid silver chloride

Balance the equation: $AgNO_3 + CaCl_2 \rightarrow Ca(NO_3)_2 + AgCl$

Working from left to right: 1 silver atom on both sides. That's fine.

The nitrate group is unchanged, so save time by counting it as a whole rather than splitting it into individual elements. There's 1 NO_3 group on the left, 2 on the right. That needs correcting. You must have started with $2AgNO_3$.

$$2AgNO_3 + CaCl_2 \rightarrow Ca(NO_3)_2 + AgCl$$

Now check the calcium: 1 on each side.

Now the chlorine: There are 2 on the left, but only 1 on the right. You need $2AgCl$.

$$2AgNO_3 + CaCl_2 \rightarrow Ca(NO_3)_2 + 2AgCl$$

Finally, check everything again. It's all OK – but it might not have been. You actually changed the numbers of silver atoms on the left hand side after you checked them at the beginning. It so happens that the problem corrected itself when you put the 2 in front of the AgCl on the right – but that won't always happen.

Example 3: ethane + oxygen $\rightarrow$ carbon dioxide + water

Balance the equation: $C_2H_6 + O_2 \rightarrow CO_2 + H_2O$

Starting from the left, balance the carbons:

$$C_2H_6 + O_2 \rightarrow 2CO_2 + H_2O$$

Now the hydrogens:

$$C_2H_6 + O_2 \rightarrow 2CO_2 + 3H_2O$$

> Don't go on until you are sure you understand why there are 7 oxygen atoms on the right-hand side.

And finally the oxygens: There are 7 oxygens (4 + 3) on the right-hand side, but only 2 on the left. The problem is that the oxygens have to go around in pairs – so how can you get an odd number (7) of them on the left-hand side?

The trick with this is to allow yourself to have halves in your equation. 7 oxygen atoms, O, is the same as 3½ oxygen molecules, O_2.

$$C_2H_6 + 3½ O_2 \rightarrow 2CO_2 + 3H_2O$$

> In fact, it is acceptable to have halves in equations, but you don't usually come across them at GCSE.

You might reasonably argue that you can't have half an oxygen molecule, but to get rid of that problem you only have to double everything.

$$2C_2H_6 + 7O_2 \rightarrow 4CO_2 + 6H_2O$$

State symbols

State symbols are often, but not always, written after the formulae of the various substances in an equation to show what physical state everything is in. You need to know four different state symbols:

(s) solid   (l) liquid   (g) gas   (aq) in aqueous solution (solution in water).

So an equation might look like this:

$$2K(s) + 2H_2O(l) \rightarrow 2KOH(aq) + H_2(g)$$

> Don't worry if this chemistry is unfamiliar to you, or if you wouldn't know at this stage what the state symbols ought to be. That doesn't matter in the least for now.

This says that solid potassium reacts with liquid water to make a solution of potassium hydroxide in water and hydrogen gas.

You should now be able to:

✓ remember the formulae for some simple covalent compounds such as water and carbon dioxide

✓ work out the formula of a simple covalent compound from its electronic structure

✓ work out formulae for simple ionic compounds from the symbols and charges of their component ions

✓ balance simple equations for familiar reactions, or reactions where you are given the names of everything involved

✓ understand and use the state symbols (s), (l), (g) and (aq).

Questions

You will need to use the Periodic Table on page 226.

1 Work out the formulae of the following compounds.

lead(II) oxide
magnesium sulfate
potassium carbonate
calcium nitrate
iron(II) sulfate
aluminium sulfate
cobalt(II) chloride
silver nitrate
ammonium nitrate
sodium sulfate

sodium bromide
zinc chloride
ammonium sulfide
iron(III) hydroxide
copper(II) carbonate
calcium hydroxide
calcium oxide
iron(III) fluoride
rubidium iodide
chromium(III) oxide

2 a) Hydrogen sulfide is a simple covalent compound of hydrogen and sulfur.

　(i) Write down the electronic structures of hydrogen and sulfur.

　(ii) Draw a dots-and-crosses diagram to show the bonding in hydrogen sulfide.

　(iii) What is the formula for hydrogen sulfide?

b) Silane is the simplest compound of silicon and hydrogen. Work out the formula of silane by drawing a dots-and-crosses diagram of it.

3 Balance the following equations:

a) $Ca + H_2O \rightarrow Ca(OH)_2 + H_2$

b) $Al + Cr_2O_3 \rightarrow Al_2O_3 + Cr$

c) $Fe_2O_3 + CO \rightarrow Fe + CO_2$

d) $NaHCO_3 + H_2SO_4 \rightarrow Na_2SO_4 + CO_2 + H_2O$

e) $C_8H_{18} + O_2 \rightarrow CO_2 + H_2O$

f) $Fe + HCl \rightarrow FeCl_2 + H_2$

g) $Zn + H_2SO_4 \rightarrow ZnSO_4 + H_2$

h) $Fe_3O_4 + H_2 \rightarrow Fe + H_2O$

i) $Mg + O_2 \rightarrow MgO$

j) $Pb + AgNO_3 \rightarrow Pb(NO_3)_2 + Ag$

k) $AgNO_3 + MgCl_2 \rightarrow Mg(NO_3)_2 + AgCl$

l) $C_3H_8 + O_2 \rightarrow CO_2 + H_2O$

m) $Fe_2O_3 + C \rightarrow Fe + CO$

4 Rewrite the following equations as balanced symbol equations:

a) sodium carbonate + hydrochloric acid (HCl) → sodium chloride + carbon dioxide + water

b) sodium hydroxide + sulfuric acid (H_2SO_4) → sodium sulfate + water

c) sodium + water → sodium hydroxide + hydrogen (H_2)

d) sodium + chlorine (Cl_2) → sodium chloride

e) iron(III) oxide + nitric acid (HNO_3) → iron(III) nitrate + water

f) zinc + oxygen (O_2) → zinc oxide

g) copper(II) oxide + hydrochloric acid → copper(II) chloride + water

h) barium chloride + sodium sulfate → barium sulfate + sodium chloride

i) zinc + lead(II) nitrate → lead + zinc nitrate

j) copper(II) sulfate + potassium hydroxide → copper(II) hydroxide + potassium sulfate

k) magnesium + copper(II) oxide → magnesium oxide + copper *l)* sodium + oxygen (O_2) → sodium oxide

m) iron + chlorine (Cl_2) → iron(III) chloride

5 Write balanced symbol equations from the following descriptions. Everything must have a state symbol attached.

a) Solid calcium carbonate reacts with a dilute solution of hydrochloric acid (HCl) to give a solution of calcium chloride and carbon dioxide gas. Water is also formed.

b) Zinc metal reacts with copper(II) sulfate solution to give solid copper and a solution of zinc sulfate.

c) Magnesium reacts with dilute sulfuric acid to give magnesium sulfate solution and hydrogen.

d) Iron(III) sulfate solution and sodium hydroxide solution react to give solid iron(III) hydroxide and a solution of sodium sulfate.

e) Solid aluminium reacts with a dilute solution of hydrochloric acid (HCl) to give a solution of aluminium chloride and hydrogen (H_2).

f) Solid iron(III) oxide reacts with a dilute solution of sulfuric acid to give iron(III) sulfate solution and water.

g) Solid lead(II) carbonate reacts with a dilute solution of nitric acid (HNO_3) to give a solution of lead(II) nitrate, carbon dioxide and water.

h) Magnesium reacts if heated in steam to produce white solid magnesium oxide and hydrogen (H_2).

i) A mixture of carbon and copper(II) oxide heated together produces copper and carbon dioxide.

Chapter 6: Rates of Reaction

Figure 6.1 *Some reactions are very fast.*

Figure 6.2 *Some reactions happen over several minutes.*

Reactions can vary in speed between those that happen within fractions of a second – explosions, for example – and those that never happen at all. Gold can be exposed to the air for thousands of years and not react in any way.

This chapter looks at the factors controlling the speeds of chemical reactions.

Figure 6.3 *Rusting takes days or weeks.*

Figure 6.4 *The weathering of limestone and the formation of stalagmites and stalactites takes a very long time.*

An investigation of the reaction between marble chips and dilute hydrochloric acid

Marble chips are made of calcium carbonate, and react with hydrochloric acid to produce carbon dioxide gas. Calcium chloride solution is also formed.

$$CaCO_3(s) + 2HCl(aq) \rightarrow CaCl_2(aq) + H_2O(l) + CO_2(g)$$

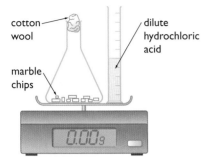

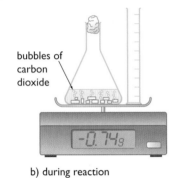

a) before reaction

b) during reaction

Figure 6.5 *Investigating the reaction between calcium carbonate and hydrochloric acid.*

Figure 6.5 shows some apparatus that can be used to measure how the mass of carbon dioxide produced changes with time. Part (a) is drawn as the apparatus would look before the reaction starts.

The flask is stoppered with cotton wool and contains marble chips. The cotton wool is to allow the carbon dioxide to escape, but to stop any acid spraying out. The measuring cylinder contains dilute hydrochloric acid. The marble is in large excess – most of it will be left over when the acid is all used up. Everything is placed on a top pan balance, which is reset to zero.

Part (b) shows what happens during the reaction. The acid has been poured into the flask and everything has been replaced on the balance.

Notice that once the reaction starts, the balance shows a negative mass. This measures the carbon dioxide escaping through the cotton wool.

The mass of carbon dioxide lost is measured at intervals, and a graph is plotted.

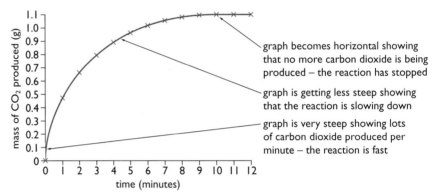

Figure 6.6 *The mass of carbon dioxide lost when calcium carbonate reacts with hydrochloric acid.*

The steeper the slope of the line, the faster the reaction. You can see from Figure 6.6 that about 0.45 g of carbon dioxide is produced in the first minute in this example. Less than 0.2 g of extra carbon dioxide is produced in the second minute – the reaction is slowing down.

The reaction is fastest at the beginning. It then slows down, until it eventually stops because all the hydrochloric acid has been used up. There will still be unreacted marble chips in the flask.

You can measure how fast the reaction is going at any point by finding the slope of the line at that point. This is called the **rate of the reaction** at that point. You might, for example, find that at a particular time, the carbon dioxide was being lost at the rate of, say, 0.12 g per minute.

Explaining what's happening

We can explain the shape of the curve by thinking about the particles present and how they interact. This is called the **collision theory**.

Reactions can happen only when particles collide. In this case, particles in the acid have to collide with the surface of the marble chips. As the acid particles get used up, the collision rate decreases, and so the reaction slows down. The marble is in such large excess that its shape doesn't change much during the reaction.

You can use a graph to find actual values for the rate of reaction at any particular time, by drawing a tangent to the line at the time you are interested in and finding its slope. If the maths of this makes you uneasy, don't worry about it. You are unlikely to be asked to do it in an exam.

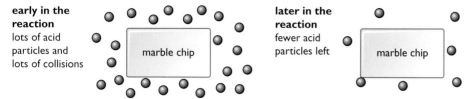

Figure 6.7 *As the reaction proceeds, the collision rate of acid particles decreases.*

A different form of graph

At GCSE, you normally plot graphs showing the mass or volume of product formed during a reaction. It is possible, however, that you may come across graphs showing the fall in the concentration of one of the reactants – in this case, the concentration of the dilute hydrochloric acid.

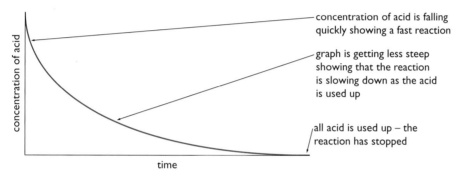

Figure 6.8 *The fall in concentration of hydrochloric acid.*

Where the graph is falling most quickly, it shows that the reaction is fastest.

Eventually, the graph becomes horizontal because the reaction has stopped.

Changing the conditions in the experiment

Using smaller marble chips

You can easily repeat the experiment using exactly the same quantities of everything, but using much smaller marble chips. The reaction with the small chips happens faster.

Both sets of results are plotted on the same graph. Notice that the same mass of carbon dioxide is produced, because you are using the same quantities of everything in both experiments. However, the reaction with the smaller chips starts off much more quickly and finishes sooner.

If you are going to investigate the effect of changing the size of the marble chips, it is important that everything else stays the exactly the same.

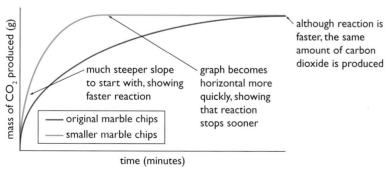

Figure 6.9 *The effect of using smaller marble chips.*

Reactions between solids and liquids (or solids and gases) are faster if the solids are present as a lot of small bits rather than a few big ones. The more finely divided the solid, the faster the reaction, because the surface area in contact with the gas or liquid is much greater.

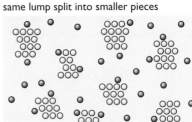

one big lump

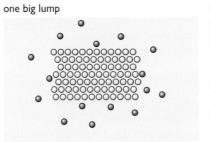

same lump split into smaller pieces

liquid (or gas) particles can't get at the particles hidden in the middle of the solid

far fewer particles are now hidden away

Figure 6.10 *The more divided the solid, the faster the reaction.*

High surface areas are frequently used to speed up reactions outside the lab. For example, a **catalytic converter** for a car uses expensive metals such as platinum, palladium and rhodium, coated onto a honeycomb structure in a very thin layer, in order to keep costs down.

In the presence of these metals, harmful substances such as carbon monoxide and nitrogen oxides are converted into relatively harmless carbon dioxide and nitrogen. The high surface area means the reaction is very rapid. This is important because the gases in the exhaust system are in contact with the catalytic converter for only a very short time.

Changing the concentration of the acid

You could repeat the experiment using the original marble chips, but using hydrochloric acid only half as concentrated as before. Everything else would be the same – the mass of marble and the volume of the acid.

You would find that the reaction would be slower, and only half as much gas would be given off.

Figure 6.11 *A real honeycomb produced by bees – in a catalytic converter, a similar structure is made of a ceramic coated with catalyst, to give a very high surface area for the exhaust gases to flow through.*

The reason you get half the mass of carbon dioxide is because you only have half the amount of acid present. (You have the same volume of acid, but it is only half as concentrated.)

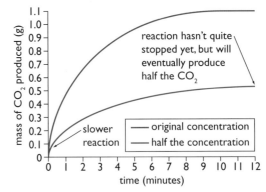

Figure 6.12 *The effect of changing the concentration of the acid.*

If you go on to do chemistry at a higher level, you will come across a few reactions in which increasing the concentration of *one* of the reactants has no effect on how fast the reaction happens. You can ignore that problem for now.

In general terms, if you increase the concentration of the reactants, the reaction becomes faster. Increasing the concentration increases the number of times the particles hit each other per second.

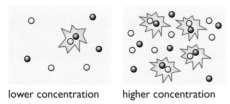

lower concentration   higher concentration

Figure 6.13 *At a higher concentration, more particles collide per second.*

Changing the temperature of the reaction

You could do the original experiment again, but this time at a higher temperature. Everything else would be exactly the same as before.

Reactions get faster as the temperature is increased. In this case, the same mass of gas would be given off, because you still have the same quantities of everything in the mixture.

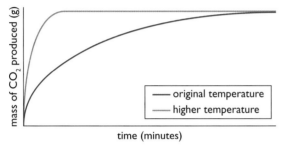

Figure 6.14 *The effect of changing the temperature of the reaction.*

As a rough approximation, a $10\,°C$ increase in temperature doubles the rate of a reaction. There are two factors at work here.

Increasing the temperature means that the particles are moving faster, and so hit each other more often. That will make the reaction go faster, but it only accounts for a small part of the increase in rate.

Not all collisions end up in a reaction. Many particles just bounce off each other. In order for anything interesting to happen, the particles have to collide with a minimum amount of energy, called **activation energy**.

A relatively small increase in temperature produces a very large increase in the number of collisions that have enough energy for a reaction to occur.

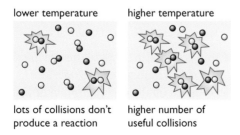

lower temperature   higher temperature

lots of collisions don't   higher number of
produce a reaction   useful collisions

Figure 6.15 *A small increase in temperature produces a large increase in the number of collisions with activation energy.*

Changing the pressure on the reaction

Changing the pressure on a reaction where the reactants are only solids or liquids makes virtually no difference to the rate of reaction – so in this case, the graphs would be unchanged. But increasing the pressure on a reaction where the reactants are gases does speed the reaction up.

If you have a fixed amount of a gas, you increase the pressure by squeezing it into a smaller volume.

This forces the particles closer together, so they hit each other more frequently. This is exactly the same as increasing the concentration of the gas.

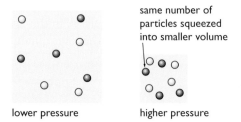

same number of particles squeezed into smaller volume

lower pressure   higher pressure

Figure 6.16 *Increased pressure means gas particles collide more frequently.*

Catalysts

What are catalysts?

Catalysts are substances that speed up chemical reactions, but aren't used up in the process. They are still there, chemically unchanged, at the end of the reaction. Because they don't get used up, small amounts of catalyst can be used to process lots and lots of reactant particles – whether atoms or molecules or ions. Different reactions need different catalysts.

Think of a catalyst as being rather like a machine tool in a factory. Because the tool doesn't get used up, one tool can process huge amounts of stainless steel into teaspoons, for example. A different tool could turn virtually endless quantities of plastic into yoghurt pots.

The catalytic decomposition of hydrogen peroxide

Bombardier beetles defend themselves by spraying a hot, unpleasant liquid at their attackers. Part of the reaction involves splitting hydrogen peroxide into water and oxygen, using the enzyme catalase. This reaction happens almost explosively, and produces a lot of heat. Enzymes are biological catalysts.

There are a lot of other things that also catalyse this reaction. One of these is manganese(IV) oxide – also called manganese dioxide, MnO_2. This is what is normally used in the lab to speed up the decomposition of hydrogen peroxide.

The reaction happening with the hydrogen peroxide is:

$$\text{hydrogen peroxide} \rightarrow \text{water} + \text{oxygen}$$
$$2H_2O_2(aq) \rightarrow 2H_2O(l) + O_2(g)$$

Figure 6.17 *Bombardier beetles use hydrogen peroxide as part of their defence mechanism.*

Notice that you don't write catalysts into the equation, because they are chemically unchanged at the end of the reaction. If you like, you can write their name over the top of the arrow.

Measuring the volume of oxygen evolved

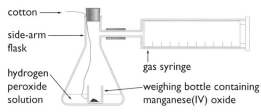

Figure 6.18 *Apparatus to measure the volume of oxygen evolved.*

When you are ready to start the reaction, shake the flask so that the weighing bottle falls over and the manganese(IV) oxide comes into contact with the hydrogen peroxide. You need to keep shaking so that an even mixture is formed.

You could use this apparatus to find out what happens to the rate of reaction if you:

- change the mass of the catalyst
- change how 'lumpy' the catalyst is
- use a different catalyst
- change the concentration of the hydrogen peroxide solution
- change the temperature of the solution.

In each case, you could measure the volume of oxygen produced at regular intervals, and produce graphs just like the ones earlier in this chapter. However, if you wanted to look in a more detailed way at how a change in concentration or temperature, for example, affects the rate of the reaction, there is a much easier way of doing it.

Exploring the very beginning of the reaction

An easy way of comparing rates under different conditions is to time how long it takes to produce a small, but constant, volume of gas – say, $5 \, cm^3$ – as you vary the conditions. You take measurements of the rate at the beginning of the reaction – the so-called **initial rate**.

This experiment uses an upturned measuring cylinder to measure the volume of the gas. The cylinder is initially full of water.

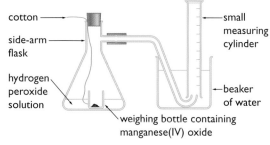

Figure 6.19 *Apparatus to explore the initial rate of the reaction.*

Using a weighing bottle like the one in Figure 6.18 is a simple way of mixing the chemicals together without losing any oxygen before you can get the bung in.
It is impossible to get the bung in quickly without forcing a bit of air into the gas syringe. That gives a misleading reading on the syringe.

You would shake the flask exactly as before to mix the hydrogen peroxide and manganese(IV) oxide.

This time you record how long it takes for $5\,cm^3$ of oxygen to be collected in the measuring cylinder.

Then you set up the experiment again, changing one of the conditions (for example, the concentration of the hydrogen peroxide) and find out how long it takes to produce the same $5\,cm^3$ this time.

Concentrations are measured in mol/dm³ (moles per cubic decimetre – also written as mol dm⁻³). If you don't know what that means, it doesn't matter for now.

Concentration (mol/dm³)	2.00	1.00	0.50	0.25
Time to collect $5\,cm^3$ of oxygen (s)	10	20	40	80

Table 6.1: *Varying the concentration – some sample results.*

You will see from Table 6.1 that every time you halve the concentration, it takes twice as long to produce the $5\,cm^3$ of gas. That means the rate of reaction has also been halved. You can see this more easily if you work out the initial rate for each reaction.

The rate of the reaction would be worked out in terms of the volume of oxygen produced per second. If it takes $10\,s$ to produce $5\,cm^3$ at the beginning of the reaction, then:

Initial rate = 5/10 = 0.5 cm³/s

If you do this for all the experiments, and then redraw Table 6.1, you get the numbers in Table 6.2.

Concentration (mol/dm³)	2.00	1.00	0.50	0.25
Initial rate (cm³/s)	0.5	0.25	0.125	0.0625

Table 6.2: *How the initial rate changes with concentration.*

Figure 6.20 shows that the rate of the reaction is proportional to the concentration – whatever you do to the concentration also happens to the rate. If you double the concentration, the rate doubles – and so on.

Varying the temperature – a sample graph

You could repeat the experiment, starting with the hydrogen peroxide solution at a range of different temperatures from room temperature up to about $50\,°C$.

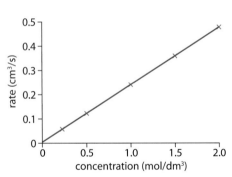

Figure 6.20 *Rate of reaction versus concentration.*

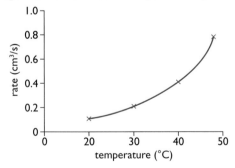

Figure 6.21 *Reaction rate versus temperature.*

This time (Figure 6.21), the graph isn't a straight line.

As a rough approximation, the rate of a reaction doubles for every 10 °C temperature rise.

Showing that a substance is a catalyst

It isn't difficult to show that manganese(IV) oxide speeds up the decomposition of hydrogen peroxide to produce oxygen. Figure 6.22 shows two flasks, both of which contain hydrogen peroxide solution. Without the catalyst, there is only a trace of bubbles in the solution. With it, oxygen is given off quickly.

How can you show that the manganese(IV) oxide is chemically unchanged by the reaction? It still looks the same, but has any been used up? You can only find out by weighing it before you add it to the hydrogen peroxide solution, and then reweighing it at the end.

You can separate it from the liquid by filtering it through a weighed filter paper, allowing the paper and residue to dry, and then reweighing it to work out the mass of the remaining manganese(IV) oxide. You should find that the mass hasn't changed.

How does a catalyst work?

You will remember that not all collisions result in a reaction happening. Collisions have to involve at least a certain minimum amount of energy, called activation energy (page 45).

You can show this on an energy diagram. In order for anything interesting to happen, the reactants have to gain enough energy to overcome the activation energy barrier.

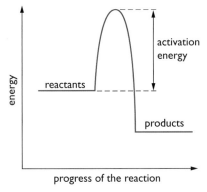

Figure 6.23 *Activation energy.*

If a reaction is slow, it means that very few collisions have this amount of energy. This means that when most collisions happen, the particles will simply bounce off each other.

Adding a catalyst gives the reaction an alternative and easier way for it to happen – involving a lower activation energy.

The approximation that reaction rates double for every 10 °C rise in temperature works for quite a lot of reactions, as long as you are within a few tens of degrees of room temperature.

Figure 6.22 *The flasks both contain hydrogen peroxide solution, the right-hand one has a little MnO$_2$ added to speed up oxygen production.*

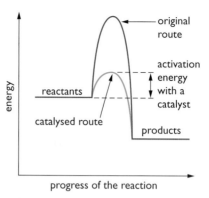

Figure 6.24 *Activation energy with a catalyst.*

Figure 6.25 *Traffic passes easily through a road tunnel under a mountain.*

If the activation energy is lower, many more collisions are likely to be successful. The reaction happens faster because the alternative route is easier.

Catalysts work by providing an alternative route for the reaction, involving a lower activation energy.

You can illustrate this with a simple everyday example. Suppose you have a mountain between two valleys. Only a few very energetic people will climb over the mountain from one valley to the next.

Now imagine building a road tunnel through the mountain. Lots of people will be able to travel easily from one valley to the next.

Warning! Be careful how you phrase the statement explaining how a catalyst works. You should say 'Catalysts provide an alternative route with a lower activation energy'.

They **do not** 'lower the activation energy' – any more than building a tunnel lowers the mountain. The original route is still there, and if particles collide with enough energy they will still use it, just as very energetic people will still choose to climb over the top of the mountain.

Catalysts in industry

Catalysts are especially important in industrial reactions because they help substances to react quickly at lower temperatures and pressures than would otherwise be needed. This saves money.

You will meet several examples of industrial use of catalysts later in the course.

End of Chapter Checklist

You should now be able to:

✓ suggest examples of reactions that happen at different rates, from very fast to very slow

✓ know and explain (in terms of collision theory) what happens to the reaction rate when you change surface area, concentration, pressure or temperature

✓ define what a catalyst is, and explain how it speeds up a reaction

✓ know why catalysts are important in industry

✓ describe simple experiments to investigate rates of reaction

✓ be able to draw and interpret simple graphs showing how the amount of either reactant or product varies with time.

Questions

1 A student carried out an experiment to investigate the rate of reaction between an excess of dolomite (magnesium carbonate) and 50 cm³ of dilute hydrochloric acid. The dolomite was in small pieces. The reaction is:

$$MgCO_3(s) + 2HCl(aq) \rightarrow MgCl_2(aq) + H_2O(l) + CO_2(g)$$

He measured the volume of carbon dioxide given off at regular intervals, with the results shown in the table below.

Time (s)	0	30	60	90	120	150	180	210	240	270	300	330	360
Volume (cm³)	0	27	45	59	70	78	85	90	94	97	99	100	100

a) Draw a diagram of the apparatus you would use for this experiment, and explain briefly what you would do.

b) Plot these results on graph paper, with time on the x-axis and volume of gas on the y-axis.

c) At what time is the gas being given off most quickly? Explain why the reaction is fastest at that time.

d) Use your graph to find out how long it took to produce 50 cm³ of gas.

e) In each of the following questions, decide what would happen to the initial rate of the reaction and to the total volume of gas given off if various changes were made to the experiment.

    (i) The mass of dolomite and the volume and concentration of acid were kept constant, but the dolomite was in one big lump instead of small bits.

    (ii) The mass of dolomite was unchanged and it was still in small pieces. 50 cm³ of hydrochloric acid was used, which had half the original concentration.

    (iii) The dolomite was unchanged again. This time 25 cm³ of the original acid was used instead of 50 cm³.

    (iv) The acid was heated to 40 °C before the dolomite was added to it.

2 The effect of concentration and temperature on the rate of a reaction can be explored using the reaction between magnesium ribbon and dilute sulfuric acid:

$$Mg(s) + H_2SO_4(aq) \rightarrow MgSO_4(aq) + H_2(g)$$

A student dropped a 2 cm length of magnesium ribbon into 25 cm³ of dilute sulfuric acid in a boiling tube (a large excess of acid). She stirred the contents of the tube continuously and timed how long it took for the magnesium to disappear.

a) What would you expect to happen to the time taken for the reaction if she repeated the experiment using the same length of magnesium with a mixture of 20 cm³ of acid and 5 cm³ of water? Explain your answer in terms of the collision theory.

b) What would you expect to happen to the time taken for the reaction if she repeated the experiment using the original quantities of magnesium and acid, but first heated the acid to 50 °C? Explain your answer in terms of the collision theory.

c) Why is it important to keep the reaction mixture stirred continuously?

3 Catalysts speed up reactions, but can be recovered chemically unchanged at the end of the reaction.

a) Explain briefly how a catalyst has this effect on a reaction.

b) Describe how you would find out whether copper(II) oxide was a catalyst for the decomposition of hydrogen peroxide solution. You need to show not only that it speeds the reaction up, but that it is chemically unchanged at the end.

End of Section A Questions

You may need to refer to the Periodic Table on page 226.

1. The diagrams show an atom and an ion.

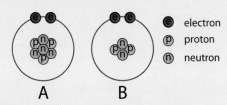

a) Which of the two structures represents an atom? Explain your choice. *(2 marks)*

b) Use the Periodic Table to help you to write the symbol (including the charge) for the structure representing an ion. *(2 marks)*

c) Complete the following table showing the relative masses and charges of the various particles.

Particle	Relative charge	Relative mass
proton	+1	
neutron	0	
electron		1/1836

(3 marks)

d) Find the elements strontium, Sr, and bromine, Br, in the Periodic Table. How many electrons are there in the outer level of each of these atoms? *(2 marks)*

e) Strontium combines with bromine to form strontium bromide. What happens to the electrons in the outer levels when strontium atoms and bromine atoms combine to make strontium bromide? *(2 marks)*

f) What is the formula for strontium bromide? *(1 mark)*

g) Would you expect strontium bromide to have a high or a low melting point? Explain your answer. *(3 marks)*

Total 15 marks

2. a) Draw dots-and-crosses diagrams to show the arrangement of the electrons in (i) a chlorine atom, (ii) a chloride ion, (iii) a chlorine molecule. *(4 marks)*

b) Dichloromethane, CH_2Cl_2, is a liquid with a low boiling point used in paint strippers. Draw a dots-and-crosses diagram to show the bonding in dichloromethane. You need only show the electrons in the outer levels of the atoms. *(3 marks)*

c) Dichloromethane contains strong carbon–hydrogen and carbon–chlorine bonds. Despite the presence of these strong bonds, dichloromethane is a liquid. Explain why. *(2 marks)*

Total 9 marks

3.

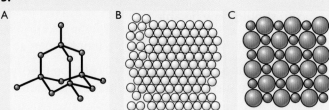

a) Which of the diagrams represents the arrangement of the particles in (i) magnesium metal, (ii) solid sodium chloride, (iii) diamond? *(2 marks)*

b) Explain why:

(i) magnesium can be stretched to form magnesium ribbon. *(1 mark)*

(ii) magnesium conducts electricity. *(2 marks)*

(iii) sodium chloride crystals are brittle. *(1 mark)*

(iv) diamond is extremely hard. *(2 marks)*

c) (i) State any one physical property of graphite which is different from diamond. *(1 mark)*

(ii) Explain how the difference arises from the arrangement of the atoms in the two substances. *(3 marks)*

Total 12 marks

4. In the nineteenth century, John Dalton put forward an atomic theory in which he suggested that atoms of a given element were all alike, but differed from the atoms of other elements. He thought that elements combined in small whole-number ratios like 1:2 or 2:3, and that chemical reactions involved rearranging existing atoms into different compounds.

a) Choose a compound with atoms arranged in the ratio 1:2, and write its formula *(1 mark)*

b) The law of conservation of mass says that in a chemical reaction, matter is neither created nor destroyed. Explain how that statement is consistent with Dalton's theory. *(2 marks)*

c) In the twentieth century, a flaw was discovered in Dalton's theory when it was found that there were two different kinds of neon atoms (Ne), one with a mass number of 20 and the other a mass number of 22.

(i) What name is given to these two different kinds of neon atom? *(1 mark)*

(ii) Write down the numbers of protons, neutrons and electrons in each of these atoms. *(2 marks)*

(iii) Would you expect there to be any differences between the chemical properties of the two sorts of neon atom? Explain your answer. *(2 marks)*

Total 8 marks

5. In an experiment to investigate the rate of decomposition of hydrogen peroxide solution in the presence of manganese(IV) oxide, $10\,cm^3$ of hydrogen peroxide solution was mixed with $30\,cm^3$ of water, and $0.2\,g$ of manganese(IV) oxide was added. The volume of oxygen evolved was measured at 60 s intervals. The results of this experiment are recorded in the table below.

Time (s)	0	60	120	180	240	300
Volume (cm³)	0	30	48	57	60	60

a) Balance the equation for the decomposition of hydrogen peroxide, including all the appropriate state symbols.

$$H_2O_2 \rightarrow H_2O + O_2$$
(2 marks)

b) Copy and complete the diagram to show how the volume of oxygen might have been measured.

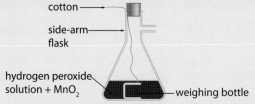

cotton ⟶

side-arm ⟶
flask

hydrogen peroxide
solution + MnO_2

weighing bottle

(2 marks)

c) Plot a graph of the results on a piece of graph paper, with time on the horizontal axis and volume of oxygen on the vertical axis.
(4 marks)

d) Use your graph to find out how long it took to produce $50\,cm^3$ of oxygen.
(1 mark)

e) Explain why the graph becomes horizontal after 240 s.
(2 marks)

f) Suppose the experiment had been repeated using the same quantities of everything, but with the reaction flask immersed in ice. Sketch the graph you would expect to get. Use the same grid as in part *(c)*. Label the new graph F.
(2 marks)

g) On the same grid as in *(c)* and *(f)*, sketch the graph you would expect to get if you repeated the experiment at the original temperature using $5\,cm^3$ of hydrogen peroxide solution, $35\,cm^3$ of water and $0.2\,g$ of manganese(IV) oxide. Label this graph G.
(2 marks)

Total 15 marks

6. During the manufacture of nitric acid from ammonia, the ammonia is oxidised to nitrogen monoxide, NO, by oxygen in the air.

$$4NH_3(g) + 5O_2(g) \rightarrow 4NO(g) + 6H_2O(g)$$

The ammonia is mixed with air and passed through a stack of large circular gauzes made of platinum–rhodium alloy at red heat (about 900 °C). The platinum–rhodium gauzes act as a catalyst for the reaction.

a) Gas particles have to collide before they can react. Use the collision theory to help you to answer the following questions.

(i) Because the gases are in contact with the catalyst for only a very short time, it is important that the reaction happens as quickly as possible. Explain why increasing the temperature to 900 °C makes the reaction very fast.
(3 marks)

(ii) Explain why the reaction rate can also be increased by increasing the pressure.
(2 marks)

(iii) Explain why the platinum–rhodium alloy is used as gauzes rather than as pellets.
(2 marks)

b) Platinum and rhodium are extremely expensive metals. Explain why the manufacturer can justify their initial cost.
(2 marks)

Total 9 marks

Section B: Some Essential Background Chemistry

Chapter 7: Oxygen and Oxides

This chapter looks at oxygen in the air and in the lab, and introduces some simple oxides.

Oxygen

The composition of the air

Figure 7.1 *Despite the extra gases added by industry . . .*

Figure 7.2 *. . . the composition of the air is much the same as it was 200 million years ago.*

The approximate percentages (by volume) of the main gases present in *unpolluted, dry* air are shown in Table 7.1.

It is important to realise that these figures apply only to *dry, unpolluted* air. Air can have anywhere between 0 and 4% water vapour. The percentage of carbon dioxide in the air, although very small, is rising steadily because of human activity.

Gas	Amount in air (%)	Amount in air (fraction)
nitrogen	78.1	about 4/5
oxygen	21.0	about 1/5
argon	0.9	
carbon dioxide	0.04	

Table 7.1: *Approximate percentages (by volume) of the main gases in unpolluted, dry air.*

There are also very small amounts of the other noble gases in the air.

Showing that air contains about one-fifth oxygen

Using copper

The apparatus shown in Figure 7.3 can be used to find the percentage of oxygen in the air.

A silica tube looks like glass, but it won't melt, however strongly you heat it with a Bunsen.

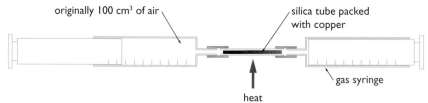

originally 100 cm³ of air

silica tube packed with copper

heat

gas syringe

Figure 7.3 *Using copper to measure the oxygen in air.*

The apparatus originally contains $100\,cm^3$ of air. This is pushed backwards and forwards over the heated copper, which turns black as copper(II) oxide is formed. The volume of gas in the syringes falls as the oxygen is used up.

$$2Cu(s) + O_2(g) \rightarrow 2CuO(s)$$

As the copper reacts, the Bunsen is moved along the tube so that it is always heating fresh copper.

Eventually, all the oxygen in the air is used up. The volume stops contracting and the copper stops turning black. On cooling, somewhere around 79 cm³ of gas is left in the syringes – 21% has been used up.

Therefore the air contained 21% of oxygen.

Using the rusting of iron

Iron rusts in damp air, using up oxygen as it does so. Figure 7.4 shows some damp iron wool in a test tube containing air. As long as the inside of the tube is wet, you could sprinkle iron filings into the tube instead of the iron wool. The iron filings will stick to the sides.

The tube is inverted in a beaker of water, and the level of the water in the tube is marked by a small rubber band. The tube is now left for a week or so for the iron to use up all the oxygen.

The water level rises in the tube as the oxygen is used up, and the new level can be marked using a second rubber band. You can find the actual volumes of the gases at the end of the experiment by filling the tube with water to each of the rubber bands in turn, and pouring it into a small measuring cylinder.

If the original volume was, say, 15 cm³, and the final volume was 12 cm³, then the oxygen used up measured 3 cm³.

The percentage of oxygen in the air was 3/15 × 100 = 20%.

Making oxygen in the lab

Oxygen is most easily made in the lab from hydrogen peroxide solution using manganese(IV) oxide as a catalyst. The reaction is known as the **catalytic decomposition** (splitting up using a catalyst) of hydrogen peroxide.

$$2H_2O_2(aq) \rightarrow 2H_2O(l) + O_2(g)$$

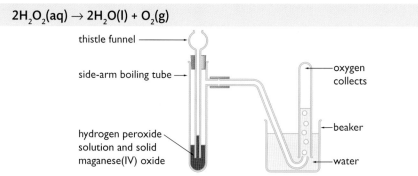

Figure 7.5 *Making oxygen in the lab.*

Testing the oxygen

Oxygen relights a glowing splint.

Burning elements in oxygen

Elements burn in oxygen much like they burn in air, only much more brightly.

Burning magnesium

Magnesium burns in air with a bright white flame to give a white, powdery ash of magnesium oxide. The flame is extremely bright in pure oxygen.

$$2Mg(s) + O_2(g) \rightarrow 2MgO(s)$$

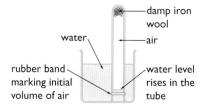

Figure 7.4 *Using iron to measure the oxygen in air*

A similar experiment can be done with a small piece of white phosphorus attached to a length of wire and held in the top of the tube. Phosphorus smoulders in air to produce two different phosphorous oxides. The iron reaction is easier to do because phosphorus is quite dangerous to handle.

Figure 7.5 shows this experiment using small-scale apparatus, rather collecting the oxygen in gas jars. If you wanted to, you could easily scale it up. But in practice, if you want gas jars of oxygen, you would almost always get it from an oxygen cylinder.

Figure 7.6 *Magnesium ribbon burning in air.*

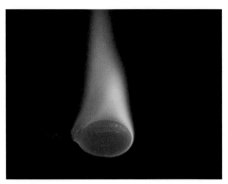

Figure 7.7 *Sulfur burning in oxygen.*

Burning sulfur

Sulfur burns in air with a tiny, almost invisible, blue flame. In oxygen it burns much more strongly, giving a bright blue flame. Poisonous, colourless sulfur dioxide gas is produced.

$$S(s) + O_2(g) \rightarrow SO_2(g)$$

Burning carbon

Carbon burns if it is heated very strongly in air or oxygen to give colourless carbon dioxide gas. The carbon may produce a small yellow-orange flame and perhaps some sparks. It depends on the purity of the carbon.

$$C(s) + O_2(g) \rightarrow CO_2(g)$$

Oxides

Metal and non-metal oxides

You will find out more about metals and non-metals in Chapter 12, see page 100.

Of the three elements we have looked at above, magnesium is a metal, whereas sulfur and carbon are non-metals. There is a pattern in the effect of water on metal and non-metal oxides.

Most metal oxides aren't soluble in water and don't react with it. If you shake some solid magnesium oxide with water, it doesn't seem to dissolve. However, if you test the pH of the mixture, you find that it is mildly alkaline. A very, very small amount does react with the water, forming some magnesium hydroxide. A very small amount of that dissolves in water, giving a slightly alkaline solution.

You might perhaps have burnt some magnesium in air, mixed the product with water and tested the pH to find that it was more alkaline than is suggested here. That's because there is some extra chemistry going on here. Magnesium also reacts with nitrogen in the air to make magnesium nitride. This reacts with water to produce ammonia, which is quite alkaline. Many books don't tell you about this, and leave you to draw a completely faulty conclusion from the experiment!

$$MgO(s) + H_2O(l) \rightarrow Mg(OH)_2(s \text{ and } aq)$$

On the other hand, many non-metal oxides react with water to give acidic solutions. For example, sulfur dioxide reacts with water to give sulfurous acid, H_2SO_3. Sulfurous acid is fairly acidic.

$$H_2O(l) + SO_2(g) \rightarrow H_2SO_3(aq)$$

Until quite recently it was thought that carbonic acid didn't actually exist as a molecule, H_2CO_3. It has now been isolated as a pure substance. *But* . . . it has been found to be completely unstable in the presence of water. Avoid ever using the term 'carbonic acid'! A solution of carbon dioxide in water is essentially just that – a solution of carbon dioxide in water.

Carbon dioxide dissolves to some extent in water, to give a solution which is sometimes called 'carbonic acid' and given the formula H_2CO_3. In fact, the reaction between carbon dioxide and water is a bit more complicated than this – but it does give a very slightly acidic solution.

Don't assume that all non-metal oxides are acidic. A few are neutral. Water (hydrogen oxide) is a good example, and so is carbon monoxide, CO.

In summary:

● most metal oxides don't either react with, or dissolve in, water – those that do tend to form alkaline solutions

● non-metal oxides often react with water to form acidic solutions – common exceptions are water (H_2O) and carbon monoxide.

Non-metal oxides and the environment

Acid rain – sulfur dioxide and oxides of nitrogen

Rain is naturally slightly acidic because of dissolved carbon dioxide. Acid rain is even more acidic because of the presence of various pollutants.

Acid rain is caused when water and oxygen in the atmosphere react with sulfur dioxide to produce sulfuric acid, or with various oxides of nitrogen, NO_x, to give nitric acid. SO_2 and NO_x come mainly from power stations and factories burning fossil fuels, or from motor vehicles.

In petrol engines, sparks are used to ignite the petrol–air mixture to power the car. These sparks also cause nitrogen and oxygen in the air to combine, to produce oxides of nitrogen.

Several oxides of nitrogen are involved, including NO and NO_2. They are often given the general formula NO_x.

Figure 7.8 *Use of very low-sulfur fuels limits the production of sulfur dioxide, but the spark in a petrol engine causes oxygen and nitrogen from the air to combine to make oxides of nitrogen, NO_x.*

Figure 7.9 *Trees dying from the effects of acid rain.*

Acid rain is worrying, mainly because of its devastating effect on trees, and on life in lakes. In some areas a high proportion of trees are affected, and are either sick or dying. In some lakes the water is so acidic that it won't support life. Limestone (calcium carbonate) and some metals such as iron are also attacked by acid rain.

The solution to acid rain involves removing sulfur from fuels, 'scrubbing' the gases from power stations and factories to remove SO_2 and NO_x, and using catalytic converters in cars. The catalyst helps to convert oxides of nitrogen into harmless nitrogen gas, but has no effect on sulfur dioxide. Unfortunately, catalytic converters don't work properly until the catalyst becomes really hot, so they aren't effective on short journeys.

Carbon dioxide and global warming – the 'greenhouse effect'

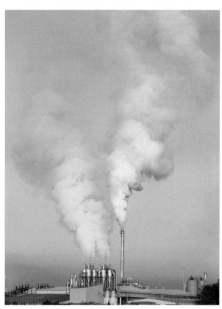

Figure 7.10 *Fossil fuels often contain sulfur compounds – burning them produces sulfur dioxide.*

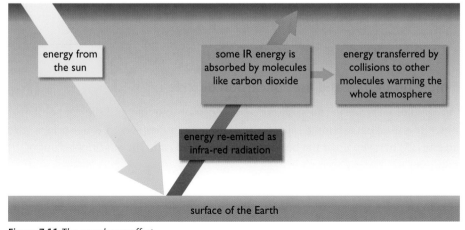

Figure 7.11 *The greenhouse effect.*

Some scientists believe that increases in carbon dioxide will cause devastating global warming. But others reject this, and claim that the increases in average world temperatures during the twentieth century were part of natural heating and cooling cycles driven by the Sun and changes to ocean currents. They believe the effect of carbon dioxide will be small compared with these.

The balance between these two views is likely to change during the lifetime of this book. Find out the current state of scientific thought by following the internet links suggested for this chapter on the accompanying website.

Carbon dioxide is also produced when many metal carbonates (such as calcium carbonate) are heated. You will find more about this in Chapter 14 (page 122).

A **precipitate** is a fine solid formed by a chemical reaction involving liquids or gases.

Figure 7.13 *Using a carbon dioxide fire extinguisher to put out an electrical fire.*

There is no argument about the fact that carbon dioxide absorbs infra-red radiation in the way Figure 7.11 shows. The absorption of infra-red radiation in this way is nothing new – it has always happened, and is one of the processes that help to maintain the Earth at a temperature suitable for life.

And there is no argument about the increasing amounts of carbon dioxide in the atmosphere. The level increases as more fossil fuels (coal, gas, and oil products such as petrol) are burnt, and as forests are cut or burnt down to make way for agriculture.

The argument is about how much real effect this will have on global temperatures. At the time of writing, this argument was still going on.

More about carbon dioxide

Making carbon dioxide in the lab

Carbon dioxide is most easily made by the reaction between dilute hydrochloric acid and calcium carbonate in the form of marble chips.

$$CaCO_3(s) + 2HCl(aq) \rightarrow CaCl_2(aq) + CO_2(g) + H_2O(l)$$

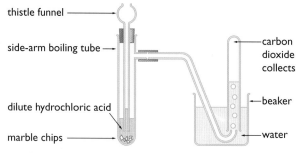

thistle funnel

side-arm boiling tube

carbon dioxide collects

beaker

dilute hydrochloric acid

water

marble chips

Figure 7.12 *Making carbon dioxide in the lab.*

Testing the carbon dioxide

Carbon dioxide turns lime water (calcium hydroxide solution) milky. It reacts to give a white precipitate of calcium carbonate.

$$Ca(OH)_2(aq) + CO_2(g) \rightarrow CaCO_3(s) + H_2O(l)$$

With an excess of carbon dioxide, the precipitate dissolves again to give a colourless solution of calcium hydrogencarbonate.

$$CaCO_3(s) + CO_2(g) + H_2O(l) \rightarrow Ca(HCO_3)_2(aq)$$

Simple properties and uses of carbon dioxide

Carbon dioxide is a colourless, odourless gas, denser than air, and slightly soluble in water. It is used in carbonated (fizzy) drinks because it dissolves in water under pressure. When you open the bottle, the pressure falls and the gas bubbles out of solution.

It is also used in fire extinguishers to put out electrical fires, or those caused by burning liquids, where using water could cause problems. The dense gas sinks onto the flames and prevents any more oxygen from reaching them.

You should now be able to:

✓ know the main gases present in the air, and their approximate percentage by volume

✓ describe an experiment to find the percentage of oxygen in the air

✓ describe how to make oxygen and carbon dioxide in the lab

✓ describe the reactions of magnesium, sulfur and carbon with oxygen

✓ know the patterns of acidity or alkalinity when metal and non-metal oxides dissolve in, or react with, water

✓ know the simple properties of carbon dioxide – limited to testing for it, its density, and its solubility in water

✓ know uses for carbon dioxide and be able to relate them to its properties

✓ know that sulfur dioxide, oxides of nitrogen, and carbon dioxide may be the causes of environmental problems.

Questions

1 **a)** Draw a labelled diagram of the apparatus you would use to collect a few test tubes of oxygen from the decomposition of hydrogen peroxide using manganese(IV) oxide as catalyst.

b) Write a balanced symbol equation for the reaction, including state symbols.

c) Describe the test for oxygen.

2 In each of the following questions, decide whether the element described is a metal or a non-metal. If you recognise the element from its description, say what you think it is.

a) A yellow, crystalline solid that burns with a bright blue flame in oxygen, giving a gas which dissolves in water to give an acidic solution.

b) A soft, silvery solid that burns in oxygen with an orange flame to give a white oxide. When water is added to the oxide, the solution is strongly alkaline.

c) A brown, flexible solid that forms a black oxide when heated in oxygen. The oxide is insoluble in water.

d) A shiny, grey solid that burns if heated very strongly in oxygen. The gas produced turns lime water milky and produces a slightly acidic solution.

3 Read the following passage and then answer the questions.

In 1895 an English physicist, Lord Rayleigh, noticed a tiny difference between the density of nitrogen made from ammonia (1.2505 g/dm³) and nitrogen obtained from the air (1.2572 g/dm³). The nitrogen was obtained from the air by removing oxygen and carbon dioxide from it.

Sir William Ramsay passed nitrogen, which had been obtained from the air, over hot magnesium. Magnesium combines with nitrogen to make solid magnesium nitride, Mg_3N_2. At the end of this, he was left with a small amount of gas that wouldn't combine with the magnesium. This gas proved to be argon, contaminated with very small quantities of other noble gases.

a) Suggest one reaction you could use to remove oxygen from the air without replacing it by another gas. Write the equation for the reaction you give.

b) How might you remove carbon dioxide from the air?

c) Write a balanced equation for the reaction between hot magnesium and nitrogen. Don't forget the state symbols.

d) By considering the density figures given, is argon denser or less dense than nitrogen? Explain your reasoning.

e) Name any two other noble gases which might be found mixed with the argon.

4 Explain why:

a) carbon dioxide is used in some fire extinguishers

b) a bottle of fizzy drink doesn't fizz until you take the top off

c) burning a fuel containing sulfur as an impurity causes acid rain

d) petrol engines produce oxides of nitrogen

e) a car with a catalytic converter can still produce pollution under some circumstances.

The reactivity series lists elements (mainly metals) in order of decreasing reactivity. It is likely that you will have come across some of this chemistry already in earlier years. This chapter reminds you about some simple reactions involving these elements and their compounds, and then uses these reactions to introduce some new and more complicated ideas.

Figure 8.1 *Rails are welded together using molten iron, produced by a reactivity series reaction between aluminium and iron(III) oxide.*

Figure 8.2 *Gold is so unreactive that it will remain chemically unchanged in contact with the air or water for ever.*

Displacement reactions involving metal oxides

The reaction between magnesium and copper(II) oxide

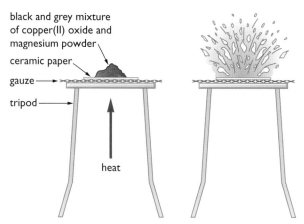

black and grey mixture of copper(II) oxide and magnesium powder

ceramic paper

gauze

tripod

heat

Figure 8.3 *How magnesium reacts with copper(II) oxide.*

At the end, traces of brown copper are left on the ceramic paper.

magnesium + copper(II) oxide → magnesium oxide + copper
$$Mg(s) + CuO(s) \rightarrow MgO(s) + Cu(s)$$

This is an example of a **displacement reaction**. The less reactive metal, copper, has been pushed out of its compound by the more reactive magnesium. Any metal higher in the series will displace one lower down from a compound.

If you heated copper with magnesium oxide, nothing would happen because copper is less reactive than magnesium. Copper isn't capable of displacing magnesium from magnesium oxide.

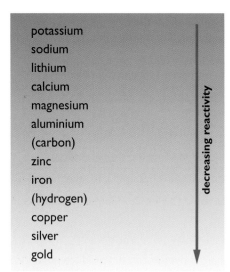

potassium
sodium
lithium
calcium
magnesium
aluminium
(carbon)
zinc
iron
(hydrogen)
copper
silver
gold

decreasing reactivity

Figure 8.4 *Elements in order of reactivity.*

The reaction between magnesium and zinc oxide

Heating magnesium with zinc oxide produces zinc metal. This time, though, because the zinc is very hot, it immediately burns in air to form zinc oxide again! This second reaction hasn't been included in the equations below.

magnesium + zinc oxide → magnesium oxide + zinc
$$Mg(s) + ZnO(s) \rightarrow MgO(s) \qquad + Zn(s)$$

The reaction between carbon and copper(II) oxide

Carbon is included in the reactivity series because it is important in extracting several metals (including iron) from their ores. Ores are often metal oxides. If the metal is below carbon in the reactivity series, then carbon can be a cheap way of removing oxygen from the oxide to leave the metal. Copper isn't, in fact, extracted like this. This reaction is just a simple lab illustration that carbon is above copper in the series.

A black mixture of carbon and copper(II) oxide is heated in a test tube to avoid the air getting at the hot copper produced and turning it back to copper(II) oxide. The carbon dioxide that is also formed escapes from the tube as a gas. The mixture glows red hot because of the heat given out during the reaction, and you are left with brown copper in the tube.

$$C(s) + 2CuO(s) \rightarrow CO_2(g) + 2Cu(s)$$

Oxidation and reduction

Oxidation and reduction – oxygen transfer

● A substance has been **oxidised** if it gains oxygen. **Oxidation** is gain of oxygen.

● A substance has been **reduced** if it loses oxygen. **Reduction** is loss of oxygen.

Figure 8.7 shows magnesium reacting with copper(II) oxide.

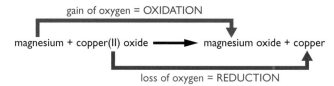

Figure 8.7 in the diagram:

gain of oxygen = OXIDATION

magnesium + copper(II) oxide ⟶ magnesium oxide + copper

loss of oxygen = REDUCTION

Figure 8.7 *Magnesium reacting with copper(II) oxide.*

A **redox** reaction is one in which both **red**uction and **ox**idation are occurring. Oxidation and reduction always go hand-in-hand.

● A **reducing agent** is a substance which reduces something else. In this case, the magnesium is the reducing agent.

● An **oxidising agent** is a substance which oxidises something else. The copper(II) oxide is the oxidising agent in this reaction.

Figure 8.5 *Magnesium reacting with zinc oxide.*

Figure 8.6 *Notice the brown copper formed at the end of the reaction between carbon and copper(II) oxide.*

There are some quite tricky ideas on this page. Take it very slowly, and make sure you understand each point before you go on to the next one. If you get to the bottom of the page and have understood what you have read (even if you don't necessarily remember it all), feel pleased with yourself.

How do you know whether a substance contains ions or not? As a rough guide for GCSE purposes only, if it is a metal (or ammonium) *compound*, or an acid in solution, it will be ionic – otherwise it's not. If you aren't sure about writing symbols for ions, read pages 33–34 in Chapter 5.

These equations are called **half equations** or **electron half equations**. They show just part of a reaction from the point of view of one of the substances present.

You now have two definitions of oxidation (and its reverse, reduction). Which are you supposed to use? Use whichever is simpler in the case you are asked about! Both definitions are true. Don't worry too much about this at the moment. With a bit of experience, you will find it is obvious which you need to use in various cases.

Oxidation and reduction – electron transfer

We are going to look very closely at what happens in the reaction between magnesium and copper(II) oxide in terms of the various particles involved. Here is the equation again:

$$Mg(s) + CuO(s) \rightarrow MgO(s) + Cu(s)$$

The magnesium and the copper are metals, and are made of metal atoms, but the copper(II) oxide and the magnesium oxide are both ionic compounds.

The copper(II) oxide contains Cu^{2+} and O^{2-} ions, and the magnesium oxide contains Mg^{2+} and O^{2-} ions. Writing those into the equation (not forgetting the state symbols) gives:

$$Mg(s) + Cu^{2+}(s) + O^{2-}(s) \rightarrow Mg^{2+}(s) + O^{2-}(s) + Cu(s)$$

Look very carefully at this equation to see what is being changed. Notice that something odd is going on – the oxide ion (O^{2-}) is completely unaffected by the reaction. It ends up with a different partner, but is totally unchanged itself. An ion like this is described as a **spectator ion**.

You don't write the spectator ions into the equation because they aren't changed in the reaction. The equation showing just those things being changed looks like this:

$$Mg(s) + Cu^{2+}(s) \rightarrow Mg^{2+}(s) + Cu(s)$$

Make sure you can see how this equation comes from the previous one. This is known as an **ionic equation**, and shows the reaction in a quite different light. It shows that the reaction has nothing to do with the oxygen.

What is actually happening is that magnesium *atoms* are turning into magnesium *ions*. The magnesium atoms lose electrons to form magnesium ions.

$$Mg(s) \rightarrow Mg^{2+}(s) + 2e^-$$

Those electrons have been gained by the copper(II) ions to make the atoms present in metallic copper.

$$Cu^{2+}(s) + 2e^- \rightarrow Cu(s)$$

Remember that we are talking about the reaction between copper(II) oxide and magnesium. We've already described this as a redox reaction, but the equations no longer have any oxygen in them! We now need a wider definition of oxidation and reduction.

Oxidation Is Loss of electrons; Reduction Is Gain of electrons
O I L R I G

In this case:

$$Mg(s) \rightarrow Mg^{2+}(s) + 2e^- \quad \text{Mg is oxidised.}$$
$$Cu^{2+}(s) + 2e^- \rightarrow Cu(s) \quad \text{Cu}^{2+} \text{ is reduced.}$$

Displacement reactions involving solutions of salts

Salts are compounds like copper(II) sulfate, silver nitrate or sodium chloride. You will find a definition of what a salt is on page 71. This section explores some reactions between metals and solutions of salts in water.

The reaction between zinc and copper(II) sulfate solution

The copper is displaced by the more reactive zinc. The blue colour of the copper(II) sulfate solution fades as colourless zinc sulfate solution is formed.

$$Zn(s) + CuSO_4(aq) \rightarrow ZnSO_4(aq) + Cu(s)$$

The zinc and the copper are metals consisting simply of atoms, but the copper(II) sulfate and the zinc sulfate are metal compounds and so are ionic.

If you rewrite the equation showing the ions, you will find that the sulfate ions are spectator ions.

$$Zn(s) + Cu^{2+}(aq) + SO_4^{2-}(aq) \rightarrow Zn^{2+}(aq) + SO_4^{2-}(aq) + Cu(s)$$

Removing the spectator ions (because they aren't changed during the reaction) leaves you with:

$$Zn(s) + Cu^{2+}(aq) \rightarrow Zn^{2+}(aq) + Cu(s)$$

This is another redox reaction.

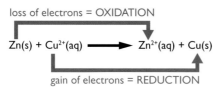

loss of electrons = OXIDATION

$$Zn(s) + Cu^{2+}(aq) \longrightarrow Zn^{2+}(aq) + Cu(s)$$

gain of electrons = REDUCTION

Figure 8.9 *Zinc reacting with copper(II) sulfate solution.*

The reaction between copper and silver nitrate solution

Silver is below copper in the reactivity series, so a coil of copper wire in silver nitrate solution will produce metallic silver. Figure 8.10 shows the silver being produced as a mixture of grey 'fur' and delicate crystals.

Notice the solution becoming blue as copper(II) nitrate is produced.

$$Cu(s) + 2AgNO_3(aq) \rightarrow Cu(NO_3)_2(aq) + 2Ag(s)$$

This time the nitrate ions are spectator ions, and the final version of the ionic equation looks like this:

$$Cu(s) + 2Ag^+(aq) \rightarrow Cu^{2+}(aq) + 2Ag(s)$$

This is yet another redox reaction.

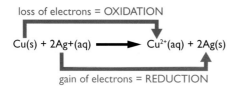

loss of electrons = OXIDATION

$$Cu(s) + 2Ag+(aq) \longrightarrow Cu^{2+}(aq) + 2Ag(s)$$

gain of electrons = REDUCTION

Figure 8.11 *Copper reacting with silver nitrate solution.*

Figure 8.8 *Zinc displaces copper from copper(II) sulfate solution.*

It wouldn't matter which copper(II) salt you started with, as long as it was soluble in water. Copper(II) chloride or copper(II) nitrate would react in exactly the same way with zinc, because the chloride ions or the nitrate ions would once again be spectator ions, taking no part in the reaction.

Figure 8.10 *Displacing silver from silver nitrate solution.*

Reactions of metals with water

A general summary

Metals above hydrogen in the reactivity series

Metals above hydrogen in the reactivity series react with water (or steam) to produce hydrogen.

If the metal reacts with *cold water*, the metal *hydroxide* and hydrogen are formed.

> **metal + cold water → metal hydroxide + hydrogen**

If the metal reacts with *steam*, the metal *oxide* and hydrogen are formed.

> **metal + steam → metal oxide + hydrogen**

As you go down the reactivity series, the reactions become less and less vigorous.

Metals below hydrogen in the reactivity series

Metals below hydrogen in the reactivity series (such as copper) don't react with water or steam. That is why copper can be used for both hot and cold water pipes.

Potassium, sodium or lithium and cold water

These reactions are described in detail on pages 102–104. They are very vigorous reactions, but become less violent in the order potassium → sodium → lithium. The equations all look like this:

> $$2X(s) + 2H_2O(l) \rightarrow 2XOH(aq) + H_2(aq)$$

Replace X by K, Na or Li, depending on which you want.

Calcium and cold water

Calcium reacts gently with cold water. The grey granules sink, but are carried back to the surface again as bubbles of hydrogen are formed around them. The mixture becomes warm as heat is produced.

Calcium hydroxide is formed. This isn't very soluble in water. Some of it dissolves to give a colourless solution, but most of it is left as a white, insoluble solid.

> $$Ca(s) + 2H_2O(l) \rightarrow Ca(OH)_2(aq \text{ and } s) + H_2(aq)$$

Magnesium and cold water

There is almost no reaction. If the magnesium is very clean, a few bubbles of hydrogen form on it, but the reaction soon stops again. This is because the magnesium becomes coated with insoluble magnesium hydroxide, which prevents water coming into contact with the magnesium.

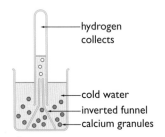

hydrogen collects
cold water
inverted funnel
calcium granules

Figure 8.12 *Calcium reacting with cold water.*

Magnesium and steam

Magnesium ribbon can be heated in steam using simple apparatus (Figure 8.13).

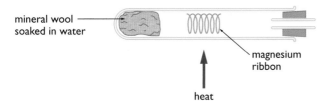

Figure 8.13 *Magnesium reacting with steam.*

The mineral wool isn't heated directly. Enough heat spreads back along the test tube to turn the water to steam.

The magnesium burns with a bright white flame in the steam, producing hydrogen, which can be ignited at the end of the delivery tube. White magnesium oxide is formed.

$$Mg(s) + H_2O(g) \rightarrow MgO(s) + H_2(g)$$

In fact, you also get a lot of black product in the tube. This is where the magnesium has reacted with the glass. Ignore this for exam purposes.

Zinc or iron and steam

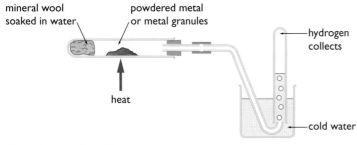

Figure 8.14 *Zinc or iron reacting with steam.*

You might wonder why there is no description for aluminium and steam. Its reactivity is supposed to be between that of magnesium and that of zinc. However, aluminium has only a very slow reaction with steam because it is covered in a very thin, but very strong, layer of aluminium oxide. It only really shows its true reactivity if that layer can be penetrated in some way. Water or steam don't do that very well. We will talk about this again when we look at reactions between metals and acids.

With both zinc and iron, the hydrogen comes off slowly enough to be collected. Neither metal burns.

Care has to be taken during this experiment to avoid 'suck-back'. If you stop heating while the delivery tube is still under the surface of the water, water is sucked back into the hot tube, which usually results in it cracking.

With zinc

Zinc oxide is formed – this is yellow when it is hot, but white on cooling.

$$Zn(s) + H_2O(g) \rightarrow ZnO(s) + H_2(g)$$

With iron

The iron becomes slightly darker grey. A complicated oxide is formed, called triiron tetroxide, Fe_3O_4.

$$3Fe(s) + 4H_2O(g) \rightarrow Fe_3O_4(s) + 4H_2(g)$$

Notice that in these equations, water now has a state symbol (g) because we are talking about it as steam.

(Remember that **metals below hydrogen** in the reactivity series, such as copper, **don't react** with water or steam.)

The general trends on this page apply to simple acids such as dilute sulfuric acid or dilute hydrochloric acid. Nitric acid behaves completely differently with most metals, as does concentrated sulfuric acid. These are problems beyond GCSE.

Reactions of metals with dilute acids

A general summary

The pattern is the same as for the reaction between the metals and water, but in each case the reaction is much more vigorous.

Metals above hydrogen in the reactivity series

Metals above hydrogen react with acids to form a salt (magnesium sulfate or zinc chloride, for example) and hydrogen. The higher the metal in the series, the more violent the reaction.

> **Metal + dilute sulfuric acid → metal sulfate + hydrogen**
> **Metal + dilute hydrochloric acid → metal chloride + hydrogen**

Metals below hydrogen in the reactivity series

These don't react with simple dilute acids such as sulfuric or hydrochloric acid.

Potassium, sodium, lithium and calcium with dilute acids

These are too reactive to add safely to acids. Calcium can be used if the acid is very dilute.

Metals from magnesium to iron in the reactivity series

Magnesium reacts vigorously with cold dilute acids, and the mixture gets very hot. A colourless solution of magnesium sulfate or chloride is formed. You will find these reactions explored in detail in Chapter 9 (page 72). With dilute sulfuric acid:

> $Mg(s) + H_2SO_4(aq) \rightarrow MgSO_4(aq) + H_2(g)$

Aluminium is slow to start reacting, but after warming it reacts very vigorously. There is a very thin, but very strong, layer of aluminium oxide on the surface of the aluminium, which stops the acid from getting to it. On heating, the acid removes this layer, and the aluminium can show its true reactivity. With dilute hydrochloric acid:

> $2Al(s) + 6HCl(aq) \rightarrow 2AlCl_3(aq) + 3H_2(g)$

Zinc and **iron** react slowly in the cold, but more rapidly on heating. The vigour of the reactions is less than that of aluminium. The zinc forms zinc sulfate or zinc chloride and hydrogen. The iron forms iron(II) sulfate or iron(II) chloride and hydrogen. For example:

> $Zn(s) + H_2SO_4(aq) \rightarrow ZnSO_4(aq) + H_2(g)$
> $Fe(s) + 2HCl(aq) \rightarrow FeCl_2(aq) + H_2(g)$

Figure 8.15 *Iron reacting with dilute hydrochloric acid.*

There are two ranges of iron salts containing either Fe^{2+} or Fe^{3+} ions. These reactions produce iron(II) salts containing Fe^{2+} ions.

Metals below hydrogen in the reactivity series

Metals such as copper, silver and gold don't react with these dilute acids.

Finding the approximate position of a metal in the reactivity series using water and dilute acids

Add a very small piece of metal to some cold water. If there is any rapid reaction, then the metal must be above magnesium in the reactivity series.

If there isn't any reaction, add a small amount of metal to some dilute hydrochloric acid (or dilute sulfuric acid). If there isn't any reaction in the cold, warm it carefully.

If there is still no reaction, the metal is probably below hydrogen in the reactivity series. If there is a reaction, then it is somewhere between magnesium and hydrogen.

Making predictions using the reactivity series

You can make predictions about the reactions of unfamiliar metals if you know their position in the reactivity series.

A problem involving manganese

Suppose you have a question as follows.

> Manganese (Mn) lies between aluminium and zinc in the reactivity series, and forms a 2+ ion. Solutions of manganese(II) salts are very pale pink (almost colourless).
> **a)** Use the reactivity series to predict whether manganese will react with copper(II) sulfate solution. If it will react, describe what you would see, name the products and write an equation for the reaction.
> **b)** Explain why you would expect manganese to react with steam. Name the products of the reaction and write the equation.

a) The reaction between manganese and copper(II) sulfate solution

Manganese is above copper in the reactivity series and so will displace it from the copper(II) sulfate.

A brown deposit of copper will be formed. The colour of the solution will fade from blue and leave a very pale pink (virtually colourless) solution of manganese(II) sulfate.

$$Mn(s) + CuSO_4(aq) \rightarrow MnSO_4(aq) + Cu(s)$$

b) The reaction between manganese and steam

Manganese is above hydrogen in the reactivity series and so reacts with steam to give hydrogen and the metal oxide – in this case, manganese(II) oxide.

You couldn't predict the colour of the manganese(II) oxide, and the question doesn't ask you to do this.

$$Mn(s) + H_2O(g) \rightarrow MnO(s) + H_2(g)$$

It would be impossible to place a metal exactly in the reactivity series using this sequence. How vigorously a metal reacts with a dilute acid depends on its position in the series, but also depends on its surface area, and whether the surface is free from dirt or an oxide coating.

You need to know the charge on the ion so that you can work out the formulae of the manganese compounds. If you aren't sure about working out the formula of an ionic compound, look again at Chapter 5.

potassium
sodium
lithium
calcium
magnesium
aluminium
manganese
zinc
iron
(hydrogen)
copper

Figure 8.16 *Where is manganese in the reactivity series?*

You should now be able to:

✓ know that the reactivity series lists elements (mainly metals) in order of decreasing reactivity, and know the positions of the elements in the list at the beginning of this chapter

✓ understand the term 'displacement reaction'

✓ describe some simple reactions involving metals with metal oxides, salt solutions, water/steam and dilute acids

✓ understand the terms oxidation, reduction and redox in terms of both oxygen transfer and electron transfer

✓ understand how to work out simple ionic equations, omitting spectator ions

✓ make simple predictions about the reactions of a metal from its position in the reactivity series.

Questions

1 a) List the following metals in order of decreasing reactivity: aluminium, copper, iron, sodium.

b) Some magnesium powder was mixed with some copper(II) oxide and heated strongly. There was a vigorous reaction, producing a lot of sparks and a bright flash of light.

    (i) Name the products of the reaction.

    (ii) Write a balanced symbol equation for the reaction.

    (iii) Which substance in the reaction has been reduced?

    (iv) Which substance is the oxidising agent?

c) If a mixture of zinc powder and cobalt(II) oxide is heated, the following reaction occurs:

$$Zn(s) + CoO(s) \rightarrow ZnO(s) + Co(s)$$

    (i) Which metal is higher in the reactivity series?

    (ii) The zinc can be described as a reducing agent. Using this example, explain what is meant by the term 'reducing agent'.

    (iii) Which substance in this reaction has been oxidised?

d) Aluminium, chromium and manganese are all moderately reactive metals. (Care! We are talking about manganese, **not** magnesium.) Use the following information to arrange them in the correct reactivity series order, starting with the most reactive one.

- Chromium is manufactured by heating chromium(III) oxide with aluminium.

- If manganese is heated with aluminium oxide there is no reaction.

- If manganese is heated with chromium(III) oxide, chromium is produced.

2 Study the following equations and, in each case, decide whether the substance in **bold type** has been oxidised or reduced. Explain your choice in terms of either oxygen transfer or electron transfer as appropriate.

a) $\mathbf{Zn(s)} + CuO(s) \rightarrow ZnO(s) + Cu(s)$

b) $\mathbf{Fe_2O_3(s)} + 3C(s) \rightarrow 2Fe(s) + 3CO(g)$

c) $\mathbf{Mg(s)} + Zn^{2+}(s) \rightarrow Mg^{2+}(s) + Zn(s)$

d) $Zn(s) + \mathbf{Cu^{2+}(aq)} \rightarrow Zn^{2+}(aq) + Cu(s)$

3 The equation for the reaction when solid magnesium and solid lead(II) oxide are heated together is:

$$Mg(s) + PbO(s) \rightarrow MgO(s) + Pb(s)$$

a) What does this tell you about the position of lead in the reactivity series? Explain your answer.

b) Rewrite the equation as an ionic equation.

4 Some iron filings were shaken with some copper(II) sulfate solution. The ionic equation for the reaction is:

$$Fe(s) + Cu^{2+}(aq) \rightarrow Fe^{2+}(aq) + Cu(s)$$

a) Write down any one change that you would observe during this reaction.

b) Which substance has been oxidised in this reaction?

c) Write down the full (not ionic) equation for this reaction.

5 Some experiments were carried out to place the metals copper, nickel and silver in reactivity series order.

Experiment 1: a piece of copper was placed in some green nickel(II) sulfate solution. There was no change to either the copper or the solution.

Experiment 2: a coil of copper wire was suspended in some silver nitrate solution. A furry grey growth appeared on the copper wire, out of which grew spiky silvery crystals. The solution gradually turned from colourless to blue.

a) Use this information to place copper, nickel and silver in reactivity series order, starting with the most reactive one.

b) In another experiment, a piece of nickel was placed in some copper(II) sulfate solution.

    (i) Write down any one change that you would observe during this reaction.

    (ii) Write the full balanced equation for this reaction. (Assume that nickel(II) sulfate solution is formed.)

    (iii) Write the ionic equation for this reaction, and use it to explain which substance has been oxidised during the reaction.

6 a) Look carefully at the following equations and then decide what you can say about the position of the metal X in the reactivity series. Explain your reasoning.

$X(s) + 2HCl(aq) \rightarrow XCl_2(aq) + H_2(g)$

$X(s) + CuSO_4(aq) \rightarrow XSO_4(aq) + Cu(s)$

$X(s) + FeSO_4(aq)$: no reaction

b) Decide whether X will react with the following substances. If it will react, write down the names of the products.

    (i) silver nitrate solution, **(ii)** zinc oxide, **(iii)** cold water, **(iv)** copper(II) chloride solution, **(v)** dilute sulfuric acid.

7 If you add some powdered aluminium to a small amount of cold dilute hydrochloric acid in a boiling tube, very little happens. If you warm this gently, it starts to fizz very rapidly.

a) Name the gas given off to produce the fizzing.

b) If you used an excess of hydrochloric acid, you would end up with a colourless solution. Name the solution.

c) Write the full balanced equation for the reaction.

d) Explain why the aluminium hardly reacts at all with the dilute acid in the cold, but reacts vigorously after even gentle heating.

8 Given some small bits of the metal titanium, and any simple apparatus that you might need, describe how you would find out the approximate position of titanium in the reactivity series using only water and dilute hydrochloric acid You need only find out that the reactivity is 'similar to iron' or 'similar to magnesium' or whatever. Your experiments should be done in an order that guarantees maximum safety. For example, if its reactivity turned out to be similar to potassium, dropping it into dilute hydrochloric acid wouldn't be a good idea!

Chapter 9: Acids

This chapter explores what acids are, and some simple patterns in their chemistry in the lab.

Figure 9.1 *Acids range from the extremely dangerous, needing protective clothing to clean up spills . . .*

Figure 9.2 *. . . to a natural part of our diet – oranges contain citric acid.*

pH and indicators

The pH scale

The pH scale ranges from about 0 to about 14, and tells you how acidic or how alkaline a solution is.

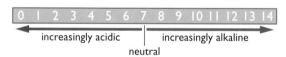

Figure 9.3 *The pH scale.*

Measuring pH

Using universal indicator

This is made from a mixture of dyes, which change colour in a gradual way over a range of pH. It can be used as a solution or as a paper. The commonest form is known as *wide range* universal indicator. It changes through a variety of colours from pH 1 right up to pH 14, but isn't very accurate.

The colour of the paper or solution is always checked against a chart to find the correct pH.

Using a pH meter

You can measure pH much more accurately using a pH meter. Before you can use a pH meter, you have to adjust it to make sure it is reading accurately. To do this, you put it into a solution with a known pH, and adjust the reading so that it gives exactly that value.

Figure 9.4 *Using universal indicator solution to measure the pH of various solutions.*

Simple indicators

Any substance that has more than one colour form depending on the pH can be used as an indicator. One of the commonest ones is **litmus**.

Figure 9.5 *The colours of litmus under different conditions.*

Litmus is red in acidic solutions and blue in alkaline ones. The neutral purple colour is an equal mixture of the red and blue forms.

Two other indicators you will come across are **methyl orange** and **phenolphthalein**. Methyl orange is yellow in alkaline solutions and red in acidic ones. Phenolphthalein is bright pink in alkaline solutions, and colourless in acidic solutions.

Reacting acids with metals

Simple dilute acids react with metals depending on their positions in the reactivity series.

● Metals below hydrogen in the series don't react with dilute acids.

● Metals above hydrogen in the series react to produce hydrogen gas.

● The higher the metal is in the reactivity series, the more vigorous the reaction. You would never mix metals such as sodium or potassium with acids because their reactions are too violent.

A summary equation for metals above hydrogen in the reactivity series

metal + acid → salt + hydrogen

Salts

All simple acids contain hydrogen. When that hydrogen is replaced by a metal, the compound formed is called a **salt**. Magnesium sulfate is a salt, and so is zinc chloride, and so is potassium nitrate.

Sulfuric acid can be thought of as the **parent acid** of all the sulfates.

Parent acid	Salts
sulfuric acid	sulfates
hydrochloric acid	chlorides
nitric acid	nitrates

Table 9.1: *Acids and salts.*

It doesn't matter if the replacement can't be done directly. For example, you can't make copper(II) sulfate from copper and dilute sulfuric acid, because they don't react. There are, however, other ways of making it from sulfuric acid. Copper(II) sulfate is still a salt.

Litmus has a big advantage because it changes colour around pH 7. That means that you can look at a piece of litmus paper and say with some confidence whether a substance is acidic, neutral or alkaline. Methyl orange and phenolphthalein change colour at a different pH. Methyl orange changes colour around pH 4, and phenolphthalein around pH 9. This doesn't matter as long as you are testing strongly acidic or alkaline substances, but neither will pick out a true 'neutral'. This isn't a problem you need to worry about at this level.

Of the common acids in the lab, nitric acid has much more complex reactions with metals. You won't be asked about this at GCSE.

Common salt is sodium chloride. This is produced if the hydrogen in hydrochloric acid is replaced by sodium.

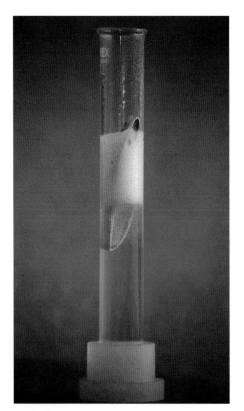

Figure 9.6 *Magnesium reacting with dilute sulfuric acid.*

You need to have read about ionic equations in Chapter 8 (pages 62–63) to understand this section.

Reactions involving magnesium and acids

With dilute sulfuric acid

There is rapid fizzing and a colourless gas is evolved, which pops with a lighted splint (the test for hydrogen). The reaction mixture gets very warm as heat is produced. The magnesium gradually disappears to leave a colourless solution of magnesium sulfate.

$$Mg(s) + H_2SO_4(aq) \rightarrow MgSO_4(aq) + H_2(g)$$

This is a displacement reaction. The more reactive magnesium has displaced the less reactive hydrogen.

With dilute hydrochloric acid

The reaction looks exactly the same. The only difference is that this time a solution of magnesium chloride is formed.

$$Mg(s) + 2HCl(aq) \rightarrow MgCl_2(aq) + H_2(g)$$

Why are the reactions so similar?

Acids in solution are ionic. Dilute sulfuric acid contains hydrogen ions and sulfate ions. Dilute hydrochloric acid contains hydrogen ions and chloride ions.

You can rewrite the equations as ionic equations. In the case of sulfuric acid:

$$Mg(s) + 2H^+(aq) + SO_4^{2-}(aq) \rightarrow Mg^{2+}(aq) + SO_4^{2-}(aq) + H_2(g)$$

You can see that the sulfate ion hasn't been changed by the reaction. It is a spectator ion, and so we leave it out of the ionic equation:

$$Mg(s) + 2H^+(aq) \rightarrow Mg^{2+}(aq) + H_2(g)$$

Repeating this with hydrochloric acid, you find that the chloride ions are also spectator ions.

$$Mg(s) + 2H^+(aq) + 2Cl^-(aq) \rightarrow Mg^{2+}(aq) + 2Cl^-(aq) + H_2(g)$$

Leaving the spectator ions out produces the ionic equation:

$$Mg(s) + 2H^+(aq) \rightarrow Mg^{2+}(aq) + H_2(g)$$

The reactions look the same because they are the same. All acids in solution contain hydrogen ions. That means that magnesium will react with any simple dilute acid in the same way.

Reactions involving zinc and acids

Again, the reactions between zinc and the two acids look exactly the same. The reactions are slower because zinc is lower down the reactivity series than magnesium. The reaction can be speeded up if it is heated or if the zinc is impure. A little copper(II) sulfate solution is often added to these reactions to make the zinc impure.

The full equations are:

$$Zn(s) + H_2SO_4(aq) \rightarrow ZnSO_4(aq) + H_2(g)$$

$$Zn(s) + 2HCl(aq) \rightarrow ZnCl_2(aq) + H_2(g)$$

The ionic equations are both the same:

$$Zn(s) + 2H^+(aq) \rightarrow Zn^{2+}(aq) + H_2(g)$$

Making hydrogen in the lab

Hydrogen is usually made from zinc and dilute sulfuric acid, with a very small amount of copper(II) sulfate solution added to speed the reaction up.

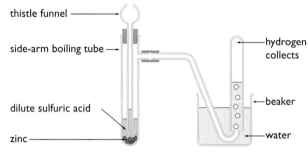

thistle funnel

side-arm boiling tube

dilute sulfuric acid

zinc

hydrogen collects

beaker

water

Figure 9.7 *Apparatus for making hydrogen in the lab.*

Testing the hydrogen

Hydrogen reacts with oxygen in the presence of a flame or a spark to give water. A lighted splint placed at the mouth of a test tube of hydrogen will give a squeaky pop as the hydrogen reacts with oxygen in the air.

$$2H_2(g) + O_2(g) \rightarrow 2H_2O(l)$$

Reacting acids with metal oxides

The metal magnesium reacts with dilute sulfuric acid; the metal copper doesn't. However, both magnesium oxide and copper(II) oxide react similarly with acids.

Reacting dilute sulfuric acid with copper(II) oxide

The black powder reacts with hot dilute sulfuric acid to produce a blue solution of copper(II) sulfate.

$$CuO(s) + H_2SO_4(aq) \rightarrow CuSO_4(aq) + H_2O(l)$$

All the metal oxide and acid combinations that you will meet at GCSE behave in exactly the same way as the reaction between copper(II) oxide and dilute sulfuric acid – producing a salt and water. Most need to be heated to get the reaction started.

A summary equation for acids and metal oxides

metal oxide + acid → salt + water

Important! Don't be tempted to describe copper(II) sulfate solution as a catalyst in this reaction. Catalysts aren't used up in a reaction, but the copper(II) sulfate is. It reacts with a small amount of the zinc to produce copper. It is the copper produced which serves as the catalyst.

Figure 9.8 *Because hydrogen is so light, it was used in airships – in 1937 the Hindenburg caught fire and 36 people were killed, most of them by jumping from the airship.*

Figure 9.9 *Copper(II) oxide reacting with hot dilute sulfuric acid.*

The ionic equation for an acid/metal oxide reaction

In the reaction between copper(II) oxide and dilute sulfuric acid, everything in the equation is ionic apart from the water.

$$Cu^{2+}(s) + O^{2-}(s) + 2H^+(aq) + SO_4{}^{2-}(aq) \rightarrow Cu^{2+}(aq) + SO_4{}^{2-}(aq) + H_2O(l)$$

Look carefully to find the spectator ions. The sulfate ion isn't changed at all, and the Cu^{2+} ion has changed only to the extent that it started as solid and ends up in solution. In this particular reaction, we count that as unchanged. Leaving the spectator ions out gives:

$$O^{2-}(s) + 2H^+(aq) \rightarrow H_2O(l)$$

This would be equally true of any simple metal oxide reacting with any acid. Oxide ions combine with hydrogen ions to make water. This is a good example of a **neutralisation reaction**. The presence of the hydrogen ions is what makes the sulfuric acid acidic. If something combines with these and removes them from solution, then obviously the acid has been neutralised.

Bases

Bases are defined as substances that combine with hydrogen ions. In the ionic equation above, an oxide ion is acting as a base because it combines with hydrogen ions to make water.

The simple metal oxides you will meet at GCSE are described as **basic oxides**.

Reacting acids with metal hydroxides

All metal hydroxides react with acids, but the ones most commonly used in the lab are the soluble hydroxides – usually sodium, potassium or calcium hydroxide solutions.

A summary equation for acids and metal hydroxides

metal hydroxide + acid → salt + water

Reacting dilute hydrochloric acid with sodium hydroxide solution

Mixing sodium hydroxide solution and dilute hydrochloric acid produces a colourless solution – not much seems to have happened. But if you repeat the reaction with a thermometer in the tube, the temperature rises several degrees, showing that there has been a chemical change. Sodium chloride solution has been formed.

$$NaOH(aq) + HCl(aq) \rightarrow NaCl(aq) + H_2O(l)$$

The ionic equation for this shows that the underlying reaction is between hydroxide ions and hydrogen ions in solution to produce water.

$$OH^-(aq) + H^+(aq) \rightarrow H_2O(l)$$

> Remember that for GCSE purposes, acids in solution and metal (and ammonium) compounds are ionic.

> The bases you will meet at GCSE include: metal oxides (because they contain oxide ions), metal hydroxides (containing hydroxide ions), metal carbonates (containing carbonate ions) and ammonia. All of these have the ability to combine with hydrogen ions.

Figure 9.10 *Sodium chloride is common salt. You don't normally make it – it occurs naturally.*

This is another good example of a neutralisation reaction. The hydroxide ion is a base because it combines with hydrogen ions. Sodium hydroxide is a soluble base.

Solutions of soluble bases are alkaline, having a pH greater than 7. This is because they contain hydroxide ions. There are soluble bases apart from hydroxides – such as ammonia and a few soluble oxides and carbonates. These are also alkaline, and they also contain hydroxide ions because of reactions with the water.

Following the course of a neutralisation reaction

If everything involved in a neutralisation reaction is a colourless solution, how can you tell when exactly enough acid has been added to an alkali to produce a neutral solution?

Using an indicator

Some indicators will change colour when you have added even one drop too much acid. You normally avoid litmus because its colour change isn't very sharp or distinct. A common alternative is **methyl orange**.

Methyl orange is yellow in alkaline solutions and red in acids. You run acid in from the burette, swirling the flask all the time. The alkali is neutralised when the solution shows the first trace of orange. If it turns red, you have added too much acid. You will find more about carrying out this experiment, called a **titration**, in Chapter 10 (pages 84–85) and Chapter 26 (page 211).

Reacting acids with carbonates

Carbonates react with cold dilute acids to produce carbon dioxide gas.

A summary equation for acids and carbonates

> carbonate + acid → salt + carbon dioxide + water

The reaction between copper(II) carbonate and dilute acids

The green copper(II) carbonate reacts with the common dilute acids to give a blue or blue-green solution of copper(II) sulfate, copper(II) nitrate or copper(II) chloride. Carbon dioxide gas is given off. You can recognise this because it turns lime water milky.

The three full equations look different:

> $CuCO_3(s) + H_2SO_4(aq) \rightarrow CuSO_4(aq) + CO_2(g) + H_2O(l)$
>
> $CuCO_3(s) + 2HNO_3(aq) \rightarrow Cu(NO_3)_2(aq) + CO_2(g) + H_2O(l)$
>
> $CuCO_3(s) + 2HCl(aq) \rightarrow CuCl_2(aq) + CO_2(g) + H_2O(l)$

But the ionic equation shows that exactly the same reaction happens each time.

> $CO_3^{2-}(s) + 2H^+(aq) \rightarrow CO_2(g) + H_2O(l)$

Because carbonate ions are combining with hydrogen ions, carbonate ions are bases.

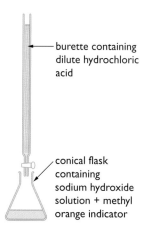

burette containing dilute hydrochloric acid

conical flask containing sodium hydroxide solution + methyl orange indicator

Figure 9.11 *Reacting dilute hydrochloric acid with sodium hydroxide solution.*

If you are really wide awake, you might remember that methyl orange changes colour around pH 4 – not the neutral point. That means that when it shows the first trace of orange, you have overshot the neutral point very slightly. In fact, it turns out to be by no more than about a drop, or even less.

Figure 9.12 *The reaction between copper(II) carbonate and dilute sulfuric acid.*

Occasionally, you might come across an acid reacting with a carbonate *solution*. In that case, replace (s) by (aq).

Theories of acids and bases

The Arrhenius theory

As a part of his work on the theory of ions, the Swedish chemist Arrhenius suggested in 1887 that acids produced hydrogen ions when they were dissolved in water. That is much the line that we have taken so far in this chapter.

He also thought that bases were solutions containing hydroxide ions. We have taken a wider view than this, defining a base as something that combines with hydrogen ions. That includes hydroxide ions, but there are other things as well.

The problem with the Arrhenius theory is that it is very restricted. A simple example of this involves hydrochloric acid and ammonia, NH_3. Ammonia gas is very soluble in water, and gives an alkaline solution with a pH of about 11. Hydrochloric acid is a solution of the gas hydrogen chloride in water.

Concentrated hydrochloric acid gives off hydrogen chloride gas, and concentrated ammonia solution releases ammonia gas. If these gases are allowed to mix, solid white ammonium chloride is produced.

$$NH_3(g) + HCl(g) \rightarrow NH_4Cl(s)$$

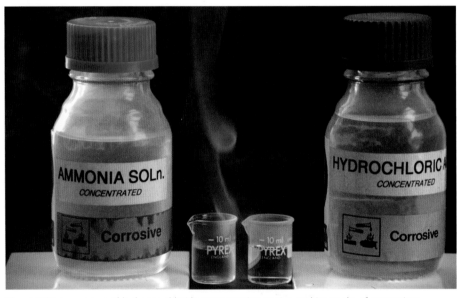

Figure 9.13 *Ammonia and hydrogen chloride gases reacting to give a white smoke of ammonium chloride.*

You would get exactly the same product if you neutralised dilute hydrochloric acid with ammonia solution. This time, the ammonium chloride would be in solution.

Despite the similarity, the Arrhenius theory wouldn't accept the reaction between the gases as being acid–base, because it doesn't involve hydrogen ions and hydroxide ions in solution in water. There are other similar examples. A resolution of the problem had to wait until 1923.

The Bronsted–Lowry theory

Bronsted was a Danish chemist; Lowry an English one. They defined acids and bases as follows.

● An **acid** is a proton (hydrogen ion) donor.

● A **base** is a proton (hydrogen ion) acceptor.

In this theory, when hydrogen chloride dissolves in water to give hydrochloric acid, a proton (a hydrogen ion) is transferred from the HCl to the water.

A hydrogen ion is just a proton – the hydrogen nucleus minus its electron.

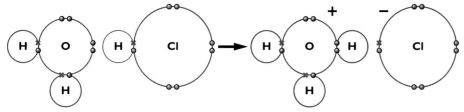

Figure 9.14 *Hydrogen chloride dissolves in water to give hydrochloric acid.*

The hydrogen nucleus breaks away from the chlorine leaving its electron behind.

In symbols:

$$H_2O(l) + HCl(g) \rightarrow H_3O^+(aq) + Cl^-(aq)$$

The $H_3O^+(aq)$ ion is called a **hydroxonium ion**. This is the ion that we normally write simply as $H^+(aq)$. You can think of it as a hydrogen ion riding on a water molecule.

In this example, according to the Bronsted–Lowry theory, the HCl is an acid because it is giving a proton (a hydrogen ion) to the water. The water is acting as a base because it is accepting the proton.

Only the outer electrons are shown in these diagrams to avoid confusion.
Notice the new bond formed between the hydrogen and the water molecule. Both electrons in the bond come from the oxygen. This is described as a **co-ordinate covalent bond** or a **dative covalent bond**. Once the bond has been made, there is absolutely no difference between this bond and the other two normal covalent bonds between the oxygen and the hydrogens.

In a similar way, hydrogen chloride gas reacts with ammonia gas to produce ammonium chloride.

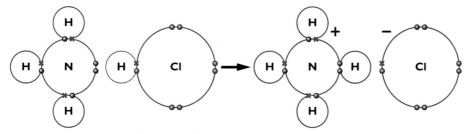

Figure 9.15 *Hydrogen chloride reacts with ammonia to produce ammonium chloride.*

The ammonia acts as a base by accepting the proton; the HCl acts as an acid by donating it. This time an ammonium ion, NH_4^+, is formed. Notice the co-ordinate bond that is formed between the nitrogen and the new hydrogen.

$$NH_3(g) + HCl(g) \rightarrow NH_4^+(s) + Cl^-(s)$$

Acids in solution

Acids in solution are acidic because of the presence of the hydroxonium ion. We would normally write a neutralisation reaction between an acid and a hydroxide, for example, as:

$$H^+(aq) + OH^-(aq) \rightarrow H_2O(l)$$

What actually happens is that the hydroxonium ion donates a proton to the base, OH^-.

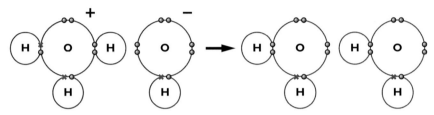

Figure 9.16 *The hydroxonium ion donates a proton to the base.*

$$H_3O^+(aq) + OH^-(aq) \rightarrow 2H_2O(l)$$

For GCSE purposes, we almost always use the simplified version:

$$H^+(aq) + OH^-(aq) \rightarrow H_2O(l)$$

Hydrogen chloride and hydrochloric acid

Both hydrogen chloride and hydrochloric acid have the formula HCl. Hydrogen chloride is a gas, and hydrochloric acid is its solution in water. As we have seen above, when hydrogen chloride dissolves in water, it reacts to give hydroxonium ions and chloride ions.

$$H_2O(l) + HCl(g) \rightarrow H_3O^+(aq) + Cl^-(aq)$$

It is easy to show that a reaction is happening by suspending a drop of water on a thermometer bulb and lowering this into a gas jar of hydrogen chloride gas. There is a large increase in temperature, showing that a reaction must have occurred.

It is the presence of the hydroxonium ions which gives hydrochloric acid its simple acidic properties – with litmus, metals and carbonates, for example.

If you dissolve hydrogen chloride gas in methylbenzene (an organic solvent also known as toluene), the solution doesn't show hydrochloric acid's simple acidic properties – provided there isn't even a trace of water present.

● It won't turn blue litmus paper red (provided the paper is also perfectly dry).

● It won't react with magnesium ribbon to produce hydrogen.

● It won't react with marble chips (calcium carbonate) to produce carbon dioxide.

If there is any trace of water present, the hydrogen chloride reacts with it, and its simple acidic properties are restored. The HCl reacts to form ions again – especially the all-important hydroxonium ion.

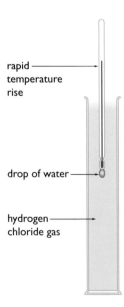

rapid temperature rise

drop of water

hydrogen chloride gas

Figure 9.17 *Hydrogen chloride reacts with water to give hydroxonium ions and chloride ions.*

You should now be able to:

✓ understand the pH scale and the use of universal indicator and simple indicators like litmus

✓ know how the reactions of metals with acids are related to the position of the metal in the reactivity series

✓ describe and write equations (full and ionic) for the reactions between common metals and dilute sulfuric or hydrochloric acid

✓ understand that simple metal oxides are bases, and know that they react with acids to form a salt and water

✓ describe and write equations (full and ionic) for the reaction of copper(II) oxide with dilute sulfuric acid

✓ know that soluble metal hydroxides are alkaline, that they contain OH⁻ ions in solution, and that they react with acids to form a salt and water

✓ write equations (full and ionic) for the reactions between common metal hydroxides and acids

✓ know that carbonates react with acids to give a salt, carbon dioxide and water, and be able to describe and write equations (full and ionic) for common examples

✓ understand what is meant by an acid and a base according to the Arrhenius theory and the Bronsted–Lowry theory

✓ explain why hydrogen chloride gas dissolved in methylbenzene doesn't show simple acidic properties, whereas a solution in water does.

Questions

1 a) Which of the following will react with dilute sulfuric acid? Copper, copper(II) oxide, copper(II) hydroxide, copper(II) carbonate.

b) In the case of each of the substances which does react, write the full equation (including state symbols) for the reaction. All of these substances are insoluble solids.

2 a) Draw a labelled diagram of the apparatus you would use to collect a few test tubes of hydrogen gas from the reaction between magnesium and dilute hydrochloric acid. Write the full equation for the reaction.

b) Describe how you would test for the hydrogen.

c) Name a metal that won't react with dilute hydrochloric acid.

d) Name a metal which it would be dangerous to add to dilute hydrochloric acid.

e) In the Hindenburg airship disaster (see page 73), most of the people who died did so because they jumped out of the airship. Those who didn't jump tended to survive the fire. This is because when the hydrogen caught fire, the flame rose very quickly instead of engulfing the passenger section of the airship.

(i) What is formed when hydrogen burns? Write the equation for the reaction.

(ii) Why do you think that, when hydrogen burns, the flame rises quickly?

3 Read this description of the chemistry of metal A and some of its compounds, and then answer the questions.

Metal A has no reaction with dilute hydrochloric acid or dilute sulfuric acid. It forms a black oxide, B, which reacts with hot dilute sulfuric acid to give a blue solution, C. Metal A also forms a green compound, D, which reacts with dilute nitric acid to give a colourless gas, E, and another blue solution, F. The colourless gas, E, turned lime water milky.

a) Name A, B, C, D, E and F.

b) Write the full equations for the reactions between

(i) B and dilute sulfuric acid

(ii) D and dilute nitric acid.

4 a) Nickel, Ni, is a silvery metal just above hydrogen in the reactivity series. Nickel(II) compounds in solution are green. Describe what you would see if you warmed some nickel with dilute sulfuric acid in a test tube. Include a description of how you would test for any gas given off.

b) Write the full equation for the reaction between nickel and dilute sulfuric acid.

c) Nickel(II) carbonate is a green, insoluble powder. Describe what you would see if you added a spatula measure of nickel(II) carbonate to some dilute hydrochloric acid in a test tube. Include a description of how you would test for any gas given off.

d) Write **(i)** a full equation and **(ii)** the ionic equation for the reaction between nickel(II) carbonate and dilute hydrochloric acid.

5 Which of the following equations represent reactions between acids and bases? For each of the equations that is an acid–base reaction, state which substance is the acid and which the base.

a) $MgO(s) + H_2SO_4(aq) \rightarrow MgSO_4(aq) + H_2O(l)$

b) $CO_3^{2-}(s) + 2H^+(aq) \rightarrow CO_2(g) + H_2O(l)$

c) $2Al(s) + 6HCl(aq) \rightarrow 2AlCl_3(aq) + 3H_2(g)$

d) $H_2O(l) + HCl(g) \rightarrow H_3O^+(aq) + Cl^-(g)$

e) $Zn(s) + Cu^{2+}(aq) \rightarrow Zn^{2+}(aq) + Cu(s)$

f) $NH_3(g) + HCl(g) \rightarrow NH_4^+(s) + Cl^-(s)$

g) $NaOH(aq) + HCl(aq) \rightarrow NaCl(aq) + H_2O(l)$

6 Sodium hydride, NaH, is a white ionic solid in which the hydrogen exists as an H⁻ ion. The electronic structures of the two ions are:

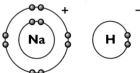

Sodium hydride reacts violently with water. The hydride ion reacts with the water like this:

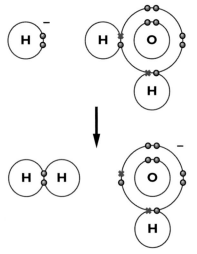

a) At the beginning of the reaction there were sodium ions, hydride ions and water molecules present.

(i) Which of these acts as an acid? Explain your reasoning.

(ii) Which of these acts as a base? Explain your reasoning.

b) Name the products of this reaction.

c) Describe what you might expect to see during the course of the reaction.

d) Assuming that you used a reasonable quantity of sodium hydride, what would you expect the pH of the final solution to be?

7 Zinc granules react slowly with cold dilute sulfuric acid to give hydrogen gas and a colourless solution of zinc sulfate.

$$Zn(s) + H_2SO_4(aq) \rightarrow ZnSO_4(aq) + H_2(g)$$

Small amounts of copper(II) sulfate solution are often added to the mixture to increase the rate of the reaction. The copper(II) sulfate reacts with some of the zinc to produce copper. The copper in contact with the zinc speeds up the reaction.

Design an experiment to find out whether the rate of the reaction depends on how much copper(II) sulfate you add.

Remember – if you do an experiment like this, it is important to change only one thing at a time. As you want to find out what happens if you change the amount of copper(II) sulfate, it is important that everything else stays the same from one part of the experiment to the next.

Your account should include a diagram of the apparatus you are going to use, and an outline of how you will do the experiment. Full practical details are not expected – to describe this in detail could take you several hours of work!

You may find it useful to look back at Chapter 6 on rates of reaction for ideas.

Chapter 10: Making Salts

Soluble and insoluble salts

The importance of knowing whether a salt is soluble or insoluble in water

You will remember that acids react with carbonates to give a salt, carbon dioxide and water. In the case of calcium carbonate (for example, marble chips) reacting with dilute hydrochloric acid, calcium chloride solution is produced.

$$CaCO_3(s) + 2HCl(aq) \rightarrow CaCl_2(aq) + CO_2(g) + H_2O(l)$$

If you try the reaction between calcium carbonate and dilute sulfuric acid, nothing much seems to happen if you use large marble chips. You will get a few bubbles when you first add the acid, but the reaction soon stops.

This chapter looks at some of the practical problems in making pure samples of salts in the lab. Remember that a salt is what is formed when the hydrogen in an acid is replaced by a metal. For example, sulfates come from sulfuric acid, chlorides from hydrochloric acid, and nitrates from nitric acid.

Figure 10.1 *Calcium carbonate reacting with dilute hydrochloric acid.*

Figure 10.2 *Calcium carbonate not reacting with dilute sulfuric acid.*

The problem is that the calcium sulfate produced in the reaction is almost insoluble in water. As soon as the reaction starts, a layer of calcium sulfate is formed around the calcium carbonate, stopping any further reaction.

You may have noticed that the bottle in the right-hand photograph is labelled as 'sulphuric acid' rather than 'sulfuric acid'. You must expect to come across both versions of this name. 'Sulphuric' is the traditional English spelling.

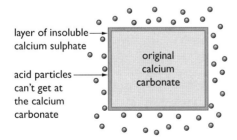

layer of insoluble calcium sulphate

acid particles can't get at the calcium carbonate

original calcium carbonate

Figure 10.3 *The reaction between calcium carbonate and sulfuric acid.*

Any attempt to produce an insoluble salt from the reaction between a solid and a liquid will fail for this reason.

How quickly the reaction stops may well depend on the size of the marble chips (because that affects the surface area), the concentration of the acid, the volume of acid added, and the amount the flask is shaken. This would make an interesting investigation – particularly if you could then explain any pattern in your results.

Chapter 10: Making Salts

Notes on the table

To keep the table simple, it includes one or two compounds (like aluminium carbonate, for example) which don't actually exist. Don't worry about these. The problem won't arise at GCSE.

Hydroxides have been included for the sake of completeness, although they are not salts. The list is in reactivity series order, apart from the ammonium group. Ammonium compounds often have similarities with sodium and potassium compounds, and so are included near them.

There is no clear cut-off between 'insoluble' and 'almost insoluble' compounds. The ones picked out as 'almost insoluble' include the more common ones that you might need to know about elsewhere in the course.

Solubility patterns

	nitrate	chloride	sulfate	carbonate	hydroxide
ammonium	soluble	soluble	soluble	soluble	soluble
potassium	soluble	soluble	soluble	soluble	soluble
sodium	soluble	soluble	soluble	soluble	soluble
barium	soluble	soluble	insoluble	insoluble	almost insoluble
calcium	soluble	soluble	almost insoluble	insoluble	almost insoluble
magnesium	soluble	soluble	soluble	insoluble	insoluble
aluminium	soluble	soluble	soluble	insoluble	insoluble
zinc	soluble	soluble	soluble	insoluble	insoluble
iron	soluble	soluble	soluble	insoluble	insoluble
lead	soluble	insoluble	insoluble	insoluble	insoluble
copper	soluble	soluble	soluble	insoluble	insoluble
silver	soluble	insoluble	soluble	insoluble	insoluble

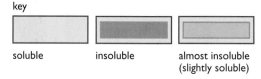

key: soluble | insoluble | almost insoluble (slightly soluble)

Figure 10.4 *Solubility patterns.*

Note that:

- all sodium, potassium and ammonium compounds are *soluble*
- all nitrates are *soluble*
- most common chlorides are *soluble*, except lead(II) chloride and silver chloride
- most common sulfates are *soluble*, except lead(II) sulfate, barium sulfate and calcium sulfate
- most common carbonates are *insoluble*, except sodium, potassium and ammonium carbonates
- most metal hydroxides are *insoluble* (or *almost insoluble*), except sodium, potassium and ammonium hydroxides.

It can seem a bit daunting to have to remember all this, but it isn't as hard as it looks at first sight.

Except for the carbonates and hydroxides, most of these compounds are soluble. Learn the exceptions in the sulfates and chlorides. The reason for the exceptions in the carbonates and hydroxides is that all sodium, potassium and ammonium compounds are soluble.

Making soluble salts (except sodium, potassium and ammonium salts)

These all involve reacting a solid with an acid. You can use any of the following mixtures:

- **acid + metal** (but only for the moderately reactive metals from magnesium to iron in the reactivity series)

- **acid + metal oxide or hydroxide**

- **acid + carbonate**.

Whatever mixture you use, the method is essentially the same.

Making magnesium sulfate crystals

Enough magnesium is added to some dilute sulfuric acid so that there is some left over when the reaction stops bubbling. This is to make sure there is no acid left in the final mixture.

$$Mg(s) + H_2SO_4(aq) \rightarrow MgSO_4(aq) + H_2(g)$$

The unused magnesium is then filtered off, and the magnesium sulfate solution is concentrated by boiling it until crystals will form when it is cooled. You can test for this by cooling a small sample of the solution quickly. If the sample crystallises, so will the whole solution.

Figure 10.5 *Dilute sulfuric acid with excess magnesium.*

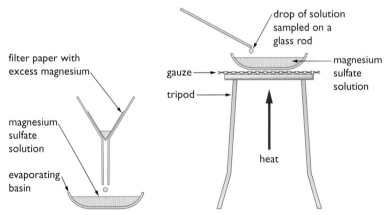

Figure 10.6 *Making magnesium sulfate crystals.*

In the diagram, a small drop on the end of a glass rod is cooled rapidly in the air to see whether crystals form.

Finally, the solution is left to form colourless magnesium sulfate crystals. Any uncrystallised solution can be poured off the crystals, and the crystals can be blotted dry with paper tissue.

Why not just evaporate the solution to dryness? Water of crystallisation

It would seem much easier to just boil off all the water rather than crystallising the solution slowly, but evaporating to dryness wouldn't give you magnesium sulfate crystals. Instead, you would produce a white powder of **anhydrous** magnesium sulfate.

'Anhydrous' means 'without water'. When many salts form their crystals, water from the solution becomes chemically bound up with the salt. This is called **water of crystallisation**. A salt which contains water of crystallisation is said to be **hydrated**.

> In the formula for the crystals, you might find either a dot or a comma between the $MgSO_4$ and the $7H_2O$.

$$MgSO_4(aq) + 7H_2O(l) \rightarrow MgSO_4 \cdot 7H_2O(s)$$

The extra water in the equation comes from the water in the solution.

Making copper(II) sulfate crystals from copper(II) oxide

The method is identical, except that you add an excess of black copper(II) oxide to hot dilute sulfuric acid. You can easily see when you have an excess because you are left with some unreacted black solid.

$$CuO(s) + H_2SO_4(aq) \rightarrow CuSO_4(aq) + H_2O(l)$$

$$CuSO_4(aq) + 5H_2O(l) \rightarrow CuSO_4 \cdot 5H_2O(s)$$

Figure 10.7 *Copper(II) sulfate crystals.*

How do you know whether you need to heat the mixture?

Carbonates react with dilute acids in the cold, and so does magnesium. Most other things that you are likely to come across need to be heated.

cold	hot
carbonates magnesium	most other substances

Figure 10.8 *Do you need to heat the mixture?*

Making sodium, potassium and ammonium salts

The need for a different method

In the method we've just been looking at, you add an excess of a solid to an acid, and then filter off the unreacted solid. You do this to make sure all the acid is used up.

The problem is that all sodium, potassium and ammonium compounds are soluble in water. The solid you added to the acid would not only react with the acid, but any excess would just dissolve in the water present. You wouldn't have any visible excess to filter off. There's no simple way of seeing when you have added just enough of the solid to neutralise the acid.

Solving the problem by doing a titration

> Before you go on, it would be a good idea to read pages 74–75 in Chapter 9 for the background to these reactions.

You normally make these salts from sodium or potassium hydroxide or ammonia solution, but you can also use the carbonates. Fortunately, solutions of all these are alkaline. That means you can find out when you have a neutral solution by using an indicator.

The method of finding out exactly how much of two solutions you need to neutralise each other is called a **titration**. The point at which an indicator changes colour during the titration is called the **end point** of the titration.

Having found out how much acid and alkali are needed, you can make a pure solution of the salt by mixing those same volumes again, but without the indicator.

Making sodium sulfate crystals

$$2NaOH(aq) + H_2SO_4(aq) \rightarrow Na_2SO_4(aq) + 2H_2O(l)$$

25 cm³ of sodium hydroxide solution is transferred to a conical flask using a pipette, and a few drops of methyl orange are added as the indicator.

Dilute sulfuric acid is run in from the burette until the indicator turns from yellow to orange.

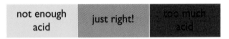

Figure 10.10 *Colour changes for methyl orange.*

The volume of acid needed is noted, and the same volumes of acid and alkali are mixed together in a clean flask without any indicator. The solution can be crystallised by evaporating it to the point that crystals will form on cooling, and then leaving it for the crystals to form. The crystals are finally separated from any remaining solution and allowed to dry.

$$Na_2SO_4(aq) + 10H_2O(l) \rightarrow Na_2SO_4 \cdot 10H_2O(s)$$

Making sodium chloride crystals

$$NaOH(aq) + HCl(aq) \rightarrow NaCl(aq) + H_2O(l)$$

You would need to do the titration using dilute hydrochloric acid rather than dilute sulfuric acid. However, once you have re-mixed the acid and the alkali without the indicator, you can then evaporate the sodium chloride solution to dryness rather than crystallising it slowly. Sodium chloride crystals don't contain any water of crystallisation, so you can save time by evaporating all the water off in one go. The disadvantage is that you end up with either a powder or very tiny crystals.

Making ammonium sulfate crystals

$$2NH_3(aq) + H_2SO_4(aq) \rightarrow (NH_4)_2SO_4(aq)$$

Using ammonia solution rather than sodium hydroxide solution makes no difference to the method. Although simple ammonium salts don't have water of crystallisation, you would still crystallise them slowly rather than evaporating them to dryness. Heating dry ammonium salts tends to break them up.

Making insoluble salts

Precipitation reactions

To make an insoluble salt, you do a **precipitation reaction**. A **precipitate** is a fine solid that is formed by a chemical reaction involving liquids or gases. A precipitation reaction is simply a reaction that produces a precipitate.

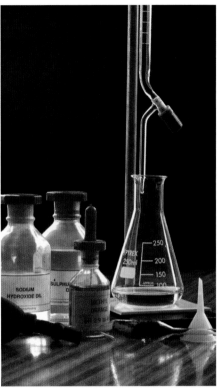

Figure 10.9 *Apparatus for carrying out a titration.*

Figure 10.11 *A precipitate of silver chloride.*

The water molecules in the solutions have been left out to avoid cluttering the diagram.

Ionic equations for precipitation reactions are simple to write. Write down the formula for the precipitate on the right-hand side of the equation. Write down the formulae for the ions that have clumped together to produce it on the left-hand side. Don't forget the state symbols.

For example, if silver chloride is produced from a reaction involving solutions, you get a white precipitate formed, because silver chloride won't dissolve in water – and so is seen as a fine white solid.

The photograph shows the results of this reaction:

$$AgNO_3(aq) + NaCl(aq) \rightarrow AgCl(s) + NaNO_3(aq)$$

Explaining what's happening

Silver nitrate solution contains silver ions and nitrate ions in solution. The positive and negative ions are attracted to each other, but the attractions aren't strong enough to make them stick together. Similarly, sodium chloride solution contains sodium ions and chloride ions – again, the attractions aren't strong enough for them to stick together.

When you mix the two solutions, the various ions meet each other. When silver ions meet chloride ions, the attractions are so strong that the ions clump together and form a solid. The sodium and nitrate ions remain in solution because they aren't sufficiently attracted to each other.

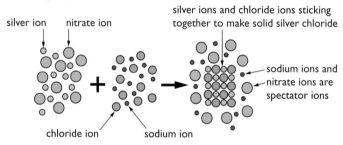

Figure 10.12 *Precipitation of silver chloride.*

Writing ionic equations for precipitation reactions

The ionic equation for a precipitation reaction is much easier to write than the full equation. All that is happening in one of these reactions is that the ions of an insoluble salt are clumping together to form the solid. The ionic equation simply shows that happening. You don't need to worry at all about the spectator ions – they aren't doing anything.

$$Ag^+(aq) + Cl^-(aq) \rightarrow AgCl(s)$$

This means that if you mix any solution containing silver ions with any solution containing chloride ions, you will get the same white precipitate of silver chloride.

Making pure barium sulfate

$$Ba^{2+}(aq) + SO_4^{2-}(aq) \rightarrow BaSO_4(s)$$

You can mix solutions of any soluble barium compound (for example, barium chloride or barium nitrate) with any soluble sulfate. The sulfate doesn't necessarily have to be a salt. Dilute sulfuric acid contains sulfate ions, so you can perfectly well use that.

Suppose you decide to use barium chloride solution and dilute sulfuric acid.

You would mix the solutions to get a white precipitate of barium sulfate. The hydrogen ions from the sulfuric acid and the chloride ions are just spectator ions and aren't involved at all.

The mixture is filtered to get the precipitate. The solid barium sulfate is impure because of the presence of the spectator ions and any excess barium chloride solution or sulfuric acid. It is washed with pure water while it is still on the filter paper and then left to dry.

In an exam, simply use the words 'filter, wash and dry the precipitate'.

Making pure lead(II) iodide

It doesn't matter if the salt is unfamiliar to you, as long as you are told that it is insoluble in water. For example, to make lead(II) iodide you would have to mix a solution containing lead(II) ions with one containing iodide ions.

$$Pb^{2+}(aq) + 2I^-(aq) \rightarrow PbI_2(s)$$

The most common soluble lead(II) salt is lead(II) nitrate. A simple source of iodide ions would be sodium or potassium iodide solution, because all sodium and potassium salts are soluble.

The photograph shows the yellow precipitate of lead(II) iodide. This can now be filtered, washed and dried.

Figure 10.13 *A precipitate of lead(II) iodide.*

Summarising the methods of making salts

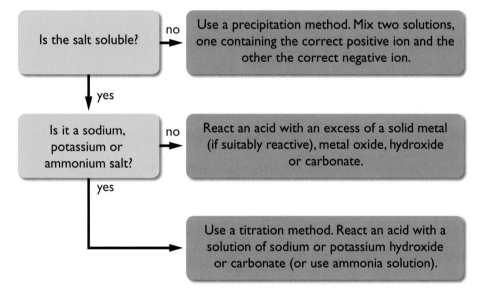

Figure 10.14 *Methods of making salts.*

You should now be able to:

✓ know which salts are soluble and which are insoluble in water

✓ give practical details of how you would make a pure, dry sample of a salt from the reaction between a suitable solid (metal, metal oxide, metal hydroxide or metal carbonate) and an acid

✓ know which salts can be made by this method

✓ describe how to make pure, dry samples of sodium, potassium or ammonium salts using a titration method

✓ describe how to make pure, dry samples of insoluble salts using precipitation reactions

✓ write ionic equations for precipitation reactions.

Questions

1   Sort the following compounds into two lists – those that are soluble in water, and those that are insoluble.

sodium chloride, lead(II) sulfate, zinc nitrate, calcium carbonate, iron(III) sulfate, lead(II) chloride, potassium sulfate, copper(II) carbonate, silver chloride, aluminium nitrate, barium sulfate, ammonium chloride, magnesium nitrate, calcium sulfate, sodium phosphate, nickel(II) carbonate, chromium(III) hydroxide, potassium dichromate(VI)

2   a)   Describe in detail the preparation of a pure, dry sample of copper(II) sulfate crystals, $CuSO_4 \cdot 5H_2O$, starting from copper(II) oxide.

   b)   Write full equations for (i) the reaction producing copper(II) sulfate solution, (ii) the crystallisation reaction.

3   a)   Read the following description of a method for making sodium sulfate crystals, $Na_2SO_4 \cdot 10H_2O$, and then explain the reasons for each of the underlined phrases or sentences.

   25 cm³ of sodium carbonate solution was transferred to a conical flask <u>using a pipette</u>, and a <u>few drops of methyl orange were added</u>. Dilute sulfuric acid was run in from a burette <u>until the solution became orange</u>. The volume of acid added was noted. That same volume of dilute sulfuric acid was added to a fresh 25 cm³ sample of sodium carbonate solution in a clean flask, but <u>without the methyl orange</u>. The mixture was <u>evaporated until a sample taken on the end of a glass rod crystallised on cooling in the air</u>. <u>The solution was left to cool</u>. The crystals formed were separated from the remaining solution and dried.

   b)   Write equations for (i) the reaction producing sodium sulfate solution, (ii) the crystallisation reaction.

4   Suggest solutions that could be mixed together to make each of the following insoluble salts. In each case, write the ionic equation for the reaction you choose.

   a)   silver chloride

   b)   calcium carbonate

   c)   lead(II) sulfate

   d)   lead(II) chloride

5   Describe in detail the preparation of a pure, dry sample of barium carbonate. Write the ionic equation for the reaction you use.

6   There are three main methods of making salts:

   A reacting an acid with an excess of a suitable solid

   B using a titration

   C using a precipitation reaction.

   For each of the following salts, write down the letter of the appropriate method, and name the substances you would react together. You should state whether they are used as solids or solutions. Write an equation (full or ionic as appropriate) for each reaction.

   a)   zinc sulfate

   b)   barium sulfate

   c)   potassium nitrate (nitric acid is HNO_3)

   d)   copper(II) nitrate

   e)   lead(II) chromate(VI) (a bright yellow insoluble solid; chromate(VI) ions have the formula CrO_4^{2-}).

Chapter 11: Separating and Analysing

Separating mixtures

Figure 11.1 *Chemists have to be able to get . . .*

Figure 11.2 *. . . pure substances from mixtures.*

This chapter starts by summarising various common methods of separating mixtures. It then goes on to look at some simple tests used to identify substances in the lab.

Making pure salt from rock salt

Rock salt consists of salt contaminated by various earthy or rocky impurities. These impurities aren't soluble in water.

If you crush the rock salt and mix it with hot water, the salt dissolves, but the impurities don't. The impurities can be filtered off, and remain on the filter paper. The salt solution (the filtrate) which drips through the filter paper can be heated to remove the water, leaving pure salt. You can boil salt solution to dryness to get solid salt because sodium chloride doesn't have water of crystallisation. You will find more about this in Chapter 10 (page 84).

This is typical of the way you can separate any mixture of two solids, one of which is soluble in water, and one of which isn't. If you want a pure sample of the solid, you must wash it with pure water while it is still on the filter paper to remove any traces of solution. Then you leave it to dry.

Figure 11.3 *Rock salt.*

Making pure water from sea water – simple distillation

The water boils and is condensed back again to a liquid by the condenser. The salt remains in the flask.

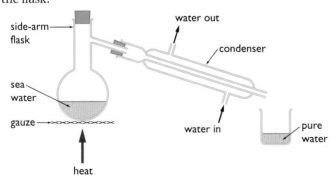

side-arm flask

water out

condenser

sea water

gauze

water in

pure water

heat

Figure 11.4 *Distilling pure water from sea water.*

To make the boiling smoother, you often put some small pieces of quartz (known as 'anti-bumping granules') into the flask with the sea water.

Notice that water is always fed into the condenser at the lower end. That way, if the flow of water stops for any reason, the condenser jacket remains full of water.

You could, of course, collect the salt from the water as well as collecting pure water. The sea water eventually becomes so concentrated that the salt will crystallise out as a white solid. This solid (known as sea salt) isn't pure sodium chloride. It contains all the other soluble substances (some good, some not so good) present in the sea water.

Fractional distillation

Fractional distillation is used to separate liquids such as alcohol (ethanol) and water. Alcohol and water are completely miscible with each other. That means you can mix them together in any proportions and they will form a single liquid layer. You can separate them by taking advantage of their different boiling points. Water boils at 100 °C; alcohol at 78 °C.

Once again, you would normally include some anti-bumping granules to make the mixture boil more smoothly.

Notice that the bulb of the thermometer has to be exactly at the side-arm of the fractionating column. You are interested in the temperature of the vapour escaping into the condenser.

The fractionating column is often packed with glass beads or something similar, although the separation of alcohol and water in the lab works perfectly well just with an empty column. For reasons that are beyond GCSE, a high surface area in the column helps separation of the two vapours. The alcohol produced by this experiment is about 96% pure. For complicated reasons, again beyond GCSE, it is impossible to remove the last 4% of water by distillation.

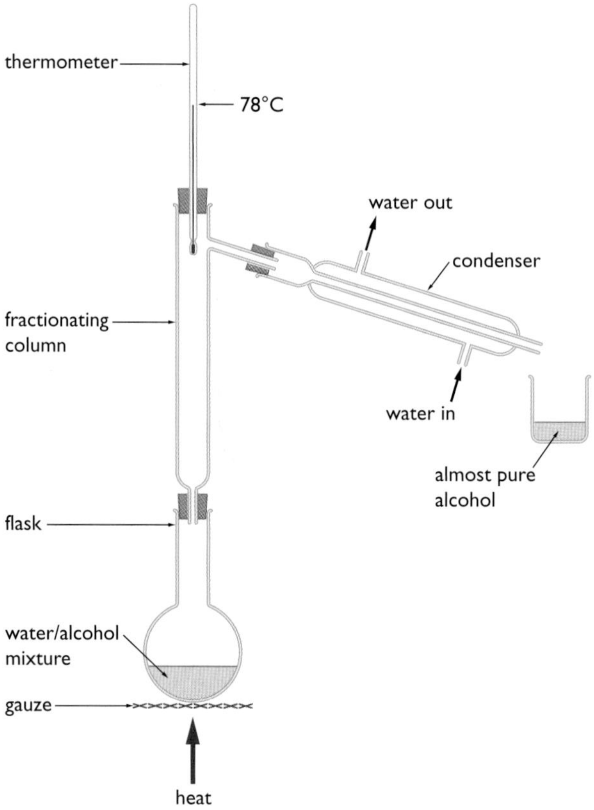

Figure 11.5 *Fractional distillation.*

Both liquids boil, but, by careful heating you control the temperature of the column so that the water all condenses in the column and trickles back into the flask. Only the alcohol remains as a vapour all the way to the top, and out into the condenser.

Separating petrol and water

Petrol and water are immiscible – they won't mix with each other, and the petrol floats on top of the water. They are easy to separate using a separating funnel to run them off into two different beakers.

Recrystallisation

This is used to purify soluble substances contaminated with small quantities of other soluble substances. The impure solid is dissolved in the minimum amount of hot water (or other suitable solvent), and then allowed to cool again. Most solids are less soluble in the cold than in the hot, and so crystals are formed again. As long as there are only small amounts of impurities, they stay in solution.

The crystals can be filtered and washed on the filter paper with a small amount of cold water (or other solvent), and then allowed to dry.

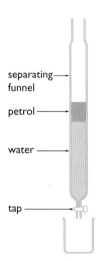

Figure 11.6 *Separating petrol and water.*

Paper chromatography

A simple example

A spot of ink is put onto some chromatography paper (an absorbent paper like filter paper or blotting paper), and the paper is hung in a boiling tube containing some solvent. You might use water, or a non-aqueous solvent (a solvent other than water). What you would use would depend on whether you are using a water-soluble ink or biro ink, which won't dissolve in water.

The solvent gradually soaks up into the paper. Having the paper in a sealed tube stops the solvent from evaporating as it travels up the paper.

The dyes that make up the ink will differ in two important ways:

● they will differ in how strongly they stick to the paper

● they will differ in how soluble they are in the solvent.

In Figure 11.7, spot C has hardly moved. Either it was not very soluble in the solvent, or it stuck very firmly to the paper (or both). On the other hand, spot A moved almost as far as the solvent. It must be very soluble in the solvent, and not very well attached to the paper. The pattern you get is called a **chromatogram**.

In the example shown, the ink must have contained a minimum of three different dyes, but there could be more. It is possible that one of the spots is made up of two similarly coloured dyes that happened to have moved the same distance. You could only find this out by trying a different solvent.

Using paper chromatography in analysis

The simple apparatus in Figure 11.7 can be scaled up to allow you to identify particular dyes in a mixture.

A pencil line is drawn on a larger sheet of paper, and pencil marks are drawn along the line to show the original positions of the various dyes placed on it (see Figure 11.8). One spot is your unknown mixture; the others are single, known dyes. The chromatogram is then allowed to develop as before.

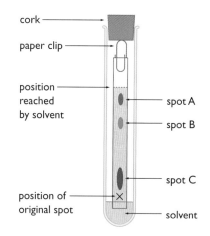

cork
paper clip
position reached by solvent
spot A
spot B
spot C
position of original spot
solvent

Figure 11.7 *Simple paper chromatography.*

You will find a photograph of a scaled-up version on page 89.

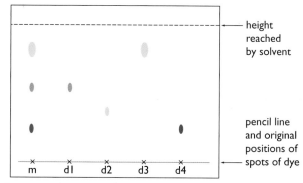

height reached by solvent

pencil line and original positions of spots of dye

m   d1   d2   d3   d4

Figure 11.8 *Scaled-up paper chromatography.*

The mixture (m) has spots corresponding to dyes 1, 3 and 4. They have the same colour as spots in the mixture, and have travelled the same distance on the paper. Although dye 2 is the same colour as one of the spots in the mixture, it has travelled a different distance and so must be a different compound.

Collecting and identifying gases

Collecting gases

Gases can be collected in different ways, as shown in Figure 11.9.

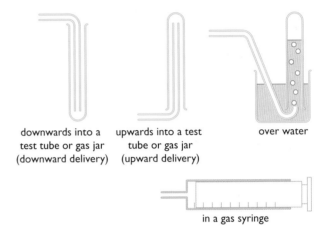

downwards into a   upwards into a test   over water
test tube or gas jar   tube or gas jar
(downward delivery)   (upward delivery)

in a gas syringe

Figure 11.9 *Methods of collecting gases.*

Collecting into a gas syringe is fine if you want to measure the volume of the gas. To test the gas, though, you would have to transfer it to a test tube using one of the first three methods.

How to collect and test individual gases

Hydrogen, H_2

Hydrogen is less dense than air and is almost insoluble in water. Collect it over water or upwards into a test tube or gas jar.

Hydrogen pops when a lighted splint is held to the mouth of the tube. The hydrogen combines explosively with oxygen in the air to make water.

$$2H_2(g) + O_2(g) \rightarrow 2H_2O(l)$$

Oxygen, O_2

Oxygen has almost the same density as air and is only slightly soluble in water. You normally collect it over water.

Oxygen relights a glowing splint.

Carbon dioxide, CO_2

Carbon dioxide is denser than air and can be collected downwards into a test tube or gas jar. It is only slightly soluble in water and so it can be collected over water as well.

Carbon dioxide turns lime water milky (or chalky). Lime water is calcium hydroxide solution. Carbon dioxide reacts with it to form a white precipitate of calcium carbonate.

$$Ca(OH)_2(aq) + CO_2(g) \rightarrow CaCO_3(s) + H_2O(l)$$

Chlorine, Cl_2

Chlorine is denser than air and is usually collected downwards into a test tube or gas jar. Because chlorine is green, it is easy to see when the tube or gas jar you are collecting it into is full. Chlorine is too soluble to collect it satisfactorily over water, but you can collect it over concentrated salt solution instead. It is less soluble in the salt solution.

Chlorine is a green gas which bleaches damp litmus paper.

Ammonia, NH_3

Ammonia is less dense than air and is extremely soluble in water. It can only be collected upwards into a test tube or gas jar.

Ammonia is the only alkaline gas that you will meet at GCSE. It turns damp red litmus paper blue.

Testing for water

Using anhydrous copper(II) sulfate

Water turns white anhydrous copper(II) sulfate blue.

Anhydrous copper(II) sulfate lacks water of crystallisation and is white. Dropping water onto it replaces the water of crystallisation, and turns it blue.

If you aren't sure about water of crystallisation, see Chapter 10 (page 83–84).

$$CuSO_4(s) + 5H_2O(l) \rightarrow CuSO_4 \cdot 5H_2O(s)$$

This test works for anything which contains water. It does *not* show that the water is pure. You can check the purity by showing that it freezes at exactly $0\,°C$ and boils at exactly $100\,°C$ at 1 atmosphere pressure.

Using cobalt chloride paper

Cobalt chloride paper is simply filter paper that has been dipped into cobalt(II) chloride solution and then dried thoroughly in a desiccator. A desiccator is a piece of glassware or a small cabinet which contains a tray of some substance which absorbs water.

When it is dry, the paper is blue. Adding water to it turns it pink.

Once again, anything that contains water will turn cobalt chloride paper from blue to pink. The water doesn't have to be pure.

Testing for ions

Flame tests

A flame test is used to show the presence of certain metal ions in a compound. A platinum or nichrome wire is cleaned by dipping it into concentrated hydrochloric acid and then holding it in a hot Bunsen flame. This is repeated until the wire doesn't give any colour to the flame.

The wire is dipped back into the acid, then into a tiny sample of the solid you are testing, and back into the flame.

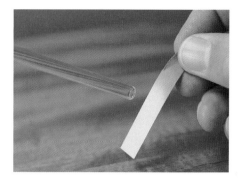

Figure 11.10 *Chlorine bleaches damp litmus paper.*

Figure 11.11 *Testing for water with anhydrous copper(II) sulfate.*

Figure 11.12 *Testing for water with cobalt chloride paper.*

Nichrome (a nickel–chromium alloy) is a cheap alternative to platinum. It does, however, always produce a faint yellow colour in the flame, which you have to ignore.

Lithium isn't the only ion to give a red flame colour. Strontium gives a very similar colour. The only way to be sure is to compare the flame colour side-by-side with a known compound of lithium or strontium.

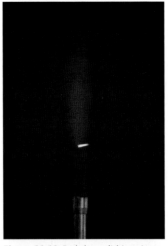

Figure 11.13 *Red shows lithium ions.*

Figure 11.14 *Strong, persistent orange shows sodium ions.*

The calcium flame test often has so much orange in it that it can be confused with sodium. The orange-red often appears for only quite a short time. You can often get a good, but very short-lived, flash of red if you dip the wire briefly back into the acid, and then return it to the flame.

Figure 11.15 *Lilac (pink) shows potassium ions.*

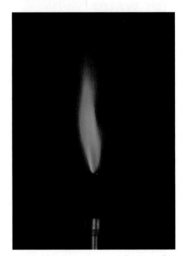

Figure 11.16 *Orange-red (brick red) shows calcium ions.*

If you aren't sure about precipitation reactions and the ionic equations for them, you must read Chapter 10 (pages 85–87) before you go on.

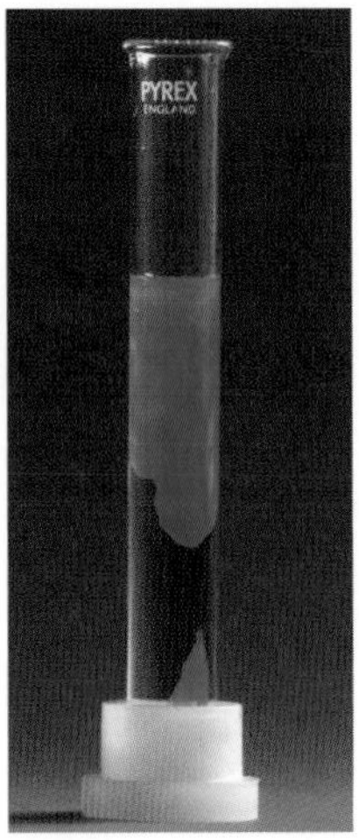

Testing for positive ions using sodium hydroxide solution

Of the common hydroxides, only sodium, potassium and ammonium hydroxides dissolve in water to any extent. Most metal hydroxides are insoluble. That means that if you add sodium hydroxide solution to a solution containing the metal ions, you will get a precipitate of the metal hydroxide.

Four simple cases where it is easy to identify the positive ions are described below.

A blue precipitate is formed

This shows the presence of copper(II) ions. The precipitate is copper(II) hydroxide.

$$Cu^{2+}(aq) + 2OH^-(aq) \rightarrow Cu(OH)_2(s)$$

Any copper(II) salt in solution will react with sodium hydroxide solution in this way. For example, with copper(II) sulfate solution, the full equation is:

$$CuSO_4(aq) + 2NaOH(aq) \rightarrow Cu(OH)_2(s) + Na_2SO_4(aq)$$

Figure 11.17 *The blue precipitate of copper(II) hydroxide.*

An orange-brown precipitate is formed

This shows the presence of iron(III) ions. The precipitate is iron(III) hydroxide.

$$Fe^{3+}(aq) + 3OH^-(aq) \rightarrow Fe(OH)_3(s)$$

Any iron(III) compound in solution will give this precipitate. An example of a full equation might be:

$$FeCl_3(aq) + 3NaOH(aq) \rightarrow Fe(OH)_3(s) + 3NaCl(aq)$$

Notice how much more complicated the full equations for these reactions are. They also hide what is going on. Use ionic equations for precipitation reactions wherever possible.

A green precipitate is formed

This shows the presence of iron(II) ions. The precipitate is iron(II) hydroxide.

$$Fe^{2+}(aq) + 2OH^-(aq) \rightarrow Fe(OH)_2(s)$$

This could be the result of reacting, say, iron(II) sulfate solution with sodium hydroxide solution.

$$FeSO_4(aq) + 2NaOH(aq) \rightarrow Fe(OH)_2(s) + Na_2SO_4(aq)$$

The green precipitate darkens on standing and turns orange-brown around the top of the tube. This is due to the iron(II) hydroxide being oxidised to iron(III) hydroxide by the air.

No precipitate, but a smell of ammonia

This shows the presence of an ammonium salt. Sodium hydroxide solution reacts with ammonium salts (either solid or in solution) to produce ammonia gas. In the cold, there is just enough ammonia gas produced for you to be able to smell it. If you warm it, you can test the gas coming off with a piece of damp red litmus paper. Ammonia is alkaline and turns the litmus paper blue.

$$NH_4^+(s \text{ or } aq) + OH^-(aq) \rightarrow NH_3(g) + H_2O(l)$$

A typical full equation might be:

$$NH_4Cl(s) + NaOH(aq) \rightarrow NaCl(aq) + NH_3(g) + H_2O(l)$$

Testing for carbonates

If you add a dilute acid to a solid carbonate, carbon dioxide is produced in the cold. It is probably best to use dilute nitric acid. Some acid–carbonate combinations can produce an insoluble salt that coats the solid carbonate and stops the reaction, but this doesn't happen if you use nitric acid because all nitrates are soluble.

Add a little dilute nitric acid, look for bubbles of gas produced in the cold, and test the gas with lime water to show that it is carbon dioxide.

The ionic equation shows any carbonate reacting with any acid.

$$CO_3^{2-}(s) + 2H^+(aq) \rightarrow CO_2(g) + H_2O(l)$$

For example, using zinc carbonate and dilute nitric acid:

$$ZnCO_3(s) + 2HNO_3(aq) \rightarrow Zn(NO_3)_2(aq) + CO_2(g) + H_2O(l)$$

Figure 11.18 *The orange-brown precipitate of iron(III) hydroxide.*

Figure 11.19 *The green precipitate of iron(II) hydroxide.*

Recognising gases by smelling them has to be done with great care. In this case, there is usually so little ammonia gas present in the cold that it is safe to smell it as long as you take the normal precautions. You shouldn't, however, make any attempt to smell the mixture when it is warm.

See Chapter 10 (page 81) for a discussion of the insoluble salt problem.

You could equally well use *nitric* acid and barium *nitrate* solution. You must never acidify the solution with sulfuric acid, because sulfuric acid contains sulfate ions. If you add those, you are bound to get a precipitate of barium sulfate, whatever else is present.

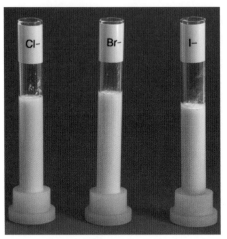

Figure 11.20 *Precipitates of silver chloride, silver bromide and silver iodide.*

All of these precipitates tend to discolour towards greys and pale purples on exposure to light.
The bromide and iodide colours are quite difficult to distinguish between in practice. There is a follow-on test involving ammonia solution which helps to sort them out, but this is beyond GCSE.

Testing for sulfates

Make a solution of your suspected sulfate in pure water, add enough dilute *hydrochloric* acid to make it acidic and then add some barium *chloride* solution. A sulfate will produce a white precipitate of barium sulfate.

$$Ba^{2+}(aq) + SO_4^{2-}(aq) \rightarrow BaSO_4(s)$$

You acidify the solution to destroy other compounds which might also produce white precipitates when you add the barium chloride solution. For example, if you didn't add acid, you would also get a white precipitate if there was a carbonate present because barium carbonate is also white and insoluble. The acid reacts with and removes the carbonate ions.

Testing for chlorides, bromides and iodides

This is very similar to the test for sulfates. Make a solution of your suspected chloride, bromide or iodide and add enough dilute *nitric* acid to make it acidic. Then add some silver *nitrate* solution.

The acid is added to react with and remove other substances which might also produce precipitates with silver nitrate solution.

A white precipitate (of silver chloride) shows the presence of chloride ions.

$$Ag^+(aq) + Cl^-(aq) \rightarrow AgCl(s)$$

A pale cream precipitate (of silver bromide) shows the presence of bromide ions.

$$Ag^+(aq) + Br^-(aq) \rightarrow AgBr(s)$$

A yellow precipitate (of silver iodide) shows the presence of iodide ions.

$$Ag^+(aq) + I^-(aq) \rightarrow AgI(s)$$

You should now be able to:

✓ describe ways of separating mixtures, including simple distillation, fractional distillation, filtration, crystallisation and paper chromatography

✓ know how to test for hydrogen, oxygen, carbon dioxide, chlorine and ammonia

✓ know how to test for the presence of water using anhydrous copper(II) sulfate or cobalt chloride paper

✓ describe how to carry out a flame test, and know the flame colours produced by lithium, sodium, potassium and calcium compounds

✓ know how to use sodium hydroxide solution to test for the presence of Cu^{2+}, Fe^{3+}, Fe^{2+} and NH_4^+ ions in solution, and write full or ionic equations for the reactions involved

✓ know how to test for carbonates using a dilute acid, and write full or ionic equations for these reactions

✓ know the tests for sulfates, chlorides, bromides and iodides, and write full or ionic equations for these reactions.

Questions

1 Four common methods of collecting gases are:

A downwards into a gas jar

B upwards into a gas jar

C over water

D in a gas syringe.

Which method would you use in each of the following cases?

a) To collect a dry sample of carbon dioxide in order to do a reaction with it.

b) To measure the amount of hydrogen produced in 10 s during the reaction between dilute sulfuric acid and magnesium.

c) To collect a sample of carbon monoxide – a colourless, odourless, poisonous gas, insoluble in water and with approximately the same density as air.

d) To collect a sample of ammonia in order to do a reaction with it.

2 Suppose you had a valuable collection of small diamonds, which you kept safe from thieves by mixing them with white sugar crystals and storing the mixture in a jar labelled 'sugar'. The time has now come when you want to sell the diamonds. Describe how you would recover all the diamonds from the sugar.

3 Name the gas being described in each of the following cases.

a) A green gas that bleaches damp litmus paper.

b) A gas that dissolves readily in water to produce a solution with a pH of about 11.

c) A gas that produces a white precipitate with calcium hydroxide solution.

d) A gas that pops when a lighted splint is placed in it.

e) A gas that relights a glowing splint.

4 In order to find out who had written a threatening letter, a sample of ink from the letter was dissolved in a solvent and then placed on some chromatography paper. Alongside it were put spots of ink from the pens of five suspects – G, M, P, R and T. The final chromatogram looked like this:

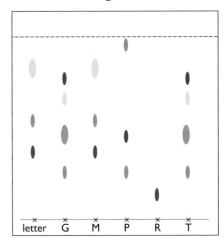

a) Which of the five suspects is using ink that matches the sample from the letter?

b) Which of the suspects is using a pen that contains ink made from a single dye?

c) Which two of the five suspects are using pens containing the same ink?

d) Whose pen contained the dye that was most soluble in the solvent?

5 Describe fully how you would carry out the following tests. In each case, describe what you would expect to happen.

a) A flame test for lithium ions in lithium chloride.

b) A test for ammonium ions in ammonium sulfate.

c) A test for sulfate ions in ammonium sulfate.

d) A test for the presence of water.

e) A test for carbonate ions in calcium carbonate.

f) A test for iodide ions in potassium iodide.

6 A is an orange solid, which dissolves in water to give an orange solution. When sodium hydroxide solution is added to a solution of A, an orange-brown precipitate, B, is formed. Adding dilute nitric acid and silver nitrate solution to a solution of A gives a white precipitate, C.

a) Identify A, B and C.

b) Write equations (full or ionic) for the reactions producing B and C.

7 D is a green crystalline solid which dissolves in water to give a very pale green solution. Addition of sodium hydroxide solution to a solution of D produces a green precipitate, E, which turns orange around the top on standing in air. Addition of dilute hydrochloric acid and barium chloride solution to a solution of D gives a white precipitate, F.

a) Identify D, E and F.

b) Write equations (full or ionic) for the reactions producing E and F.

8 G is a colourless crystalline solid which reacts with dilute nitric acid to give a colourless solution, H, and a colourless, odourless gas, I, which turns lime water milky. G has a lilac flame colour.

a) Identify G, H and I.

b) Write an equation (full or ionic) for the reaction between G and dilute nitric acid.

9 Suppose you had some potassium nitrate contaminated with small amounts of potassium carbonate. Potassium carbonate is more soluble in water than potassium nitrate is.

a) Describe how you would make a pure sample of potassium nitrate from the impure mixture.

b) How could you test your final product to show that it no longer contained any carbonate ions?

10 (Hint: This question is deliberately designed to be confusing! You can't, for example, identify A for certain just by reading the first paragraph. You need information from later in the question as well. Read through the question and just write down the things you can be sure about, until it all falls into place. A good starting point would be solution C.)

A is a green powder that, on heating, gives a black solid, F, and a colourless gas, G, which turns lime water milky.

A reacts with an acid, B, to give a blue solution, C, and a gas, D, which turns lime water milky.

Solution C gave a blue precipitate, I, when sodium hydroxide solution was added to it.

Solution C also gave a white precipitate, E, with dilute hydrochloric acid and barium chloride solution.

The black solid, F, reacts with hot dilute hydrochloric acid to give a green solution, H.

a) Identify substances A to I.

b) Write equations (full or ionic) for:

(i) the reaction between A and B

(ii) the reaction between solution C and barium chloride solution

(iii) the reaction between solution C and sodium hydroxide solution

(iv) the reaction between F and dilute hydrochloric acid

(v) the effect of heat on A.

Chapter 12: The Periodic Table

The Modern Periodic Table

The search for patterns in chemistry during the nineteenth century led eventually to the modern Periodic Table. The elements are arranged in order of atomic number – the number of protons in the nuclei of the atoms.

The modern Periodic Table is one of the most important tools that a chemist has. This chapter explores how it works.

The vertical columns are called **groups**

	1	2											3	4	5	6	7	0
1					H													He
2	Li	Be											B	C	N	O	F	Ne
3	Na	Mg											Al	Si	P	S	Cl	Ar
4	K	Ca	Sc	Ti	V	Cr	Mn	Fe	Co	Ni	Cu	Zn	Ga	Ge	As	Se	Br	Kr
5	Rb	Sr	Y	Zr	Nb	Mo	Tc	Ru	Rh	Pd	Ag	Cd	In	Sn	Sb	Te	I	Xe
6	Cs	Ba	La•	Hf	Ta	W	Re	Os	Ir	Pt	Au	Hg	Tl	Pb	Bi	Po	At	Rn
7	Fr	Ra	Ac:															

The horizontal rows are called **periods**

inner transition elements

•Ce	Pr	Nd	Pm	Sm	Eu	Gd	Tb	Dy	Ho	Er	Tm	Yb	Lu
:Th	Pa	U	Np	Pu	Am	Cm	Bk	Cf	Es	Fm	Md	No	Lr

Figure 12.1 *The modern Periodic Table.*

The inner transition elements are usually dropped out of their proper places and written separately at the bottom of the Periodic Table. The reason for this isn't very subtle. If you put them where they should be (as in Figure 12.2), everything has to be drawn slightly smaller to fit on the page. That makes it more difficult to read.

For a larger version of the Periodic Table, including atomic numbers and other information, see page 226.

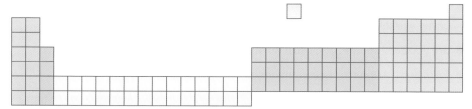

Figure 12.2 *The real shape of the Periodic Table.*

Most GCSE Periodic Tables stop at the end of the second inner transition series, even though more elements keep on being discovered. Some tables omit the inner transition series altogether, because they mainly contain either uncommon or highly radioactive elements.

The Periodic Table and atomic structure

Remember that the atomic number counts the number of protons in the atoms of the element, which is equal to the number of electrons in the neutral atom. Elements in the same Group have the same number of electrons in their outer energy levels (shells). That governs how they react, and means that elements in the same Group will have similar chemical properties.

Now would be a good time to revise electronic structures (Chapter 2, pages 6–12).

There is, however, a change in properties (sometimes gradual, sometimes quite rapid) from the top to the bottom of a Group. You will find examples later in this chapter.

Metals and non-metals in the Periodic Table

groups

1	2											3	4	5	6	7	0
						H											He
Li	Be											B	C	N	O	F	Ne
Na	Mg											Al	Si	P	S	Cl	Ar
K	Ca	Sc	Ti	V	Cr	Mn	Fe	Co	Ni	Cu	Zn	Ga	Ge	As	Se	Br	Kr
Rb	Sr	Y	Zr	Nb	Mo	Tc	Ru	Rh	Pd	Ag	Cd	In	Sn	Sb	Te	I	Xe
Cs	Ba	La•	Hf	Ta	W	Re	Os	Ir	Pt	Au	Hg	Tl	Pb	Bi	Po	At	Rn
Fr	Ra	Ac:															

inner transition elements

•Ce	Pr	Nd	Pm	Sm	Eu	Gd	Tb	Dy	Ho	Er	Tm	Yb	Lu
:Th	Pa	U	Np	Pu	Am	Cm	Bk	Cf	Es	Fm	Md	No	Lr

☐ metal

☐ non-metal

Figure 12.3 *Metals and non-metals.*

Although the division into metals and non-metals is shown as clear-cut, in practice there is a lot of uncertainty on the dividing line. For example, arsenic, As, has properties of both metals and non-metals.

Differences between metals and non-metals

Metals:

- tend to be solids with high melting and boiling points, and with relatively high densities (but as with several of the properties in this list, there are exceptions – for example, mercury is a liquid – look for the words 'tend to' in each statement)

- are shiny when they are polished (known as a *metallic lustre*), and tend to be easily workable

- are good conductors of electricity and heat

- form positive ions in their compounds

- have oxides which tend to be basic, reacting with acids to give a salt and water.

Non-metals:

- tend to have low melting and boiling points (carbon and silicon are obvious exceptions)

- tend to be brittle as solids and, even if they are crystalline, they don't have the same sort of shine as metals

- don't usually conduct electricity – carbon (in the form of graphite) and silicon are again exceptions

- are poor conductors of heat

- tend to form negative ions and covalent compounds

- have oxides which are acidic or neutral.

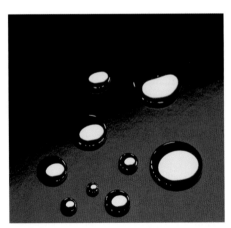

Figure 12.4 *Mercury has most of the properties of a metal (high density, shiny, conducts electricity, forms positive ions) – except that it is a liquid.*

Figure 12.5 *Sulfur crystals are shiny, but you wouldn't mistake them for a metal.*

Group 0 – the noble gases

Physical properties

The noble gases are all colourless gases. Radon, at the bottom of the Group, is radioactive. Argon makes up almost 1% of the air. Helium has the second lowest density of any gas (after hydrogen).

All the gases are **monatomic**. That means their molecules consist of single atoms.

Their densities and boiling points illustrate typical patterns (trends) in physical properties as you go down a Group in the Periodic Table.

Figure 12.6 *The noble gases.*

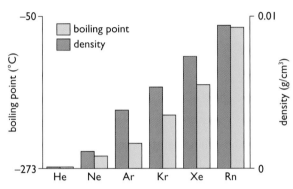

Figure 12.7 *Boiling point and density patterns in the noble gases.*

The density increases as the atoms get heavier. The boiling points also increase as you go down the Group. This is because the attractions between one molecule and its neighbours get stronger as the atoms get bigger. More energy is needed to break the stronger attractions. In helium, these intermolecular attractions are very, very weak. Very little energy is needed to break these attractions, and so helium's boiling point is very low.

Chemical reactivity

The noble gases don't form stable ions, and so don't produce ionic compounds. They are reluctant to form covalent bonds because, in most cases, it costs too much energy to rearrange the full energy levels to produce the single electrons that an atom needs if it is to form simple covalent bonds by sharing electrons. That means that these gases are generally unreactive.

Until the 1960s, scientists thought the noble gases were completely unreactive. Then they found that they could make xenon combine with fluorine just by heating the two together. After that, a number of other compounds of both xenon and krypton were found – mainly combined with fluorine and oxygen, such as XeF_4, XeO_3, $XeOF_4$, KrF_2 and several more.

I have included some formulae, not because you are expected to learn them, but to show that it is perfectly possible to have compounds of some of the noble gases. They don't fit easily into a GCSE view of covalent bonding, but you will certainly be able to explain the bonding in, say, XeF_4 if you do chemistry to a higher level.

Figure 12.8 *The alkali metals.*

Nobody is expecting you to remember these values! They are here just to show the patterns. You *will* be expected to know those patterns.

Figure 12.9 *Lithium, sodium and potassium have to be kept in oil to stop them reacting with oxygen in the air.*

Group 1 – the alkali metals

This Group contains the familiar reactive metals sodium and potassium as well as some less common ones.

Francium, at the bottom of the Group, is radioactive. One of its isotopes is produced during the radioactive decay of uranium-235, but is extremely short-lived. Once you know about the rest of Group 1, you can predict what francium would be like, but you can't realistically observe its properties. We will make those predictions later.

Physical properties

	Melting point (°C)	Boiling point (°C)	Density (g/cm³)
Li	181	1342	0.53
Na	98	883	0.97
K	63	760	0.86
Rb	39	686	1.53
Cs	29	669	1.88

Notice that the melting and boiling points of the elements are very low for metals, and get lower as you go down the Group.

Their densities tend to increase – although not as tidily as the noble gases. Lithium, sodium and potassium are all less dense than water, and so will float on it.

The metals are also very soft and are easily cut with a knife, becoming softer as you go down the Group. They are shiny and silver when freshly cut, but tarnish within seconds on exposure to air.

Storage and handling

All these metals are extremely reactive, and get more reactive as you go down the Group. They all react quickly with air to form oxides, and react between rapidly and violently with water to form strongly alkaline solutions of the metal hydroxides.

To stop them reacting with oxygen or water vapour in the air, lithium, sodium and potassium are stored under oil. If you look carefully at Figure 12.9, you will see traces of bubbles in the beaker containing the sodium. There must have been a tiny amount of water present in the oil that the sodium was placed in.

Rubidium and caesium are so reactive that they have to be stored in sealed glass tubes to stop any possibility of oxygen getting at them.

Great care must be taken not to touch any of these metals with bare fingers. There could be enough sweat on your skin to give a reaction producing lots of heat and a very corrosive metal hydroxide.

The reactions with water

All these metals react with water to produce a metal hydroxide and hydrogen.

> **metal + cold water → metal hydroxide + hydrogen**

The main difference between the reactions is how fast they happen. The reaction between sodium and water is typical.

With sodium

> $2Na(s) + 2H_2O(l) \rightarrow 2NaOH(aq) + H_2(g)$

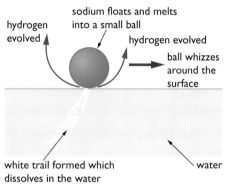

Figure 12.10 *Sodium reacting with water.*

Strictly speaking, most of the time the sodium is reacting, it is present as molten sodium – not solid sodium. Writing (l) for the state symbol, though, has the potential to confuse an examiner, and is probably best avoided!

The sodium floats because it is less dense than water. It melts because its melting point is low and a lot of heat is produced by the reaction. Because the hydrogen isn't given off symmetrically around the ball, the sodium is pushed around the surface of the water – literally like a jet-propelled hovercraft.

The white trail formed is the sodium hydroxide, which dissolves to make a strongly alkaline solution. All these metals react with water to produce alkaline metal hydroxides. That's why the Group is often called the 'alkali metals'.

Lithium

> $2Li(s) + 2H_2O(l) \rightarrow 2LiOH(aq) + H_2(g)$

The reaction is very similar to sodium's reaction, except that it is slower. Lithium's melting point is higher and the heat isn't produced so quickly, so the lithium doesn't melt.

Potassium

> $2K(s) + 2H_2O(l) \rightarrow 2KOH(aq) + H_2(g)$

Potassium's reaction is faster than sodium's. Enough heat is produced to ignite the hydrogen, which burns with a lilac flame. The reaction often ends with the potassium spitting around.

The lilac colour is due to contamination of the normally blue hydrogen flame by potassium compounds.

Rubidium and caesium

These react even more violently than potassium, and the reaction can be explosive. Rubidium hydroxide and caesium hydroxide are formed.

As you go down the Group, the metals become more reactive.

Be aware that if you look on the internet for video clips of these metals reacting with water, some of the most dramatic video clips you will find have been faked using explosives!

Explaining the increase in reactivity

In all these reactions, the metal atoms are losing electrons and forming metal ions in solution. For example:

$$Na(s) \rightarrow Na^+(aq) + e^-$$

The electrons released by the metal are gained by the water molecules, producing hydroxide ions and hydrogen gas.

$$2H_2O(l) + 2e^- \rightarrow 2OH^-(aq) + H_2(g)$$

The differences between the reactions depend in part on how easily the outer electron of the metal is lost in each case. That depends on how strongly it is attracted to the nucleus in the original atom. Remember that the nucleus of an atom is positive because it contains protons, and so attracts the negative electrons.

> You are unlikely to need this part of the reaction for GCSE purposes. It is included here just for completeness.

> The outer electron is **shielded** or **screened** from the full attraction of the nucleus by all the inner electrons.
> In the case of lithium, the outer electron feels the pull of 3+ charges from the protons offset by 2– charges from the inner electrons.
> In the case of sodium, the pull of 11+ charges is offset by the 10– charges from the inner electrons.

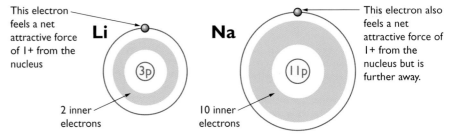

This electron feels a net attractive force of 1+ from the nucleus

Li (3p)

2 inner electrons

This electron also feels a net attractive force of 1+ from the nucleus but is further away.

Na (11p)

10 inner electrons

Figure 12.11 *Electrons of lithium and sodium.*

In every single atom in this Group, the outer electron will feel an overall attractive force of 1+ from the nucleus, but the effect of the force falls very quickly as distance increases. The bigger the atom, the more easily the outer electron is lost.

Compounds of the alkali metals

All Group 1 metal ions are colourless. That means that their compounds will be colourless or white unless they are combined with a coloured negative ion. Potassium dichromate(VI) is orange, for example, because the dichromate(VI) ion is orange. Group 1 compounds are typical ionic solids and are mostly soluble in water.

Summarising the main features of the Group 1 elements

Group 1 elements:

- are metals
- are soft with melting points and densities which are very low for metals
- have to be stored out of contact with air or water
- react rapidly with air to form coatings of the metal oxide
- react with water to produce an alkaline solution of the metal hydroxide and hydrogen gas
- increase in reactivity as you go down the Group
- form compounds in which the metal has a 1+ ion
- have mainly white compounds which dissolve to produce colourless solutions.

Figure 12.12 *Potassium dichromate(VI) solution is orange because the dichromate(VI) ion is orange.*

Using these features to predict the properties of francium

If you followed the trends in Group 1, you could predict that:

- francium is very soft, with a melting point just above room temperature

- its density is probably just over 2 g/cm³

- francium will be a silvery metal, but will tarnish almost instantly in air

- it would react violently with water to give francium hydroxide and hydrogen

- francium hydroxide solution will be strongly alkaline

- francium compounds are white and dissolve in water to give colourless solutions.

Remember that francium is highly radioactive and short-lived. You couldn't actually observe any of these things.

Group 7 – the halogens

The name 'halogen' means 'salt-producing'. When they react with metals, these elements produce a wide range of salts, including calcium fluoride, sodium chloride, silver bromide and potassium iodide.

The halogens are non-metallic elements with diatomic molecules: F_2, Cl_2, etc. As the molecules get larger towards the bottom of the Group, the melting and boiling points increase. Fluorine and chlorine are gases. Bromine is a liquid which turns to vapour very easily, and iodine is a solid.

Astatine is radioactive and is formed during the radioactive decay of other elements, such as uranium and thorium. Most of its isotopes are so unstable that their lives can be measured in seconds or fractions of a second.

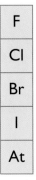

Figure 12.13 *The halogens.*

	State	Colours
F_2	gas	yellow
Cl_2	gas	green
Br_2	liquid	dark red liquid – red/brown vapour
I_2	solid	dark grey solid – purple vapour

Table 12.1: *The halogens.*

Figure 12.14 *Chlorine, bromine and iodine.*

Figure 12.15 *Iodine has a purple vapour.*

Notice that in small quantities, chlorine gas is a fairly yellowish green.

Because the halogens are non-metals, they will be poor conductors of heat and electricity. When they are solid (for example, iodine at room temperature), their crystals will be brittle.

Safety

Fluorine is so dangerously reactive that you would never expect to come across it in a school lab.

Apart from any safety problems due to the reactivity of the elements (especially fluorine and chlorine), all the elements have extremely poisonous vapours and have to be handled in a fume cupboard.

Liquid bromine is also very corrosive, and great care has to be taken to keep it off the skin. It is a good idea to have a beaker of dilute sodium thiosulfate solution handy whenever you use bromine. This reacts at once with any bromine you might have got on your skin or the bench, without being particularly harmful itself.

Reactions with hydrogen

The halogens react with hydrogen to form **hydrogen halides** – hydrogen fluoride, hydrogen chloride, hydrogen bromide and hydrogen iodide. For example:

$$H_2(g) + Br_2(g) \rightarrow 2HBr(g)$$

> Notice that you would react hydrogen with bromine vapour – not liquid bromine.

> You will find more about the acidity of hydrogen chloride and hydrochloric acid in Chapter 9, pages 77–78.

The hydrogen halides are all steamy, acidic, poisonous gases. In common with all the compounds formed between the halogens and non-metals, the gases are covalently bonded. They are very soluble in water, reacting with it to produce solutions of acids. For example, hydrochloric acid is a solution of hydrogen chloride in water.

The reactivity falls quickly as you go down the Group.

Halogen	Reaction with hydrogen
F_2	violent explosion, even in the cold and dark
Cl_2	violent explosion if exposed to a flame or to sunlight
Br_2	mild explosion if a bromine vapour/hydrogen mixture is exposed to a flame
I_2	partial reaction to form hydrogen iodide if iodine vapour is heated continuously with hydrogen

Table 12.2: *Reactions between halogens and hydrogen.*

The reaction between sodium and chlorine

Sodium burns in chlorine with its typical orange flame to produce white solid sodium chloride.

$$2Na(s) + Cl_2(g) \rightarrow 2NaCl(s)$$

Sodium chloride is, of course, an ionic solid. Typically, when the halogens react with metals from Groups 1 and 2, they form ions.

It is useful to look at this from the point of view of the sodium and of the chlorine separately by investigating the ionic equation for the reaction.

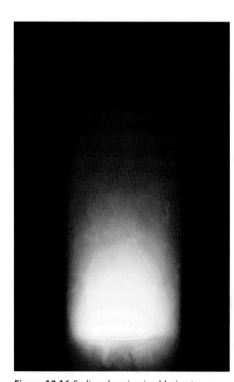

Figure 12.16 *Sodium burning in chlorine to produce sodium chloride.*

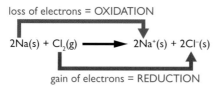

Figure 12.17 *The reaction between sodium and chlorine.*

If you aren't sure about ionic equations or oxidation and reduction, you should read pages 61–63 in Chapter 8.

The sodium has lost electrons and so has been oxidised to sodium ions. That means chlorine is acting as an oxidising agent. That is typical of the reactions of chlorine. It is a strong **oxidising agent**.

Displacement reactions involving the halogens

Just as you can use the reactivity series of metals to make sense of their displacement reactions, so you can also use a corresponding reactivity series for the halogens.

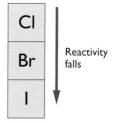

Figure 12.18 *Reactivity series for the halogens.*

Reacting chlorine with potassium bromide or potassium iodide solutions

If you add chlorine solution to colourless potassium bromide solution, the solution becomes orange as bromine is formed.

We shall concentrate on the three commonly used halogens, but the trend continues for the rest of the Group.

$$2KBr(aq) + Cl_2(aq) \rightarrow 2KCl(aq) + Br_2(aq)$$

The more reactive chlorine has displaced the less reactive bromine from potassium bromide.

Similarly, adding chlorine solution to potassium iodide solution gives a dark reddish-brown solution of iodine. If an excess of chlorine is used, you may get a dark grey precipitate of iodine.

$$2KI(aq) + Cl_2(aq) \rightarrow 2KCl(aq) + I_2(aq \text{ or } s)$$

In each case, the chlorine is acting as an oxidising agent.

Figure 12.19 *Bromine and iodine displaced from potassium bromide and potassium iodide solutions.*

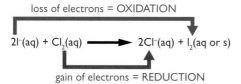

Figure 12.20 *The reaction between chlorine and potassium bromide (top) or potassium iodide (below).*

These are all redox reactions. The potassium ions are spectator ions. The reaction would be the same with any soluble bromide or iodide.

Figure 12.21 *Bromine displaces iodine from potassium iodide solution.*

Warning! This argument falls down if you try to include fluorine. Fluorine atoms don't, in fact, accept electrons more readily than chlorine atoms do – for reasons which are beyond GCSE. The greater reactivity of fluorine has to be explained in a more complicated way. However, there have been cases in the past where some examiners at GCSE have asked students to compare fluorine and chlorine. If that happens, you will have to use the explanation described here – even though it would be wrong!

The reaction of bromine with potassium iodide solution

In exactly the same way, the more reactive bromine displaces the less reactive iodine from potassium iodide solution.

Adding bromine solution ('bromine water') to colourless potassium iodide solution gives a dark reddish-brown solution of iodine (or a dark grey precipitate if an excess of bromine is added).

$$2KI(aq) + Br_2(aq) \rightarrow 2KBr(aq) + I_2(aq \text{ or } s)$$

The ionic equation shows bromine acting as an oxidising agent.

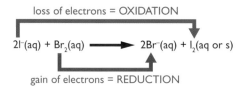

Figure 12.22 *The reaction between bromine solution and potassium iodide solution.*

Explaining the trend in the reactivity of the halogens

As you go down the Group, the oxidising ability of the halogens falls.

When a halogen oxidises something, it does so by removing electrons from it.

Each halogen has the ability to oxidise the ions of those underneath it in the Group, but not those above it. Chlorine can remove electrons from bromide or iodide ions, and bromine can remove electrons from iodide ions.

Chlorine is a strong oxidising agent because its atoms readily attract an extra electron to make chloride ions. Bromine is less successful at attracting electrons, and iodine is less successful still.

You have to consider the amount of attraction the incoming electron feels from the nucleus. In chlorine, there are 17 positively charged protons offset by the 10 negatively charged electrons in the inner energy levels (shells). That means the new electron feels an overall pull of 7+ from the centre of the atom.

A similar argument with bromine shows that the new electron also feels an overall pull from the nucleus of 7+, but in the bromine case, it is further away.

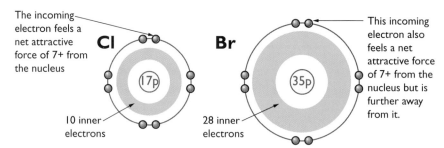

Figure 12.23 *Comparing chlorine and bromine.*

The incoming electron is further and further from the nucleus as you go down the Group, and so it is less strongly attracted. That means the ion is less easily formed – and that, in turn, means that the elements get less reactive as you go down the Group.

Summarising the main features of the Group 7 elements

Group 7 elements:

- have diatomic molecules, X_2
- go from gases to liquid to solid as you go down the Group
- have coloured poisonous vapours
- form ionic salts with metals and covalent compounds with non-metals
- become less reactive towards the bottom of the Group
- are oxidising agents with oxidising ability decreasing down the Group
- will displace elements lower down the Group from their salts.

Transition metals

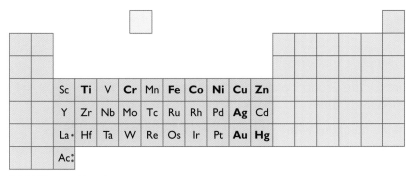

Figure 12.24 *The transition elements.*

The bold type in Figure 12.24 simply picks out some of the more familiar transition elements. This table leaves out the inner transition elements, because you are unlikely to come across them in the lab. The red dots in the table show where they should be. See page 226 for the full Periodic Table.

These are all typically metallic elements. They are good conductors of heat and electricity, workable, strong, and mostly with high densities. With the exception of liquid mercury, Hg, they have melting points which range from fairly high to very high.

They are much less reactive than the metals in Groups 1 and 2, and so they don't react as rapidly with air or water.

Because of their useful physical properties and relative lack of reactivity, several of the transition elements are important in everyday life. You will find examples of uses of iron in Chapter 17.

Figure 12.25 *Solutions of some common transition metal compounds.*

Transition metals form coloured compounds

The majority of transition metal compounds are coloured. Figures 12.25 and 12.26 show examples, both in and out of the lab.

Transition metals and their compounds are often useful catalysts

Examples you will come across elsewhere in this book include:

- iron in the manufacture of ammonia
- vanadium(V) oxide, V_2O_5, in the manufacture of sulfuric acid
- manganese(IV) oxide, MnO_2, in the decomposition of hydrogen peroxide.

Figure 12.26 *Weathering on the copper-covered spire of Truro cathedral.*

End of Chapter Checklist

You should now be able to:

✓ know that in the modern Periodic Table, the 100 or so elements are arranged in order of their atomic (proton) numbers

✓ understand the use of the terms *group*, *period* and *transition element (metal)*

✓ decide whether an element is a metal or a non-metal from its position in the Periodic Table

✓ know the main differences between metals and non-metals – particularly with regard to electrical conductivity and the acid–base behaviour of their oxides

✓ know that the Group 0 elements are generally unreactive gases, and be able to explain that lack of reactivity

✓ describe and explain the reactions of the Group 1 metals with water

✓ know that reactivity increases as you go down Group 1, and be able to explain that increase in reactivity

✓ know that compounds of the Group 1 metals are normally white (or colourless) soluble solids

✓ know the trends in physical properties for the Group 7 elements (the halogens), and the precautions that have to be taken when using them

✓ describe and explain the reactions of the halogens with hydrogen, and in displacement reactions involving other members of the Group

✓ know that the halogens become less reactive as you go down the Group, and be able to explain that fall in reactivity for chlorine, bromine and iodine

✓ know that the transition elements are typical metals and are less reactive than Group 1 metals

✓ know that the transition elements form coloured compounds and that the metals or their compounds may act as catalysts.

Questions

You will need to use the Periodic Table on page 226.

1 Answer the questions which follow using *only* the elements in this list:

caesium, chlorine, molybdenum, neon, nickel, nitrogen, strontium, tin.

a) Name an element which is

   (i) in group 2

   (ii) in the same period as silicon

   (iii) in the same group as phosphorus.

b) How many electrons are there in the outer levels of atoms of **(i)** strontium, **(ii)** chlorine, **(iii)** nitrogen?

c) Divide the list of elements at the beginning of the question into metals and non-metals.

d) Name the two elements which are likely to have the greatest number of coloured compounds.

e) Name **(i)** the most reactive metal, **(ii)** the least reactive element.

2 This question concerns the chemistry of the elements Li, Na, K, Rb and Cs on the extreme left-hand side of the Periodic Table. In each case, you should name the substances represented by letters.

a) A is the least dense of all metals.

b) When metal B is dropped onto water it melts into a small ball and rushes around the surface. A gas, C, is given off and this burns with a lilac flame. A white trail dissolves into the water to make a solution of D.

c) When metal E is heated in a green gas F it burns with an orange flame and leaves a white solid product G.

d) Write equations for:

   (i) the reaction of B with water

   (ii) the reaction between E and F.

e) What would you expect to see if solution D was tested with red and blue litmus paper?

f) Explain why B melts into a small ball when it is dropped onto water.

3 This question is about astatine, At, at the bottom of Group 7 of the Periodic Table. Astatine is radioactive, and extremely rare. You are asked to make some predictions about astatine and its chemistry.

a) Showing only the outer electrons, draw dots-and-crosses diagrams to show the arrangement of electrons in an astatine *atom*, an astatide *ion* and an astatine *molecule*.

b) What physical state would you expect astatine to be in at room temperature?

c) Would you expect astatine to be more or less reactive than iodine?

d) Describe hydrogen astatide, and suggest a likely pH for a reasonably concentrated solution of it in water.

e) What would you expect caesium astatide to look like? Will it be soluble in water? Explain your reasoning.

f) Write an ionic equation for the reaction that will occur if you add chlorine water to a solution of sodium astatide. Assume that astatine is insoluble in water. Explain clearly why this reaction would be counted as a redox reaction.

4 Predict any five properties of the element palladium, Pa (atomic number 46), or its compounds. The properties can be either physical or chemical.

5 Explain as fully as you can why:

a) neon is an unreactive monatomic gas

b) potassium is more reactive than sodium

c) chlorine displaces bromine from potassium bromide solution.

6 In this question you will be given some information about three elements. You should say, with reasons, where you might expect to find them in the Periodic Table. You can choose between:

Group 1 or 2 element
transition element
Group 7 element
noble gas.

a) Element A

melting point (°C)	–112
boiling point (°C)	–108
density at 0°C (g/cm³)	0.0059
reaction with chlorine	none
reaction with oxygen	none
reaction with sodium	none

b) Element B

B melts at 1890 °C and is a good conductor of electricity. It has no reaction with cold water, but will react with chlorine on heating. It reacts very slowly with dilute hydrochloric acid and dilute sulfuric acid. Compounds of B are highly coloured – including blue, green, purple, orange and yellow.

c) Element C

melting point (°C)	850
boiling point (°C)	1487
reaction with cold water	steady production of hydrogen
reaction with dilute hydrochloric acid	very vigorous reaction producing hydrogen and a colourless solution
reaction with oxygen	burns to give a white solid

7 Suppose you were given a sample of a solid element and were asked to do some simple tests on it to find out whether it was a metal or a non-metal. You can assume that you have all the normal equipment and chemicals available in a school lab, as well as the means to measure melting points up to about 1000 °C.

Draw up a table like this:

Test	Observation
1 appearance	
2	
3	
4	

Suggest three more tests that you might do, and record all your (imaginary) findings in the 'Observation' column. As a result of these findings, decide (with reasons) whether the element is a metal or non-metal.

(Hint: keep it simple! Decide whether you want your element to be a metal or a non-metal, and then make up results that all point that way. Your results *do not* have to correspond to any real element.)

Chapter 13: Electrolysis

The photograph shows what happens if you connect a solution of potassium iodide into a simple electrical circuit.

If you look at what is happening in the solution, you can see obvious signs of chemical change. Some coloured substance is being produced at the positive carbon electrode, and a gas is being given off at the negative electrode.

This chapter explores the effect of electricity on chemical compounds in the lab. Examples of applications of this in industry will be found in later chapters.

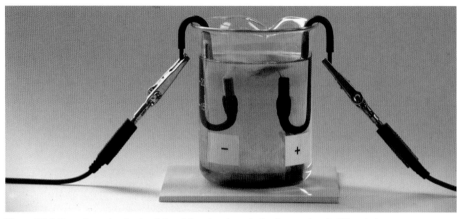

Figure 13.1 *Part of an electric circuit involving the electrolysis of potassium iodide solution.*

For the reason why metals conduct electricity, see Chapter 4 (page 24). For the reason why graphite conducts electricity, see Chapter 4 (page 29). The carbon rods used are essentially made up of very, very tiny graphite crystals.

Some important background

The conduction of electricity by metals and carbon

In a metal or carbon, electricity is simply a flow of electrons. The movement of the electrons doesn't produce any chemical change in the metal or the carbon.

Metals and carbon contain mobile electrons, and it is these that move. That's equally true even for a liquid metal such as mercury. In an electrical circuit, you can think of a battery or a power pack as an 'electron pump', pushing the electrons through the various bits of metal or carbon.

Passing electricity through compounds – electrolysis

Hardly any solid compounds conduct electricity. On the other hand, a lot of compounds will conduct electricity when they are molten or when they are dissolved in water. All of these show signs of a chemical reaction while they are conducting.

Defining electrolysis

Electrolysis is a chemical change caused by passing an electric current through a compound which is either molten or in solution.

The reason that some compounds undergo electrolysis will be explored in the rest of this chapter.

Some other important words

An **electrolyte** is a substance that undergoes electrolysis. Electrolytes all contain ions. The movement of the ions is responsible for both the conduction of electricity and the chemical changes that take place. Covalent compounds are ***not*** electrolytes, because they don't contain ions.

In a solid electrolyte, the ions aren't free to move, and so nothing happens.

The electricity is passed into and out of the electrolyte via two **electrodes**. Carbon is frequently used for electrodes because it conducts electricity and is chemically fairly inert. Platinum is also fairly inert and can be used instead of carbon. Various other metals are sometimes used as well.

The positive electrode is called the **anode**. The negative electrode is called the **cathode**.

Remember **PANC** – positive anode, negative cathode.

The electrolysis of molten compounds

Electrolysing molten lead(II) bromide, PbBr$_2$

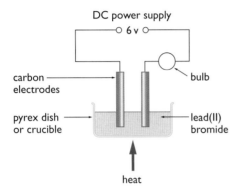

Figure 13.2 *Electrolysing molten lead(II) bromide.*

The power supply can be a 6 volt battery or a power pack. It doesn't matter which. The voltage isn't very critical either.

Nothing at all happens until the lead(II) bromide melts. Then:

● the bulb lights up, showing that electrons are flowing through it

● there is bubbling around the electrode (the anode) connected to the positive terminal of the power source as brown bromine gas is given off

● nothing seems to be happening at the electrode (the cathode) connected to the negative terminal of the power source, but afterwards metallic lead is found underneath it

● when you stop heating and the lead(II) bromide solidifies again, everything stops – there is no more bubbling and the bulb goes out.

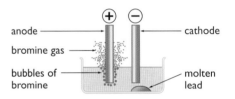

Figure 13.3 *What happens when the lead(II) bromide melts (the bulb also lights up).*

Explaining what is happening

Lead(II) bromide is an ionic compound. The solid consists of a giant structure of lead(II) ions and bromide ions packed regularly in a crystal lattice. It doesn't have any mobile electrons, and the ions are locked tightly in the lattice and aren't free to move. The solid lead(II) bromide doesn't conduct electricity.

As soon as the solid melts, the ions do become free to move around, and it is this movement that enables the electrons to flow in the external circuit. This is how it works . . .

As soon as you connect the power source, it pumps any mobile electrons away from the left-hand electrode towards the right-hand one (Figure 13.4). At the moment, the lead(II) bromide is still solid.

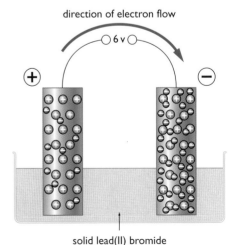

Figure 13.4 *The build-up of charges on the electrodes.*

The excess of electrons on the right-hand electrode makes it negatively charged. The left-hand electrode is positively charged because it is short of electrons. There is a limit to how many extra electrons the 'pump' can squeeze into the negative electrode because of the repulsion by the electrons already there.

Things change when the lead(II) bromide melts, and the ions become free to move.

In Figures 13.5 and 13.6, the lead(II) ions and bromide ions are drawn much bigger than the remains of the atoms in the electrode (the green, positively charged circles, which represent the nuclei and the non-mobile electrons). This is so that it is easier to see what is happening.

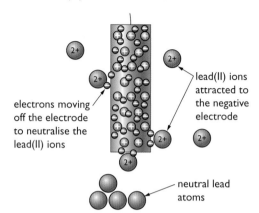

electrons moving off the electrode to neutralise the lead(II) ions

lead(II) ions attracted to the negative electrode

neutral lead atoms

Figure 13.5 *The reaction at the cathode.*

The positive lead(II) ions are attracted to the cathode. When they get there, each lead(II) ion picks up two electrons from the electrode and forms neutral lead atoms. These fall to the bottom of the container as molten lead.

$$Pb^{2+}(l) + 2e^- \rightarrow Pb(l)$$

This leaves spaces in the electrode that more electrons can move into. The power source pumps new electrons along the wire to fill those spaces.

Bromide ions are attracted to the positive anode. When they get there, the extra electron which makes the bromide ion negatively charged moves onto the electrode because this electrode is short of electrons.

The loss of the extra electron turns each bromide ion into a bromine atom. These join in pairs to make bromine molecules. Overall:

$$2Br^-(l) \rightarrow Br_2(g) + 2e^-$$

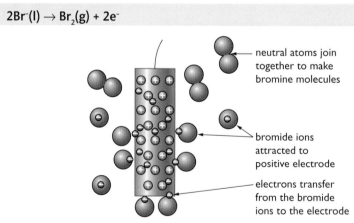

neutral atoms join together to make bromine molecules

bromide ions attracted to positive electrode

electrons transfer from the bromide ions to the electrode

Figure 13.6 *The reaction at the anode.*

The new electrons on the electrode are pumped away by the power source to help fill the spaces being created at the cathode. Because electrons are flowing in the external circuit, the bulb lights up.

Electrons can flow in the external circuit because of the chemical changes to the ions arriving at the electrodes. We say that the ions are **discharged** at the electrodes. Discharging an ion simply means that it loses its charge – either giving up electron(s) to the electrode or receiving electron(s) from it.

Electrolysis and redox

If you look back at the electrode equations on the previous page, you will see that the lead(II) ions gain electrons at the cathode. Gain of electrons is reduction. The lead(II) ions are reduced to lead atoms.

Remember: OIL RIG.

The bromide ions lose electrons at the anode. Loss of electrons is oxidation. Bromide ions are oxidised to bromine molecules.

The electrolysis of other molten substances

In each case, the positive ions are attracted to the negative cathode, where they are discharged by gaining electrons. Positive ions are known as **cations** because they are attracted to the cathode. The negative ions move to the anode, where they are discharged by giving electrons to the electrode. Negative ions are known as **anions**.

Remember that the cathode is negative and that a cation is attracted to it – so must be positive.

Not all ionic compounds can be electrolysed molten. Some break up into simpler substances before their melting point. For example, copper(II) carbonate breaks into copper(II) oxide and carbon dioxide, even on gentle heating. It is impossible to melt it.

Other ionic compounds have such high melting points that it isn't possible to melt them in the lab, although it can be done industrially. For example, it is difficult to keep sodium chloride molten in the lab because its melting point is 801 °C. If you could keep it molten you would get sodium at the cathode and chlorine at the anode. Sodium is manufactured by electrolysing molten sodium chloride.

| At the cathode: | $Na^+(l) + e^- \rightarrow Na(l)$ | molten sodium is produced |
| At the anode: | $2Cl^-(l) \rightarrow Cl_2(g) + 2e^-$ | chlorine gas is produced |

The electrolysis of aqueous solutions

The electrolysis of sodium chloride solution

You might have thought you would get the same products if you electrolysed sodium chloride solution as if you electrolysed it molten. You would be wrong! Although chlorine is formed at the anode as you might expect, hydrogen is produced at the cathode rather than sodium. The hydrogen at the cathode is coming from the water.

Water is a very **weak electrolyte**. It ionises very slightly to give hydrogen ions and hydroxide ions.

$$H_2O(l) \rightleftharpoons H^+(aq) + OH^-(aq)$$

The reversible sign shows that as water molecules break up to form hydrogen ions and hydroxide ions, these ions are recombining to make water again.

Whenever you have water present, you have to consider these ions *as well* as the ions in the compound you are electrolysing.

A simple apparatus for electrolysing solutions

The reason you don't appear to get as much chlorine as you do hydrogen is that chlorine is slightly soluble, and some of it dissolves in the water that is present.

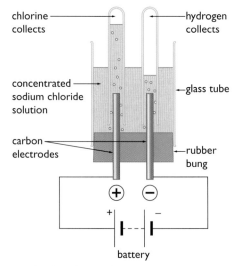

Figure 13.7 *A simple apparatus for electrolysing solutions.*

At the cathode

For positive ions, the lower an element is in the reactivity series, the more easily it will accept an electron.

The solution contains $Na^+(aq)$ and $H^+(aq)$, and these are both attracted to the negative cathode. The $H^+(aq)$ gets discharged because it is much easier to persuade a hydrogen ion to accept an electron than it is a sodium ion. Each hydrogen atom formed combines with another one to make a hydrogen molecule.

$$2H^+(aq) + 2e^- \rightarrow H_2(g)$$

Remember that the hydrogen ions come from water molecules splitting up. Each time a water molecule ionises, it also produces a hydroxide ion. There is a build up of these in the solution around the cathode.

Because the hydrogen ions are discharged, they can no longer react with the hydroxide ions and reform water. The ionisation of the water becomes a one-way process.

You may find an alternative way of looking at this cathode reaction, starting from simple neutral water molecules, which can be thought of as taking electrons directly from the cathode:

$2H_2O(l) + 2e^- \rightarrow H_2(g) + 2OH^-(aq)$
Whichever method you use, it is a simplification. How the reaction happens almost certainly depends on the pH of the solution. This is too complicated to worry about at GCSE, and so we simplify it. Either method is fine for exam purposes.

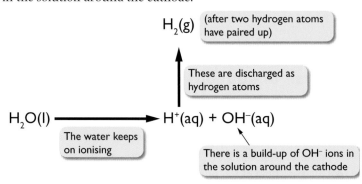

Figure 13.8 *The process of electrolysing solutions.*

These hydroxide ions make the solution strongly alkaline in the region around the cathode. Because of the presence of the sodium ions attracted to the cathode, you can think of the electrolysis as also forming sodium hydroxide solution.

At the anode

If the sodium chloride solution is dilute, you get noticeable amounts of oxygen produced as well as chlorine. This comes from the discharge of the hydroxide ions:

$4OH^-(aq) \rightarrow 2H_2O(l) + O_2(g) + 4e^-$

$Cl^-(aq)$ and $OH^-(aq)$ are both attracted by the positive anode. The hydroxide ion is *slightly* easier to discharge than the chloride ion is, but there isn't that much difference. There are far, far more chloride ions present in the solution, and so it is mainly these that are discharged.

$$2Cl^-(aq) \rightarrow Cl_2(g) + 2e^-$$

The electrolysis of some other solutions using carbon electrodes

How to work out what will happen

- If the metal is high in the reactivity series, you get hydrogen produced instead of the metal.

- If the metal is below hydrogen in the reactivity series, you get the metal produced.

- If you have reasonably concentrated solutions of halides (chlorides, bromides or iodides), you get the halogen (chlorine, bromine or iodine). With other common negative ions, you get oxygen.

This leaves the problem of what you get if you have a moderately reactive metal such as zinc, for example. Reasonably concentrated solutions will give you the metal. Very dilute solutions will give you mainly hydrogen. In between, you will get both.

At GCSE you probably won't have to worry about this. The examples you will meet in exams are always clear-cut.

The table shows some simple examples of these rules.

	Cathode		Anode	
	Product	**Equation**	**Product**	**Equation**
KI(aq)	hydrogen	$2H^+(aq) + 2e^- \rightarrow H_2(g)$	iodine	$2I^-(aq) \rightarrow I_2(aq) + 2e^-$
$MgBr_2(aq)$	hydrogen	$2H^+(aq) + 2e^- \rightarrow H_2(g)$	bromine	$2Br^-(aq) \rightarrow Br_2(aq) + 2e^-$
$H_2SO_4(aq)$	hydrogen	$2H^+(aq) + 2e^- \rightarrow H_2(g)$	oxygen	$4OH^-(aq) \rightarrow 2H_2O(l) + O_2(g) + 4e^-$
$CuSO_4(aq)$	copper	$Cu^{2+}(aq) + 2e^- \rightarrow Cu(s)$	oxygen	$4OH^-(aq) \rightarrow 2H_2O(l) + O_2(g) + 4e^-$

Table 13.1: *The electrolysis of solutions using carbon electrodes.*

The electrolysis of copper(II) sulfate solution using carbon electrodes

The copper(II) ions and hydrogen ions (from the water) will be attracted to the cathode. Copper is below hydrogen in the reactivity series, which means that its ion is easier to discharge. The carbon electrode will get coated with brown copper.

$$Cu^{2+}(aq) + 2e^- \rightarrow Cu(s)$$

Sulfate ions and hydroxide ions (from the water) will be attracted to the anode. Sulfate ions are very stable and aren't discharged. Instead, you get oxygen from the discharge of hydroxide ions from the water.

$$4OH^-(aq) \rightarrow 2H_2O(l) + O_2(g) + 4e^-$$

It is interesting to think about what would happen if you continued with the electrolysis for a long time. The copper(II) ions will eventually all be used up, and so the colour of the solution will fade from blue to colourless.

What is left in the solution? Hydrogen ions from the water aren't being discharged and neither are the sulfate ions. The solutions turns into dilute sulfuric acid. The electrolysis will then continue as for dilute sulfuric acid (see below).

You may find an alternative way of looking at this anode reaction, just as there is at the cathode. The equation this time is:

$2H_2O(l) \rightarrow O_2(g) + 4H^+(aq) + 4e^-$

As before, how the reaction happens almost certainly depends on the pH of the solution, and is too complicated to worry about at GCSE, and so we simplify it. Either method is fine for exam purposes.

The electrolysis of dilute sulfuric acid using carbon electrodes

In this case, the only positive ions arriving at the cathode are hydrogen ions (from the acid and the water). These are discharged to give hydrogen gas.

$$2H^+(aq) + 2e^- \rightarrow H_2(g)$$

At the anode – just as with copper(II) sulfate solution – sulfate ions and hydroxide ions (from the water) arrive. The sulfate ions are too stable to be discharged, and so you get oxygen from discharge of hydroxide ions from the water.

$$4OH^-(aq) \rightarrow 2H_2O(l) + O_2(g) + 4e^-$$

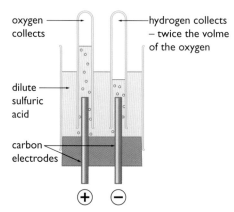

Figure 13.9 *The electrolysis of dilute sulfuric acid using carbon electrodes.*

Twice as much hydrogen is produced as oxygen.

Look at the equations above. For every four electrons that flow around the circuit, you would get one molecule of oxygen. But four electrons would produce two molecules of hydrogen.

You get twice the number of molecules of hydrogen as of oxygen. Twice the number of molecules occupy twice the volume.

This is the result of Avogadro's law. See Chapter 23 (page 189) if you are interested.

What would happen with non-electrolytes?

If you have understood the last few pages, you will realise that for electrolysis to work, there have to be ions present. The current in the external circuit (with the bulb and power source) can flow only if there are ions which can move and be discharged.

If you tried to electrolyse a covalent compound (either molten or in solution), there wouldn't be a current flow, because there aren't any ions. Nothing else would happen either. Sugar, for example, is a non-electrolyte – it doesn't undergo electrolysis. It won't conduct electricity, and won't be decomposed by it – either in solution or when molten.

There are cases, of course, where it is impossible to test the substance in this way. It was mentioned above that copper(II) carbonate can't be electrolysed molten because it decomposes before melting. It isn't soluble in water either. So you can't test it, despite the fact that it does contain ions.

Simple experiments like those described in this chapter give you an easy way of finding out whether a substance is ionic or not. If it undergoes electrolysis, either molten or in solution, it must contain ions. If it doesn't undergo electrolysis, it doesn't contain ions.

End of Chapter Checklist

You should now be able to:

✓ understand that the flow of electricity in metals and carbon is due to movement of delocalised (mobile) electrons, and that there is no chemical change involved

✓ understand what is meant by *electrolysis, electrolyte, non-electrolyte, electrode, anode, cathode*

✓ know that electricity is conducted through electrolytes (molten or in solution) by the movement and discharge of ions

✓ know the products of electrolysis of simple molten electrolytes like lead(II) bromide, explaining the electrolysis with the help of electrode equations

✓ describe and explain the electrolysis of aqueous solutions such as sodium chloride, copper(II) sulfate and dilute sulfuric acid, including electrode equations

✓ deduce the products of electrolysis of other aqueous solutions in simple cases

✓ describe a simple experiment to find out whether a substance is an electrolyte or a non-electrolyte.

You will find calculations involving electrolysis on pages 196–201.

Questions

1 Say what is formed at the cathode and at the anode during the electrolysis of the following substances. Assume that carbon electrodes were used each time. You don't need to write electrode equations.

a) molten lead(II) bromide

b) molten zinc chloride

c) sodium iodide solution

d) molten sodium iodide

e) copper(II) chloride solution

f) dilute hydrochloric acid

g) magnesium sulfate solution

h) sodium hydroxide solution.

2 Some solid potassium iodide was placed in an evaporating basin. Two carbon electrodes were inserted and connected to a 12 volt DC power source and a light bulb. The potassium iodide was heated. As soon as the potassium iodide was molten, the bulb came on. Purple fumes were seen coming from the positive electrode, and lilac flashes were seen around the negative one.

a) Explain why the bulb didn't come on until the potassium iodide melted.

b) What name is given to the positive electrode?

c) Name the purple fumes seen at the positive electrode, and write the electrode equation for their formation.

d) The lilac flashes seen around the negative electrode are caused by the potassium which is formed. The potassium burns with a lilac flame. Write the electrode equation for the formation of the potassium.

e) What differences would you expect to observe if you used molten sodium bromide instead of potassium iodide?

f) Write the electrode equations for the reactions occurring during the electrolysis of molten sodium bromide.

3 For each of the following electrolytes **(i)** write the cathode equation, **(ii)** write the anode equation, **(iii)** say what has been oxidised and what has been reduced.

a) molten lead(II) bromide using carbon electrodes

b) sodium chloride solution using carbon electrodes

c) calcium bromide solution using carbon electrodes

d) copper(II) sulfate solution using carbon electrodes

e) aluminium nitrate solution using carbon electrodes

f) molten magnesium iodide using carbon electrodes

g) dilute hydrochloric acid using carbon electrodes.

4 You are asked to find out whether two compounds, S and T, are electrolytes or non-electrolytes. S melts at 1261 °C and is soluble in water. T melts at 265 °C and is insoluble in water. Describe, with the aid of diagrams, how you would find out if each of these substances was an electrolyte or a non-electrolyte. In each case, say what you would look for to help you to decide.

Chapter 13: Electrolysis

Some chemical reactions produce heat. Others need to be heated constantly to make them occur at all. This chapter explores some examples of both kinds of reaction.

Exothermic and endothermic changes

Exothermic reactions

It is common experience that a lot of chemical reactions give out energy in the form of heat. A reaction that gives out heat is said to be **exothermic**.

Combustion reactions

Any reaction that produces a flame must be exothermic. Burning things produces heat energy.

Figure 14.1 *Burning fuel produces enough energy to launch a rocket.*

Figure 14.2 *The flare stack at an oil refinery is a safety device. If a process goes wrong (for example, if pressures get too high), reactants and products can be sent to the flare stack, where they burn off safely.*

You will be familiar with testing for hydrogen by lighting it and getting a squeaky pop. That is an obvious sign of energy being released – an exothermic change. This can be harnessed in oxy-hydrogen cutting equipment, which can be used underwater.

$$2H_2(g) + O_2(g) \rightarrow 2H_2O(l)$$

Apart from burning, other simple exothermic changes include:

● the reactions of metals with acids

● neutralisation reactions

● adding water to calcium oxide.

Figure 14.3 *The burning of hydrogen is used in oxy-hydrogen cutting equipment underwater.*

The reactions of metals with acids

For example, when magnesium reacts with dilute sulfuric acid, the mixture gets very warm.

$$Mg(s) + H_2SO_4(aq) \rightarrow MgSO_4(aq) + H_2(g)$$

This reaction is described in detail in Chapter 9 (page 72).

Neutralisation reactions

About the only interesting thing that you can observe happening when sodium hydroxide solution reacts with dilute hydrochloric acid is that the temperature rises!

$$NaOH(aq) + HCl(aq) \rightarrow NaCl(aq) + H_2O(l)$$

You can read about this reaction in Chapter 9 (pages 74–75).

Adding water to calcium oxide

If you add water to solid calcium oxide, the heat produced is enough to boil the water and produce steam. Calcium hydroxide is produced.

$$CaO(s) + H_2O(l) \rightarrow Ca(OH)_2(s)$$

Calcium oxide is known as **quicklime**. Adding water to it is described as **slaking** it. The calcium hydroxide produced is known as **slaked lime**.

Showing an exothermic change on an energy diagram

In an exothermic reaction, the reactants have more energy than the products. As the reaction happens, energy is given out in the form of heat. That energy warms up both the reaction itself and the surroundings.

Remember that in a chemical reaction the reactants are the chemicals you start with.

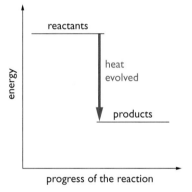

Figure 14.4 *An exothermic change.*

You can measure the amount of heat energy released. It is given the symbol ΔH.

ΔH is given a minus or a plus sign to show whether heat is being given out or absorbed by the reaction. You always look at it from the point of view of the substances taking part. For an exothermic reaction, ΔH is given a *negative* number, because the reactants are *losing* energy as heat. That heat is transferred to the surroundings, which then get warmer. ΔH is measured in units of kJ mol^{-1} ('kilojoules per mole').

ΔH is pronounced 'delta H'. The Greek letter Δ is used to mean 'change in'. ΔH means 'change in heat'. The mole is a particular quantity of a substance. You can read about it in chapter 22, but you probably don't need to worry about it at the moment. In the case of magnesium, 1 mole weighs 24.3 g.

In an equation, this would be shown as, for example:

$$Mg(s) + H_2SO_4(aq) \rightarrow MgSO_4(aq) + H_2(g) \qquad \Delta H = -466.9 \, kJ \, mol^{-1}$$

This means that 466.9 kJ of heat is given out when one mole of magnesium reacts in this way. You know it has been given out because ΔH has a negative sign.

Endothermic reactions

A reaction that absorbs energy is said to be **endothermic**. The energy absorbed may be in the form of light, heat taken from the surroundings, or electrical energy. For the purposes of this course, we are only considering energy being absorbed in the form of heat.

The effect of heat on carbonates

These are simple examples of endothermic reactions. You have to heat a carbonate constantly to make it react.

Most carbonates split up to give the metal oxide and carbon dioxide when you heat them. This is a good example of **thermal decomposition** – breaking something up by heating it.

For example, copper(II) carbonate is a green powder which decomposes on heating to produce black copper(II) oxide.

$$CuCO_3(s) \rightarrow CuO(s) + CO_2(g)$$

Zinc carbonate is a white powder which decomposes on heating to give zinc oxide, which is yellow when it is hot, but turns back to white on cooling.

$$ZnCO_3(s) \rightarrow ZnO(s) + CO_2(g)$$

Calcium carbonate doesn't decompose unless it is heated at quite high temperatures. This is a commercially important reaction because it is used to convert limestone (calcium carbonate) into quicklime (calcium oxide).

$$CaCO_3(s) \rightarrow CaO(s) + CO_2(g)$$

Showing an endothermic change on an energy diagram

Group 1 carbonates (apart from lithium carbonate) won't decompose at the temperatures you can reach with a Bunsen burner (about 1000°C).

Figure 14.5 *Copper(II) carbonate turns black on heating.*

Figure 14.6 *Limestone being heated in a lime kiln to produce quicklime (calcium oxide).*

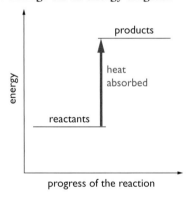

Figure 14.7 *An endothermic change.*

In an endothermic change, the products have more energy than the reactants. That extra energy has to come from somewhere, and it is taken from the surroundings. In the case of the decomposition of the carbonates, it comes from the Bunsen burner, or the fuel in the lime kiln.

Because the reactants are *gaining* energy, ΔH is given a *positive* sign.

For example:

$$CaCO_3(s) \rightarrow CaO(s) + CO_2(g) \qquad \Delta H = +178 \text{ kJ mol}^{-1}$$

Again, don't worry if you don't understand the units of ΔH. It isn't important for now.

This means that it needs 178 kJ of heat energy to convert 1 mole of calcium carbonate (in this case 100 g) into calcium oxide and carbon dioxide.

Why do reactions either give out or absorb heat?

During chemical reactions, bonds in the reactants have to be broken, and new ones formed to make the products. Breaking bonds needs energy, and energy is released when new bonds are made.

Think about what happens when hydrogen burns in oxygen to make water.

$$2H_2(g) + O_2(g) \rightarrow 2H_2O(l)$$

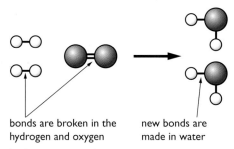

bonds are broken in the
hydrogen and oxygen

new bonds are
made in water

Figure 14.8 *Hydrogen burning in oxygen to make water.*

Energy has to be supplied to break the bonds in the hydrogen molecules and in the oxygen molecule. Energy is released when new bonds are formed between the hydrogen and oxygen atoms in the water molecules.

In this particular reaction, you get much more energy released when the new bonds are formed than was used to break the original ones. This surplus energy is given out as heat during the reaction – an exothermic change.

When you heat calcium carbonate, breaking up the original bonds in the compound costs more energy than you get out when the new ones are made. That means that when the reaction is finished, more energy has been absorbed than is released again – an endothermic change.

You will find calculations involving energy changes covered in Chapter 25.

If you want to be really accurate about this, the water would originally be formed as steam. Heat is also given out when the steam condenses to form liquid water. This is due to setting up attractive forces between the molecules in liquid water. Setting up attractions always releases energy, whatever kind of attractions you are talking about.

End of Chapter Checklist

You should now be able to:

✓ understand the meaning of the terms *exothermic* and *endothermic*, and give examples of reactions of each type

✓ understand simple energy diagrams showing the relative energies of reactants and products

✓ know that energy is needed to break bonds and is released when bonds are made.

Questions

1 **a)** Explain what is meant by an exothermic reaction, and write balanced equations for any two exothermic changes (apart from the combustion of heptane given in part **(b)**).

b) Heptane, C_7H_{16}, is a hydrocarbon found in petrol. The equation for the combustion of heptane is:

$$C_7H_{16}(l) + 11O_2(g) \rightarrow 7CO_2(g) + 8H_2O(l)$$

$\Delta H = -4817 \, kJ \, mol^{-1}$

Draw a simple energy diagram to show the combustion of heptane. Show clearly how the figure of -4817 fits onto your diagram.

c) Explain in terms of breaking and making bonds why this reaction is exothermic.

2 **a)** Explain what is meant by an endothermic reaction, and write balanced equations for any two endothermic changes (apart from the photosynthesis reaction given in part **(b)**.

b) Photosynthesis involves the conversion of carbon dioxide and water into carbohydrates such as glucose, $C_6H_{12}O_6$, and oxygen, in the presence of sunlight and chlorophyll.

$$6CO_2(g) + 6H_2O(l) \rightarrow C_6H_{12}O_6(aq) + 6O_2(g)$$

$\Delta H = +2820 \, kJ \, mol^{-1}$

Draw a simple energy diagram to show the process of photosynthesis. Show clearly how the figure of $+2820$ fits onto your diagram.

3 Classify each of the following changes as exothermic or endothermic. In some cases, you will have to rely on your previous knowledge of chemistry. Several reactions are likely to be entirely new to you.

a) The reaction between sodium and water.

b) Burning ethanol.

c) The reaction between sodium carbonate and ethanoic acid. A thermometer placed in the reaction mixture shows a temperature drop.

d) $S(s) + O_2(g) \rightarrow SO_2(g)$ $\quad \Delta H = -297 \, kJ \, mol^{-1}$

e) $CuSO_4(s) \rightarrow CuO(s) + SO_3(g)$ $\quad \Delta H = +220 \, kJ \, mol^{-1}$

f) If you dissolve solid sodium hydroxide in water, the solution gets very hot.

4 Self-heating cans are used to provide warm food in situations where it is inconvenient to use a more conventional form of heat. By doing an internet (or other) search, find out how self-heating cans work. Write a short explanation of your findings (not exceeding 200 words). You should include equation(s) for any reaction(s) involved, and a diagram or picture if it is useful.

Chapter 15: Introducing Reversible Reactions

Reversibility and dynamic equilibria

Two simple reversible reactions

Heating copper(II) sulfate crystals

If you heat blue copper(II) sulfate crystals gently, the blue crystals turn to a white powder and water is driven off. Heating causes the crystals to lose their water of crystallisation, and white anhydrous copper(II) sulfate is formed. 'Anhydrous' simply means 'without water'.

$$CuSO_4 \cdot 5H_2O(s) \rightarrow CuSO_4(s) + 5H_2O(l)$$

Anhydrous copper(II) sulfate is used to test for the presence of water. If you add water to the white solid, it turns blue – and also gets very warm. See Figure 11.11 (page 93).

The original change has been exactly reversed. Even the heat that you put in originally has been given out again.

$$CuSO_4(s) + 5H_2O(l) \rightarrow CuSO_4 \cdot 5H_2O(s)$$

Heating ammonium chloride

If you heat ammonium chloride, the white crystals disappear from the bottom of the tube and reappear further up. Heating ammonium chloride splits it into the colourless gases ammonia and hydrogen chloride.

$$NH_4Cl(s) \rightarrow NH_3(g) + HCl(g)$$

These gases recombine further up the tube, where it is cooler.

$$NH_3(g) + HCl(g) \rightarrow NH_4Cl(s)$$

The reaction reverses when the conditions are changed from hot to cool.

Reversible reactions under 'closed' conditions

'Closed' conditions means that no substances are added to the reaction mixture and no substances escape from it. On the other hand, heat may be either given off or absorbed.

Imagine a substance that can exist in two forms – one of which we'll represent by a blue square and the other by a yellow one. Suppose you start off with a sample which is entirely blue.

This chapter explores the idea of 'reversibility' in a reaction, and how you can control such reactions in order to get as much as possible of what you want.

Figure 15.1 *Copper(II) sulfate crystals are split into anhydrous copper(II) sulfate and water on gentle heating.*

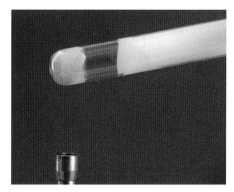

Figure 15.2 *Heating ammonium chloride.*

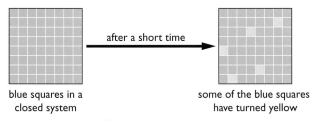

blue squares in a closed system → after a short time → some of the blue squares have turned yellow

Figure 15.3 *Blue squares converting to yellow ones.*

Chapter 15: Introducing Reversible Reactions

Suppose you started with 64 blue squares, and in any second there was a one in four chance of each of them changing colour. In the first second, 16 would change colour, leaving 48 blue squares. In the next second, a quarter of these change colour – but that's only 12, leaving 36 blue ones. In the third second, nine would change colour – and so on. The rate of change falls as the number of blue squares falls.

Because you are starting with a high concentration of blue squares, at the beginning of the reaction the rate at which they turn yellow will be relatively high in terms of the number of squares changing colour per second. The number changing colour per second (the rate of change) will fall as the blue gradually gets used up.

But the yellow squares can also change back to blue ones again – it is a reversible reaction. At the start, there aren't any yellow squares, so the rate of change from yellow into blue is zero. As their number increases, the rate at which yellow change to blue also increases.

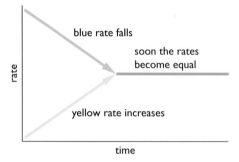

Figure 15.4 *The rates of both reactions become equal.*

Soon the rates of both reactions become equal. At that point, blue ones are changing into yellow ones at exactly the same rate that yellow ones are turning blue.

What would you see in the reaction mixture when that happens? The total numbers of blue squares and of yellow squares would remain constant, but the reaction would still be going on. If you followed the fate of any one particular square, sometimes it would be blue and sometimes yellow.

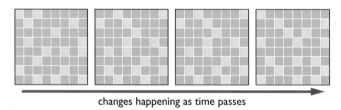

changes happening as time passes

Figure 15.5 *The reaction continues, but total numbers of blue and yellow squares remain constant.*

This is an example of a **dynamic equilibrium**. It is *dynamic* in the sense that the reactions are still continuing. It is an *equilibrium* in the sense that the total amounts of the various things present are now constant.

Notice that you can set up a dynamic equilibrium only if the system is closed. If, for example, you removed the yellow ones as soon as they were formed, they would never get the chance to turn blue again. What was a reversible reaction will now go entirely in one direction as blue squares turn yellow without being replaced.

Writing equations for reactions in dynamic equilibrium

Taking a general case where A and B react reversibly to give C and D:

$$A + 2B \rightleftharpoons C + D$$

The special two-way arrows show a reversible reaction in a state of dynamic equilibrium. The reaction between A and B (the left-to-right reaction) is described as the **forward reaction**. The reaction between C and D (the right-to-left reaction) is called the **back reaction**.

Manipulating reversible reactions

If your aim in life was to produce substance C in the last equation as efficiently as possible, you might not be too pleased if it kept reacting back to produce A and B all the time.

This section looks at what can be done to alter the **position of equilibrium** so as to produce as much as possible of what you want in the equilibrium mixture. 'Position of equilibrium' is just a reference to the proportions of the various things in the equilibrium mixture.

If, for example, the equilibrium mixture contains a high proportion of C and D, we would say that the 'position of equilibrium lies towards C and D', or the 'position of equilibrium lies to the right'.

Le Chatelier's principle

If a dynamic equilibrium is disturbed by changing the conditions, the reaction moves to counteract the change.

This is a useful guide to what happens if you change the conditions in a system in dynamic equilibrium. It is essentially a 'law of chemical cussedness'! The reaction sets about counteracting any changes you make.

Things we might try to do to influence the reaction include:

- increasing or decreasing the concentrations of substances present

- changing the pressure

- changing the temperature

- adding a catalyst (in fact, this turns out to have no effect on the position of equilibrium).

Adding and removing substances

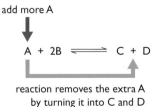

Figure 15.6 *Adding more of substance A.*

If you add more A, the system responds by removing it again. That produces more C and D – which is what you probably want. You might choose to increase the amount of A if it was essential to convert as much B as possible into products – because it was expensive, for example.

The reason for using '2B' will become obvious later on when we look at the effect of pressure on the reaction.

Important! Le Chatelier's principle is no more than a useful rule-of-thumb to help you to decide what happens if various conditions are changed. It is *not the reason* why the reaction responds in that way.

Alternatively, if you remove C as soon as it is formed, the reaction will respond by replacing it again by reacting more A and B. Removing a substance as soon as it is formed is a useful way of moving the position of equilibrium to generate more products.

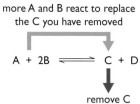

Figure 15.7 *Removing substance C as soon as it is formed.*

Changing the pressure

This only really applies to gas reactions, and where the total number of molecules on both sides of the equation are different. In our example, there are three molecules on the left, but only two on the right.

$$A(g) + 2B(g) \rightleftharpoons C(g) + D(g)$$

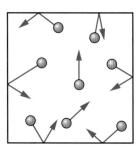

Figure 15.8 *Pressure is caused by molecules hitting the walls of their container – the more molecules, the greater the pressure.*

Pressure is caused by molecules hitting the walls of their container. If you have fewer molecules in the same volume at the same temperature, you will have a lower pressure.

According to Le Chatelier's principle, if you increase the pressure, the reaction will respond by reducing it again. It can reduce the pressure by producing fewer molecules to hit the walls of the container – in this case by creating more C and D. Increasing the pressure will always help the reaction go in the direction which produces the smaller number of molecules.

If there are the same number of molecules on both sides of the equation, changing the pressure will make no difference to the position of equilibrium.

Changing the temperature

Suppose the forward reaction is *exothermic*. This is shown in an equation by writing a negative sign in front of the quantity of heat energy. For example:

$$A + 2B \rightleftharpoons C + D \qquad \Delta H = -100 \, kJ \, mol^{-1}$$

If you aren't happy about this, you ought to read Chapter 14 before you go on. In a reversible reaction, the value of ΔH quoted always applies to the *forward* reaction as written in the equation. The value of ΔH is given as if the reaction was a one-way process.

The back reaction would be *endothermic* by exactly the same amount.

Suppose you changed the conditions by decreasing the temperature of the equilibrium – for example, if the reaction was originally in equilibrium at 500 °C, you lower the temperature to 100 °C. The reaction will respond in such a way as to increase the temperature again. How can it do that?

If more C and D is produced, more heat is given out because of the exothermic change. That extra heat which is produced will warm the reaction mixture up again – as Le Chatelier suggests. In other words, decreasing the temperature will cause more C and D to be formed.

Increasing the temperature will have exactly the opposite effect. The reaction will move to get rid of the extra heat by absorbing it in an endothermic change. This time the back reaction is favoured.

Adding a catalyst

Adding a catalyst speeds up reactions. In a reversible change, it speeds up the forward and back reactions by the same proportion. For example, if it speeds up the forward reaction ten times, it speeds up the back reaction ten times as well.

The net effect of this is that there is no change in the position of equilibrium if you add a catalyst. The catalyst is added to increase the rate at which equilibrium is reached. You will find examples of this in practice in the industrial examples in Chapter 16.

A simple example to illustrate Le Chatelier's principle

Nitrogen dioxide, NO_2, is a dark brown, poisonous gas. It can join up in pairs (dimerise) to make molecules of dinitrogen tetroxide, N_2O_4, which is colourless. There is a dynamic equilibrium between the two forms:

$$2NO_2(g) \rightleftharpoons N_2O_4(g) \quad \Delta H = -57 \, kJ \, mol^{-1}$$

brown   colourless

The effect of pressure

If you increase the pressure, the equilibrium will move to reduce it again by producing fewer molecules. In other words, it will produce more dinitrogen tetroxide.

If you lower the pressure, the equilibrium will move to increase it again by producing more molecules. Therefore you will get a higher proportion of the brown nitrogen dioxide in the equilibrium mixture.

The effect of temperature

Notice from the equation that the change from nitrogen dioxide to dinitrogen tetroxide is exothermic. The negative sign for ΔH shows that heat is given out by the forward reaction.

If you decrease the temperature, the equilibrium will move to produce more heat to counteract the change you have made. In other words, at a lower temperature there will be more dinitrogen tetroxide in the equilibrium mixture, and the colour will fade.

If you increase the temperature, the equilibrium will move to lower it again by favouring the endothermic change. In other words, more nitrogen dioxide will be formed and the colour of the gas will darken.

You can see this happening in Figure 15.9. Of the three tubes containing this equilibrium mixture, one is at lab temperature, one is in ice, and one is in hot water. Notice that the hot one is very dark brown and therefore contains a high proportion of nitrogen dioxide.

The one in the ice is slightly paler than the one in the air, showing that it must have a slightly greater proportion of the colourless dinitrogen tetroxide.

Warning! You have to be very careful here about predicting exactly what colour changes you would see. If you increase the pressure, for example, you squeeze the same number of molecules into a smaller space and so the colour will darken initially. Then it fades a bit as the equilibrium re-establishes – but not to its original colour. The gases are still compressed.

At the time of writing, there were some excellent video clips on www.youtube.com showing this reaction. Visit the page of links for this chapter on the website accompanying this book for up-to-date links.

Figure 15.9 *Tubes containing the NO_2/N_2O_4 equilibrium at different temperatures.*

End of Chapter Checklist

You should now be able to:

✓ understand what is meant by a reversible reaction using simple examples such as the effect of heat on copper(II) sulfate crystals or ammonium chloride

✓ understand that a reversible reaction in a closed system can reach a state of dynamic equilibrium

✓ using Le Chatelier's principle, predict what happens to the position of equilibrium if you add or subtract substances, change the temperature, or change the pressure

✓ know that a catalyst has no effect on the position of equilibrium.

Questions

1 **a)** State Le Chatelier's principle.

b) At room temperature, nitrogen dioxide gas consists of a *dynamic equilibrium* involving nitrogen dioxide and dinitrogen tetroxide.

$$2NO_2(g) \rightleftharpoons N_2O_4(g)$$

(i) Explain what is meant by the term *dynamic equilibrium*. Be sure that you have explained what both of the words mean.

(ii) Predict the effect of an increase in pressure on the proportions of the two gases present in the equilibrium mixture. Explain your answer.

(iii) The forward reaction (the conversion of nitrogen dioxide into dinitrogen tetroxide) is exothermic. Predict the effect of lowering the temperature of the mixture on the proportions of the two gases present. Explain your answer.

2 Hydrogen can be made by the reaction between methane (natural gas) and steam. The reaction can be carried out by passing a mixture of methane and steam over a nickel catalyst at pressures between 2 and 30 atmospheres and a temperature of about 1000 °C.

$$CH_4(g) + H_2O(g) \rightleftharpoons CO(g) + 3H_2(g) \qquad \Delta H = +210 \, kJ \, mol^{-1}$$

a) The pressure used is relatively low. What would be the effect on the conversion of the methane into carbon monoxide and hydrogen if the pressure was higher?

b) Explain why a high temperature is used in order to get a good conversion of methane into hydrogen.

c) A catalyst has no effect on the proportions of the substances present in an equilibrium mixture. What, then, is the point of using a nickel catalyst?

d) The equation shows the methane and steam in a 1:1 ratio. Explain why an excess of steam might be used in the process.

3 The indicator litmus is a weak acid – it only ionises partially in solution. It is a complicated molecule containing a hydrogen atom which can break free to form an ion. In the equation, Lit represents the rest of the molecule.

$$HLit(aq) \rightleftharpoons H^+(aq) + Lit^-(aq)$$

In litmus solution there is a dynamic equilibrium involving the HLit molecules and the two ions. Because litmus is a weak acid, the position of equilibrium lies well to the left.

HLit molecules are red and Lit⁻ ions are blue. Explain why litmus:

a) turns red when you add an acid [a source of $H^+(aq)$] to it

b) turns blue when you add an alkali [a source of $OH^-(aq)$] to it.

4 Ammonia, NH_3, is manufactured by passing a mixture of nitrogen and hydrogen over an iron catalyst at a pressure of 200 atmospheres or more, and a temperature of 450 °C.

$$N_2(g) + 3H_2(g) \rightleftharpoons 2NH_3(g) \qquad \Delta H = -92 \, kJ \, mol^{-1}$$

a) Explain why this reaction will produce a higher percentage conversion into ammonia if the pressure is very high.

b) 200 atmospheres is a high pressure, but not very high. Can you think of any reason(s) why most ammonia manufacturers don't use a pressure of, say, 1000 atmospheres?

c) Use Le Chatelier's principle to work out whether you would get the best yield of ammonia in the equilibrium mixture at a low or a high temperature.

d) The temperature used, 450 °C, is neither very high nor very low. Can you suggest why a manufacturer might choose a temperature which gave less than an ideal percentage conversion? (Hint: think about rates of reaction.)

You may need to refer to the Periodic Table on page 226.

1. This question is about copper(II) sulfate solution, which contains $Cu^{2+}(aq)$ and $SO_4^{2-}(aq)$ ions.

   a) The presence of the sulfate ions can be shown by adding dilute hydrochloric acid and barium chloride solution to produce a white precipitate.

     (i) Name the white precipitate.

     (ii) Write the ionic equation for its formation.   *(2 marks)*

   b) Describe a test that would show the presence of the copper(II) ions in the solution.   *(2 marks)*

   c) An excess of zinc powder was added to some copper(II) sulfate solution and the mixture was shaken thoroughly. A displacement reaction occurred. The ionic equation for the reaction is

     $Zn(s) + Cu^{2+}(aq) \rightarrow Zn^{2+}(aq) + Cu(s)$

     (i) Describe two changes that you would expect to see during the reaction.

     (ii) Which substance in the reaction has been oxidised? Explain your answer.   *(4 marks)*

   d) Copper can also be produced from copper(II) sulfate by electrolysis.

     (i) At which electrode is the copper produced?

     (ii) Write the equation for the reaction taking place at the electrode.

     (iii) What type of reaction is occurring at this electrode? Explain your answer.   *(4 marks)*

                          Total 12 marks

2. This question is about salts.

   a) What would you add to dilute hydrochloric acid to make each of the following salts? In each case, say whether you would add it as a solid or in solution.

     (i) copper(II) chloride

     (ii) sodium chloride

     (iii) silver chloride   *(3 marks)*

   b) Potassium sulfate is produced when dilute sulfuric acid reacts with potassium hydroxide solution.

     $2KOH(aq) + H_2SO_4(aq) \rightarrow K_2SO_4(aq) + 2H_2O(l)$

     Given solutions of potassium hydroxide and dilute sulfuric acid, an indicator and suitable titration apparatus, describe how you would make a pure, neutral solution of potassium sulfate by a titration method. You should name the indicator you would choose to use, and state any important colour change(s).   *(6 marks)*

                          Total 9 marks

3. Sodium chloride solution was electrolysed using the apparatus in the diagram.

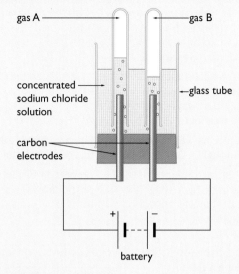

   a) Name: (i) gas A, (ii) gas B.   *(2 marks)*

   b) Describe how you would test for: (i) gas A, (ii) gas B.   *(4 marks)*

   c) Suppose the sodium chloride solution was replaced by potassium iodide solution. What differences would you observe (if any) at: (i) the positive electrode, (ii) the negative electrode?   *(3 marks)*

   d) The same apparatus was used to electrolyse another solution, C. A brown solid was formed on the negative electrode, and an orange solution around the positive one. Suggest a possible identity for solution C.   *(2 marks)*

                          Total 11 marks

4. *a)* Chlorine was bubbled through a solution of potassium iodide.

     (i) Balance the ionic equation for the reaction involved:

     $Cl_2(g) + I^-(aq) \rightarrow Cl^-(aq) + I_2(s)$

     (ii) Describe what you would expect to see happen in the solution.

     (iii) Describe the function of the chlorine in the reaction with the iodide ions.   *(5 marks)*

b) Samples of a very pale green solution, G, were tested as follows:

Test	Observation
A sample of solution was acidified with dilute nitric acid and silver nitrate solution was added.	A white precipitate (H) was formed.
A small amount of sodium hydroxide solution was added to a sample of G.	A dark green precipitate (I) was formed.
Chlorine was bubbled through a sample of G.	The pale green solution turned yellow (solution J).
A small amount of sodium hydroxide solution was added to solution J.	An orange-brown precipitate (K) was formed.

(i) Use the results from the first two tests to identify solution G.

(ii) Identify precipitates I and K.

(iii) Suggest the identity of solution J.

(iv) Write an ionic equation for the formation of I.

(6 marks)

Total 11 marks

5. Mendeleev produced the first Periodic Table by arranging the elements in order of their atomic mass. When argon was discovered, its atomic mass turned out to be slightly higher than that of potassium. In this instance, Mendeleev reversed the usual order in the Periodic Table.

Mendeleev's order			Atomic mass order		
Group 0	Group 1	Group 2	Group 0	Group 1	Group 2
Ne	Na	Mg	Ne	Na	Mg
Ar	K	Ca	K	Ar	Ca

a) State one physical property of potassium that suggests that it should be in the same Group as sodium rather than with neon. *(1 mark)*

b) Give any one chemical property of potassium that is similar to that of sodium. Say what the potassium reacts with, and what is formed. Write the balanced equation for the reaction. *(4 marks)*

c) (i) Draw dots-and-crosses diagrams to show the electronic structures of sodium and potassium atoms.

(ii) What happens to these structures when sodium or potassium reacts to form compounds?

(iii) Explain why potassium is more reactive than sodium.

(6 marks)

d) Argon is chemically unreactive and its molecules are monatomic. What is a monatomic molecule? Explain why argon's molecules are monatomic. *(3 marks)*

Total 14 marks

6. Reactions can be described as (among other things): neutralisation, precipitation, redox, thermal decomposition. Decide which of these types of reaction each of the following equations represents.

a) $Zn(s) + CuO(s) \rightarrow ZnO(s) + Cu(s)$ *(1 mark)*

b) $ZnCO_3(s) \rightarrow ZnO(s) + CO_2(g)$ *(1 mark)*

c) $ZnCO_3(s) + H_2SO_4(aq) \rightarrow ZnSO_4(aq) + CO_2(g) + H_2O(l)$ *(1 mark)*

d) $Zn^{2+}(aq) + CO_3^{2-}(aq) \rightarrow ZnCO_3(s)$ *(1 mark)*

e) $Zn(s) + Pb^{2+}(aq) \rightarrow Zn^{2+}(aq) + Pb(s)$ *(1 mark)*

(f) $Zn(s) + 2HCl(aq) \rightarrow ZnCl_2(aq) + H_2(g)$ *(1 mark)*

Total 6 marks

7. At temperatures above 150°C, brown nitrogen dioxide gas dissociates (splits up reversibly) into colourless nitrogen monoxide and oxygen.

$$2NO_2(g) \rightleftharpoons 2NO(g) + O_2(g) \qquad \Delta H = +114\,kJ\,mol^{-1}$$

a) Explain what is meant by the symbol ΔH, and the significance of it having a positive value. *(2 marks)*

b) Predict what would happen to the proportion of the nitrogen dioxide splitting up if you:

(i) increase the temperature

(ii) increase the pressure. *(2 marks)*

c) Nitrogen monoxide is formed when mixtures of nitrogen and oxygen gases are subjected to an electric spark. This happens in petrol engines, where a spark is used to ignite a petrol/air mixture. The nitrogen monoxide converts into nitrogen dioxide in the atmosphere by the reverse of the reaction above. The nitrogen dioxide then dissolves in water.

(i) Write a balanced equation for the formation of nitrogen monoxide from nitrogen and oxygen. *(1 mark)*

(ii) Name the environmental problem that this overall process gives rise to, and give a consequence of the problem. *(2 marks)*

(iii) Name another gas which also contributes to this problem. *(1 mark)*

Total 8 marks

Chapter 16: Manufacturing Chemicals

Figure 16.1 *The chemical industry is large and often messy . . .*

Figure 16.2 *. . . but its products find their way into almost every aspect of modern life.*

This chapter looks at the manufacture of some important inorganic chemicals, putting into practice ideas that you have already come across in lab-based chemistry.

The manufacture and uses of ammonia

The Haber process

The Haber process takes nitrogen from the air and hydrogen produced from natural gas, and combines them into ammonia, NH_3.

$$N_2(g) + 3H_2(g) \rightleftharpoons 2NH_3(g) \qquad \Delta H = -92\,kJ\,mol^{-1}$$

The raw materials: nitrogen (from the air)
                      hydrogen (made from natural gas)

The proportions: 1 volume of nitrogen to 3 volumes of hydrogen

The temperature: 450 °C

The pressure: 200 atmospheres

The catalyst: iron

Each time the gases pass through the reaction vessel, only about 15% of the nitrogen and hydrogen combine to make ammonia. The reaction mixture is cooled and the ammonia condenses as a liquid. The unreacted nitrogen and hydrogen can simply be recycled through the reactor.

Remember that the negative sign for ΔH shows that the reaction is exothermic.

The reaction to produce the hydrogen from natural gas (which is mainly methane) is complicated. You will find the first stage of the process in Q2 on page 130. Further reactions are then needed to separate the hydrogen from the carbon monoxide. Hydrogen can also be obtained by cracking other hydrocarbons bigger than methane. Cracking is explained on pages 166–167. If you are asked in an exam for the raw material that the hydrogen is obtained from, say 'natural gas', not 'methane'.

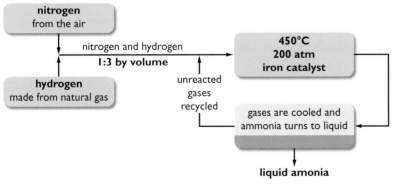

Figure 16.3 *A flow scheme for the Haber process.*

The actual pressure varies in different manufacturing plants, but is always very high.

Don't try to read any further unless you are happy about equilibria and Le Chatelier's principle from Chapter 15.

The reason for the proportions of nitrogen and hydrogen

Equation proportions are used: 1 of nitrogen to 3 of hydrogen. An excess of either would clutter the reaction vessel with molecules which wouldn't have anything to react with.

The reason for the temperature

According to Le Chatelier's principle, the forward reaction (an exothermic change) would be favoured by a low temperature, but the temperature used, 450 °C, isn't a low temperature.

If the temperature was genuinely low, the reaction would be so slow that it would take a very long time to produce much ammonia. 450 °C is a **compromise temperature**, producing a reasonable yield of ammonia reasonably quickly.

The reason for the pressure

There are 4 gas molecules on the left-hand side of the equation, but only 2 on the right-hand side.

$$N_2(g) + 3H_2(g) \rightleftharpoons 2NH_3(g)$$

A reaction that produces fewer gaseous molecules is favoured by a high pressure. A high pressure would also produce a fast reaction rate because the molecules are brought closely together.

The 200 atmospheres actually used is high, but not *very high*. This is another compromise. Generating high pressures and building the vessels and pipes to contain them is very expensive. Pressures much higher than 200 atmospheres cost more to generate than you would get back in the value of the extra ammonia produced.

The catalyst

The iron catalyst speeds the reaction up, but has no effect on the proportion of ammonia in the equilibrium mixture. If the catalyst wasn't used, the reaction would be so slow that virtually no ammonia would be produced.

Uses of ammonia

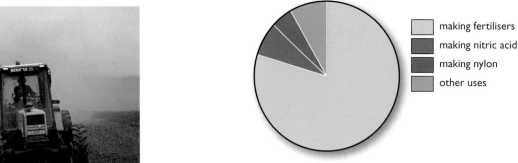

- making fertilisers
- making nitric acid
- making nylon
- other uses

Figure 16.5 *Uses of ammonia.*

A high proportion of ammonia is used to make fertilisers. Most of the ammonia used to make nitric acid eventually ends up in fertilisers as well.

Figure 16.4 *Most of the ammonia produced ends up in fertilisers.*

The manufacture and uses of sulfuric acid

The Contact Process

At the heart of this process is a reversible reaction in which sulfur dioxide is converted to sulfur trioxide, but first you have to produce sulfur dioxide.

Stage 1: making sulfur dioxide

Either burn sulfur in air:

$$S(s) + O_2(g) \rightarrow SO_2(g)$$

or heat sulfide ores strongly in air:

$$4FeS_2(s) + 11O_2(g) \rightarrow 2Fe_2O_3(s) + 8SO_2(g)$$

FeS_2 is *pyrite* or *iron pyrites*. You will find a photograph of some crystals of pyrite in Chapter 17 (page 139).

Stage 2: Making sulfur trioxide

Now the sulfur dioxide is converted into sulfur trioxide using an excess of air from the previous processes.

$$2SO_2(g) + O_2(g) \rightleftharpoons 2SO_3(g) \qquad \Delta H = -196\,kJ\,mol^{-1}$$

Notice that the forward reaction is an exothermic change.

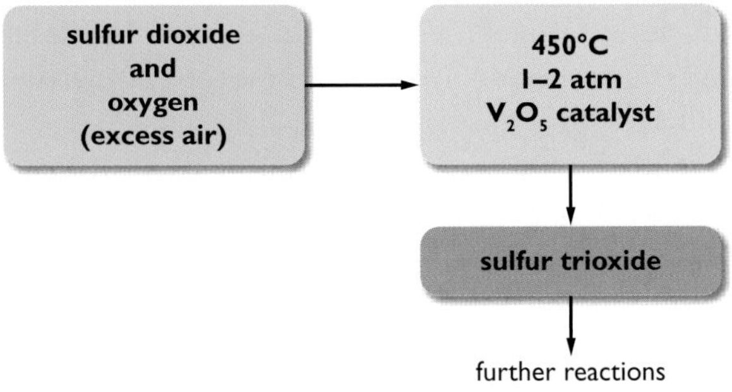

Figure 16.6 *Sulfur dioxide is converted into sulfur trioxide.*

An excess of oxygen is used in this reaction, because it is important to make sure as much sulfur dioxide as possible is converted into sulfur trioxide. Having sulfur dioxide left over at the end of the reaction is wasteful, and could cause possibly dangerous pollution.

Because the forward reaction is exothermic, there would be a higher percentage conversion of sulfur dioxide into sulfur trioxide at a low temperature. However, at a low temperature the rate of reaction would be very slow. $450\,°C$ is a compromise. Even so, there is about a 99.5% conversion.

You will need to be familiar with equilibria and Le Chatelier's principle from Chapter 15 to make sense of this.

There are 3 gas molecules on the left-hand side of the equation, but only 2 on the right. Reactions in which the numbers of gas molecules decrease are favoured by high pressures. In this case, though, the conversion is so good at low pressures that it isn't economically worthwhile to use higher ones.

The catalyst, vanadium(V) oxide, has no effect on the percentage conversion, but helps to speed up the reaction. Without the catalyst, the reaction would be extremely slow.

Stage 3: Making the sulfuric acid

In principle, you can react sulfur trioxide with water to make sulfuric acid. In practice, this produces an uncontrollable fog of concentrated sulfuric acid. Instead, the sulfur trioxide is absorbed in concentrated sulfuric acid to give **fuming sulfuric acid** (also called **oleum**).

$$H_2SO_4(l) + SO_3(g) \rightarrow H_2S_2O_7(l)$$

This is converted into twice as much concentrated sulfuric acid by careful addition of water.

$$H_2S_2O_7(l) + H_2O(l) \rightarrow 2H_2SO_4(l)$$

Uses of sulfuric acid

Sulfuric acid has a wide range of uses throughout the chemical industry. The highest single use is in making fertilisers (including ammonium sulfate and 'superphosphate' – essentially a mixture of calcium phosphate and calcium sulfate).

It is also used in the manufacture of detergents and paints. If you look at the list of ingredients on any industrial or domestic detergents (including shampoos and liquid 'hand soaps'), and find the words 'sulfate' or 'sulfonate', then sulfuric acid was used in the manufacturing process. Even those simply labelled as containing 'anionic surfactants' almost certainly contain these sorts of ingredients, even if they don't name them.

In paint manufacture, sulfuric acid is used in extracting the white pigment titanium dioxide, TiO_2, from titanium ores.

The chlor-alkali industry

Salt can be extracted from underground deposits by **solution mining**. Very hot water under pressure is pumped down into the salt deposits. The salt dissolves and the solution is pumped back to the surface.

The diaphragm cell

The concentrated salt solution can be electrolysed to produce three useful chemicals – sodium hydroxide, chlorine and hydrogen. The electrolysis can be carried out in a **diaphragm cell**.

Figure 16.7 *A selection of detergents from the author's kitchen and bathroom, all listed as containing sulfates or sulfonates.*

If you haven't done any electrolysis recently, you may need to read pages 115–116 in Chapter 13, which describe and explain the electrolysis of sodium chloride solution in the lab. The industrial process is a straightforward modification of this.

The diaphragm is made of a porous material. The solution can seep through it from the anode compartment into the cathode side. Notice that there is a higher level of liquid on the anode side. That makes sure that the flow of liquid is always from left to right – preventing any of the sodium hydroxide solution formed finding its way back to where chlorine is being produced.

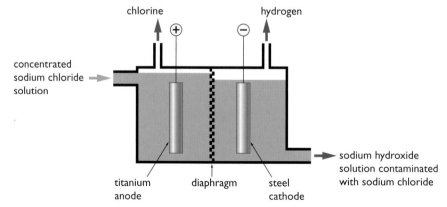

Figure 16.8 *The industrial electrolysis of sodium chloride solution.*

The cell is designed to keep the products apart. If chlorine comes into contact with sodium hydroxide solution, it reacts to make bleach – a mixture of sodium chloride and sodium chlorate(I) solution. If chlorine comes into contact with hydrogen, it produces a mixture which would explode violently on exposure to sunlight or heat to give hydrogen chloride.

Explaining what's happening

At the titanium anode, chloride ions are discharged to produce **chlorine** gas.

$$2Cl^-(aq) \rightarrow Cl_2(g) + 2e^-$$

At the steel cathode, it is too difficult to discharge sodium ions, so **hydrogen** ions from the water are discharged instead to produce hydrogen gas.

$$2H^+(aq) + 2e^- \rightarrow H_2(g)$$

More and more water keeps splitting up to replace the hydrogen ions as soon as they are discharged. Each time a water molecule splits up it produces a hydroxide ion as well. That means that there will be a build-up of sodium ions and hydroxide ions in the right-hand compartment – **sodium hydroxide solution** is formed. This is contaminated with unchanged sodium chloride.

The sodium hydroxide solution is concentrated by evaporating it. During this process, most of the sodium chloride crystallises out as solid salt. This can be separated, redissolved in water and recycled back through the cell again.

Uses of sodium hydroxide and chlorine

Uses of sodium hydroxide include:

- the purification of bauxite to make aluminium oxide ('alumina') as a part of the manufacture of aluminium (see page 140) – the alumina industry is the largest user of sodium hydroxide in Australia, for example

- paper-making – the sodium hydroxide helps break the wood down into pulp

- soap-making – sodium hydroxide reacts with animal and vegetable fats and oils to make compounds, such as sodium stearate, that are present in soap

- making bleach – bleach is formed when sodium hydroxide and chlorine react together in the cold; it is a mixture of sodium chloride and sodium chlorate(I) solution.

$$2NaOH(aq) + Cl_2(g) \rightarrow NaCl(aq) + NaOCl(aq) + H_2O(l)$$

Uses of chlorine include:

- sterilising water to make it safe to drink

- making hydrochloric acid (by controlled reaction with hydrogen)

- making bleach.

This is the most difficult part of this explanation. If you aren't happy about it, read page 116 where it is explained in more detail.
You will also find an alternative way of looking at the cathode reaction in a margin note on that page.

If you get sodium hydroxide on your skin, it feels soapy. That's because it is reacting with fats and oils in your skin, turning you into soap!

Sodium chlorate(I) is also known as sodium hypochlorite. You may find its formula written as either NaOCl or NaClO. There are logical reasons for both forms.

You should now be able to:

✓ know the conditions for the Haber process, including recycling the unreacted gases after the ammonia has been liquefied

✓ know that ammonia is used to make nitric acid and fertilisers

✓ describe the manufacture of sulfuric acid by the Contact Process

✓ know that sulfuric acid is used in the manufacture of detergents, fertilisers and paints

✓ describe the manufacture of sodium hydroxide and chlorine using a diaphragm cell, including the electrode equations

✓ recall important uses of sodium hydroxide and chlorine.

Questions

1 Describe, including equations and essential conditions, the production of sulfuric acid starting from sulfur.

2 The reaction at the centre of the Haber process for the manufacture of ammonia is:

$$N_2(g) + 3H_2(g) \rightleftharpoons 2NH_3(g) \qquad \Delta H = -92\,kJ\,mol^{-1}$$

a) What would happen to the percentage of ammonia in the equilibrium mixture and to the rate of the reaction if you:

(i) increased the temperature

(ii) increased the pressure

(iii) added a catalyst?

b) In the light of your answer to (ii), explain why ammonia plants usually operate with pressures of about 200 atmospheres.

c) State the sources of the nitrogen and the hydrogen used in the Haber process.

3 Refer back to the description of the manufacture of sodium hydroxide and chlorine on pages 136–137.

a) Explain why it is important that the liquid level in the left-hand compartment of a diaphragm cell is higher than that in the right-hand one.

b) Which of the metal electrodes is the cathode, and which the anode?

c) Sodium chloride solution will contain the following ions: $Na^+(aq)$, $Cl^-(aq)$, $H^+(aq)$ and $OH^-(aq)$.

(i) Write an equation to show the source of the hydrogen and hydroxide ions.

(ii) Which of these four ions are attracted towards the cathode?

(iii) Which ion is discharged at the cathode?

(iv) Use your answer to parts (i) and (ii) to help to explain the formation of sodium hydroxide solution in the cathode compartment.

d) Give a use for (i) sodium hydroxide solution; (ii) chlorine.

4 a) Given solutions of ammonia and dilute sulfuric acid and any indicator of your choice, describe how you would make a pure solution of ammonium sulfate.

b) Design a simple experiment to show that your ammonium sulfate solution could function as a fertiliser.

5 This question is about the manufacture of nitric acid from ammonia, and will probably be new to you. Ammonia gas is mixed with air and passed over a platinum–rhodium catalyst at about 850 °C. The ammonia combines with oxygen in the air to make nitrogen monoxide and steam.

$$4NH_3(g) + 5O_2(g) \rightarrow 4NO(g) + 6H_2O(g)$$
$$\Delta H = -906\,kJ\,mol^{-1}$$

a) The catalyst has to be heated at the start of the reaction, but then no further heating is necessary. Explain why.

b) Platinum and rhodium are very expensive metals. How can a manufacturer justify the cost of using them as a catalyst?

c) On cooling, the nitrogen monoxide reacts with more oxygen in the air to give nitrogen dioxide, NO_2. Write a balanced equation for this reaction.

d) Nitrogen dioxide is converted into nitric acid by reacting it with water and even more oxygen. Balance the equation:

$$H_2O(l) + NO_2(g) + O_2(g) \rightarrow HNO_3(aq)$$

e) Most nitric acid is turned into ammonium nitrate to be used as a fertiliser. Find a non-fertiliser use for nitric acid.

Chapter 17: Metals

Extracting metals from their ores

> *This chapter explores the extraction and uses of two important metals.*

Minerals and ores

Most metals are found in the Earth's crust combined with other elements. The individual compounds are called minerals.

Figure 17.1 *Pyrite (iron pyrites), FeS$_2$.*

Figure 17.2 *Magnetite, Fe$_3$O$_4$.*

Figure 17.3 *Haematite, Fe$_2$O$_3$.*

Figures 17.1–17.3 show pure samples of some iron-containing minerals, but they are normally found mixed with other unwanted minerals in rocks. An **ore** contains enough of the mineral for it to be worthwhile to extract the metal.

The price of a metal is affected by how common the ore is, and how difficult it is to extract the metal from the ore.

A few very unreactive metals, such as gold, are found **native**. That means that they exist naturally as the uncombined element. Silver and copper are also sometimes found native – although much more rarely.

Extracting the metal

Many ores are either oxides or compounds that are easily converted to oxides. Sulfides like sphalerite (zinc blende), ZnS, can be easily converted into an oxide by heating in air – a process known as **roasting**.

> If you have forgotten about oxidation and reduction, you might find it useful to re-read Chapter 8.

$$2ZnS(s) + 3O_2(g) \rightarrow 2ZnO(s) + 2SO_2(g)$$

To obtain the metal from the oxide, you have to remove the oxygen. Removal of oxygen is called reduction. Metals exist as positive ions in their ionic compounds, and to produce the metal you would have to add electrons to the positive ion. Addition of electrons is also called reduction.

Methods of extraction and the reactivity series

How a metal is extracted depends to a large extent on its position in the reactivity series. A manufacturer obviously wants to use the cheapest possible method of reducing an ore to the metal. There are two main economic factors to take into account:

- the cost of energy
- the cost of the reducing agent.

potassium
sodium
calcium
magnesium
aluminium
(carbon)
zinc
iron
copper

Figure 17.4 *A part of the reactivity series.*

Figure 17.5 *Aluminium production needs huge amounts of expensive electricity.*

Figure 17.6 *Bronze is an alloy of copper and tin.*

Figure 17.7 *Bauxite – essentially impure aluminium oxide.*

For metals up to zinc in the reactivity series, the cheapest method of reducing the ore is often to heat it with carbon or carbon monoxide. Carbon is cheap and can also be used as the source of heat. The extraction of iron is a good example of this.

Ores of metals higher in the reactivity series than zinc can't be reduced using carbon at reasonable temperatures.

Metals above zinc are usually produced by electrolysis. The metal ions are given electrons directly by the cathode. Unfortunately, the large amounts of electricity involved make this an expensive process, and so a metal like aluminium is much more expensive than one like iron.

Some metals, such as titanium, are extracted by heating the compound with a more reactive metal. This is also bound to be an expensive method, because the more reactive metal itself will have had to be extracted by an expensive process first.

The reactivity series and the history of metal use

Why was the Bronze Age before the Iron Age? Why wasn't aluminium discovered until 1827?

Bronze is an alloy of copper and tin, both of which are low in the reactivity series. Both can be made easily from their ores by heating them with carbon. You can imagine the metals being found accidentally when charcoal (a form of impure carbon) in a fire came into contact with stones containing copper or tin ores.

Iron can also be made from its ores by heating them with carbon, but higher temperatures are needed. The iron produced is also more difficult to purify into a useful form than copper is. Iron therefore wasn't in common use until much later than bronze.

Because aluminium is above carbon in the reactivity series, it can't be made accidentally by heating aluminium oxide with carbon. It has to be extracted using electrolysis, and so it was impossible to get metallic aluminium before the discovery of electricity. This is true of all the metals from aluminium upwards in the reactivity series.

Aluminium

Extraction

Aluminium is the most common metal in the Earth's crust, making up 7.5% by mass. Its main ore is **bauxite** – a clay mineral which you can think of as impure aluminium oxide.

The bauxite is first treated to produce pure aluminium oxide. You don't need to know how this is done for GCSE purposes.

Because aluminium is a fairly reactive metal, it has to be extracted using electrolysis. Aluminium oxide, however, has a very high melting point, and it isn't practical to electrolyse molten aluminium oxide. Instead, the aluminium oxide is dissolved in molten **cryolite**.

Cryolite is another aluminium compound that melts at a more reasonable temperature. The electrolyte is a solution of aluminium oxide in molten cryolite at a temperature of about 1000 °C.

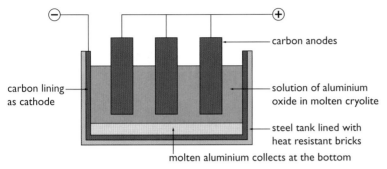

Figure 17.9 *A simplified view of the electrolysis cell.*

Figure 17.8 *The cell room in an aluminium plant.*

Figure 17.9 shows a very simplified view of the electrolysis cell. The molten aluminium is siphoned off from time to time, and fresh aluminium oxide is added to the cell. The cell operates at about 5–6 volts, but with currents of up to about 100,000 amps. The heat generated by the huge current keeps the electrolyte molten. The large amounts of electricity needed are a major expense.

If you aren't sure about electrolysis, you ought to read Chapter 13 before you go on.

The chemistry of the process

Aluminium ions are attracted to the cathode and are reduced to aluminium by gaining electrons.

$$Al^{3+}(l) + 3e^- \rightarrow Al(l)$$

The molten aluminium produced sinks to the bottom of the cell.

The oxide ions are attracted to the anode and lose electrons to form oxygen gas.

$$2O^{2-}(l) \rightarrow O_2(g) + 4e^-$$

This creates a problem. Because of the high temperatures, the carbon anodes burn in the oxygen to form carbon dioxide. The anodes have to be replaced regularly, and this also adds to the expense of the process.

Figure 17.10 *Aluminium resists corrosion, has a low density and is strong.*

Uses of aluminium

Pure aluminium isn't very strong, so aluminium alloys are normally used instead. The aluminium can be strengthened by adding other elements, such as silicon, copper or magnesium.

Figures 17.10 to 17.12 show some examples of the uses of aluminium.

Aluminium's uses depend on its low density and strength (when alloyed), its ability to conduct electricity and heat, its appearance, and its ability to resist corrosion.

Aluminium resists corrosion because it has a very thin, but very strong, layer of aluminium oxide on the surface. This prevents anything else getting to the surface and reacting with it.

Figure 17.11 *Aluminium has a shiny appearance, resists corrosion, has a low density and is a good conductor of heat.*

Figure 17.12 *Aluminium resists corrosion, has a low density and is a good conductor of electricity – the aluminium in the cables is strengthened by a core of steel.*

Iron

Extraction using a blast furnace

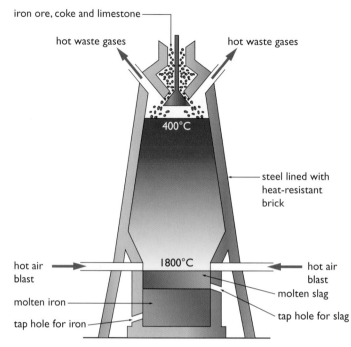

Figure 17.13 *A blast furnace.*

The hot waste gases at the top of the furnace are piped away and used to heat the air blast at the bottom.

Coke is impure carbon, and it burns in the hot air blast to form carbon dioxide. This is a strongly exothermic reaction.

An exothermic reaction is one that gives out heat.

$$C(s) + O_2(g) \rightarrow CO_2(g)$$

At the high temperatures in the furnace, the carbon dioxide is reduced by more carbon to give carbon monoxide.

$$CO_2(g) + C(s) \rightarrow 2CO(g)$$

It is the carbon monoxide which is the main reducing agent in the furnace – especially in the cooler parts. Assuming that the iron ore is haematite, Fe_2O_3:

$$Fe_2O_3(s) + 3CO(g) \rightarrow 2Fe(l) + 3CO_2(g)$$

The iron melts and flows to the bottom of the furnace, where it can be tapped off.

In the hotter parts of the furnace, some of the iron oxide is also reduced by carbon itself.

$$Fe_2O_3(s) + 3C(s) \rightarrow 2Fe(l) + 3CO(g)$$

Notice that carbon monoxide is formed, rather than carbon dioxide, at these temperatures.

Figure 17.14 *Molten iron being tapped from a blast furnace.*

The limestone is added to the furnace to remove impurities in the ore which would otherwise clog the furnace with solid material.

The furnace is hot enough for the limestone (calcium carbonate) to undergo thermal decomposition. It splits up into calcium oxide and carbon dioxide. This is an endothermic reaction (it absorbs heat) and it is important not to add too much limestone to avoid cooling the furnace.

$$CaCO_3(s) \rightarrow CaO(s) + CO_2(g)$$

Calcium oxide is a basic oxide, and its function is to react with acidic oxides such as silicon dioxide, SiO_2. Silicon dioxide occurs naturally as quartz, and is typical of the sort of impurities that need to be removed from the furnace.

$$CaO(s) + SiO_2(s) \rightarrow CaSiO_3(l)$$

The product is calcium silicate. This melts and trickles to the bottom of the furnace as a molten **slag**, which floats on top of the molten iron and can be tapped off separately.

Properties and uses of the different kinds of iron

Cast iron

Molten iron straight from the furnace can be cooled rapidly and solidified by running it into sand moulds. This is known as **pig iron**. If the pig iron is remelted and cooled under controlled conditions, **cast iron** is formed. This is very impure iron, containing about 4% carbon as its main impurity.

Cast iron is very fluid when it is molten and doesn't shrink much when it solidifies, and that makes it ideal for making castings. Unfortunately, although cast iron is very hard, it is also very brittle – tending to shatter if it is hit hard. It is used for things like manhole covers, guttering and drainpipes, and cylinder blocks in car engines.

Mild steel

Mild steel is iron containing up to about 0.25% of carbon. This small amount of carbon increases the hardness and strength of the iron. It is used for (among other things) wire, nails, car bodies, ship building, girders and bridges.

Thermal decomposition is splitting a compound into simpler bits using heat.

Calcium oxide is a basic oxide, because it reacts with acids to form salts. Calcium silicate is a salt formed when calcium oxide and silicon dioxide react. Silicon dioxide, a non-metal oxide, is therefore described as an acidic oxide.

Figure 17.15 *The first ever iron bridge (at Ironbridge on the River Severn in the UK) was made of cast iron.*

Figure 17.16 *Mild steel is used for car bodies . . .*

Figure 17.17. *. . . and for simple nails – and lots more.*

Wrought iron

Pure iron is known as **wrought iron**. It was once used to make decorative gates and railings, but has now been largely replaced by mild steel. The purity of the iron makes it very easy to work because it is fairly soft, but the softness and lack of strength mean that it isn't useful for structural purposes.

High-carbon steel

High-carbon steel is iron containing up to 1.5% carbon. Increasing the carbon content makes the iron harder, but at the same time it gets more brittle. High-carbon steel is used for cutting tools and masonry nails. Masonry nails are designed to be hammered into concrete blocks or brickwork where a mild steel nail would bend. If you miss-hit a masonry nail, it tends to break into two bits because of its increased brittleness.

Stainless steel

Stainless steel is an alloy of iron with chromium and nickel. Chromium and nickel form strong oxide layers in the same way as aluminium, and these oxide layers protect the iron as well. Stainless steel is therefore very resistant to corrosion.

Obvious uses include kitchen sinks, saucepans, knives and forks, and gardening tools, but there are also major uses for it in the brewing, dairy and chemical industries, where corrosion-resistant vessels are essential.

Figure 17.18 *A mild steel spade tarnishes – a stainless steel one doesn't.*

Types of iron	Iron mixed with	Some uses
wrought iron	(pure iron)	decorative work such as gates and railings
mild steel	up to 0.25% carbon	nails, car bodies, ship building, girders
high-carbon steel	0.25–1.5% carbon	cutting tools, masonry nails
cast iron	about 4% carbon	manhole covers, guttering, engine blocks
stainless steel	chromium and nickel	cutlery, cooking utensils, kitchen sinks

Table 17.1: *A summary of types of iron.*

Rusting of iron

Iron rusts in the presence of oxygen and water. Rusting is accelerated in the presence of electrolytes such as salt.

Warning! Many metals corrode, but it is only the corrosion of iron that is referred to as *rusting*.

The formula of rust is $Fe_2O_3 \cdot xH_2O$, where x is a variable number. It simply behaves as a mixture of iron(III) oxide and water.

Forming this from iron is a surprisingly complicated process. The iron loses electrons to form iron(II) ions, Fe^{2+}, which are then oxidised by the air to iron(III) ions, Fe^{3+}. Reactions involving the water produce the actual rust.

Figure 17.19 *Rusting is accelerated by salty water.*

Preventing rusting by using barriers

The most obvious way of preventing rusting is to keep water and oxygen away from the iron. You can do this by painting it, or coating it in oil or grease, or covering it in plastic, but once the coating is broken, the iron will rust. Coating the iron with a metal below it in the reactivity series (for example, to make tin plate) is just a barrier method. Once the layer of tin on the iron is scratched, a tin can, for example, will rust very quickly.

Preventing rusting by alloying the iron

We have already seen that alloying the iron with chromium and nickel to produce stainless steel prevents the iron from rusting. Even if the surface is scratched, the stainless steel still won't rust. Unfortunately, stainless steel is expensive.

Preventing rusting by using sacrificial metals

Galvanised iron is iron that is coated with a layer of zinc. As long as the zinc layer is unscratched, it serves as a barrier to air and water. However, the iron still doesn't rust, even when the surface is broken.

Zinc is more reactive than iron, and so corrodes instead of the iron. During the process, the zinc loses electrons to form zinc ions.

$$Zn(s) \rightarrow Zn^{2+}(aq) + 2e^-$$

Those electrons flow into the iron. Any iron atom which has lost electrons to form an ion immediately regains them. If the iron can't form ions, it can't rust.

Zinc blocks are attached to metal hulls or keels of boats for the same reason. The corrosion of the more reactive zinc prevents the iron from rusting. Such blocks are called **sacrificial anodes**.

Underground pipelines are also protected using sacrificial anodes. In this case, sacks containing lumps of magnesium are attached at intervals along the pipe. The very reactive magnesium corrodes in preference to the iron. The electrons produced as the magnesium forms its ions prevent the ionisation of the iron.

Figure 17.20 *Galvanised iron doesn't rust even in constant contact with air and water.*

Figure 17.21 *A sacrificial anode attached to a boat.*

End of Chapter Checklist

You should now be able to:

✓ understand that the method of extraction of a metal, and how long it has been in use, are related to its position in the reactivity series

✓ describe and explain (including electrode equations) the extraction of aluminium from purified aluminium oxide

✓ describe and explain (including equations) the extraction of iron from iron oxide

✓ give uses for aluminium and iron, and relate those uses to the properties of the metal

✓ state the conditions necessary for iron to rust, and explain the various ways of preventing rusting.

Questions

1 Sodium is the sixth most abundant element in the Earth's crust, occurring in large quantities as common salt, NaCl, and yet sodium metal wasn't first produced until the early nineteenth century.

   a) From your knowledge of the position of sodium in the reactivity series, suggest a method for manufacturing sodium from sodium chloride. You aren't expected to give details of the manufacturing process, but should describe and explain (including equation/s where relevant) how sodium is formed in your process.

   b) Explain why sodium wasn't produced until the early nineteenth century.

   c) Suggest three other metals which might have been first isolated from their compounds at the same sort of time.

   d) What is bronze? Why has bronze been known for thousands of years?

2 a) Name the ore from which aluminium is extracted.

   b) Aluminium is manufactured using electrolysis. Carbon electrodes are used. Describe the nature of the electrolyte.

   c) At which electrode is the aluminium produced?

   d) Write the electrode equation for the formation of the aluminium. Is this an example of oxidation or reduction?

   e) Oxygen gas is formed at the other electrode. Explain why that causes a problem.

   f) Aluminium alloys are used in aircraft construction.

   (i) What property of aluminium makes it particularly suitable for this purpose?

   (ii) Why are aluminium alloys used in preference to pure aluminium?

3 The following reactions take place in a blast furnace:

   A: $C(s) + O_2(g) \rightarrow CO_2(g)$ $\qquad \Delta H = -394 \, kJ \, mol^{-1}$
   B: $CO_2(g) + C(s) \rightarrow 2CO(g)$ $\qquad \Delta H = +172 \, kJ \, mol^{-1}$
   C: $Fe_2O_3(s) + 3CO(g) \rightarrow 2Fe(l) + 3CO_2(g)$ $\quad \Delta H = -4 \, kJ \, mol^{-1}$
   D: $CaCO_3(s) \rightarrow CaO(s) + CO_2(g)$ $\qquad \Delta H = +178 \, kJ \, mol^{-1}$

   a) Which one of these reactions provides the heat to maintain the temperature of the furnace?

   b) What materials are put into the furnace to provide sources of **(i)** carbon, **(ii)** oxygen, **(iii)** iron(III) oxide, **(iv)** calcium carbonate?

   c) The calcium oxide produced in reaction D takes part in the formation of slag. Write an equation for the formation of the slag.

   d) Some iron is also produced by reaction between iron(III) oxide and carbon. Balance the following equation:

   $Fe_2O_3(s) + C(s) \rightarrow Fe(l) + CO(g)$

4 a) Cast iron or pig iron from the bottom of the blast furnace contains an important impurity which limits its usefulness.

   (i) What is the impurity, and approximately what percentage of the cast iron does it make up?

   (ii) What effect does this impurity have on the properties of cast iron that limits its usefulness?

   b) Describe the composition of stainless steel, and explain why it resists corrosion. State one use for stainless steel.

   c) Car bodies used to be made from mild steel, which was then painted. In more recent cars, the mild steel is galvanised before it is painted.

   (i) What is meant by *galvanised steel*?

   (ii) Describe and explain the effect that galvanised steel has on the life of the car.

You may need to refer to the Periodic Table on page 226.

1. Iron is produced in a blast furnace by the reduction of its ore, haematite (Fe_2O_3).

   a) What do you understand by the term 'reduction'? *(1 mark)*

   b) Give the proper chemical name for haematite. *(1 mark)*

   c) The main heat source in the furnace is provided by burning coke in air.

   $$C(s) + O_2(g) \rightarrow CO_2(g)$$

   What name is given to a reaction which produces heat? *(1 mark)*

   d) The main reducing agent in the furnace is carbon monoxide. Write an equation to show its formation. *(1 mark)*

   e) Balance the equation: $Fe_2O_3(s) + CO(g) \rightarrow Fe(l) + CO_2(g)$ *(1 mark)*

   f) Limestone is added to the furnace to help in the removal of impurities in the ore, such as silicon dioxide (SiO_2). Explain the chemistry of this. *(3 marks)*

   g) The impure iron from the blast furnace can be used to make cast iron, but most is converted into various steels.

   (i) Give one use in each case for cast iron, mild steel, high-carbon steel and stainless steel. *(4 marks)*

   (ii) Give two effects of increasing the proportion of carbon mixed with the iron. *(2 marks)*

   Total 14 marks

2. *a)* Aluminium is manufactured by the electrolysis of aluminium oxide dissolved in molten cryolite.

   (i) Name the ore from which aluminium oxide is obtained. *(1 mark)*

   (ii) At which electrode is the aluminium produced? *(1 mark)*

   (iii) Oxygen is released at the other electrode. Explain why that creates a problem. *(2 marks)*

   (iv) Aluminium is the commonest metal in the Earth's crust, and yet it is relatively expensive because its extraction is expensive. Why is the extraction expensive? *(1 mark)*

   b) High-voltage overhead electricity cables are made of aluminium with a steel core, supported on galvanised steel pylons.

   (i) Aluminium is not such a good conductor of electricity as copper. Why is aluminium used for overhead power cables, instead of copper? *(1 mark)*

   (ii) Iron is a less good conductor of electricity than aluminium. Why are the cables constructed with a steel core? *(1 mark)*

   (iii) Suggest two reasons why the pylons are made of steel, rather than aluminium. *(2 marks)*

   (iv) What is 'galvanised' iron? *(1 mark)*

   (v) Explain how galvanising iron helps to prevent it from rusting. *(2 marks)*

   Total 12 marks

3. Zinc occurs naturally as sphalerite (zinc blende), ZnS.

   In the extraction of zinc, the zinc sulfide is first heated strongly in air to produce zinc oxide.

   $$2ZnS(s) + 3O_2(g) \rightarrow 2ZnO(s) + 2SO_2(g)$$

   The zinc oxide can be reduced to zinc in two ways. In the first method, it is heated with carbon in a blast furnace at a temperature in excess of 1000 °C. Zinc boils at 907 °C, and so is produced as a vapour that can be condensed. In the second method, the zinc oxide is converted into zinc sulfate solution, which is then electrolysed.

   a) Suggest a use for the sulfur dioxide produced during the formation of the zinc oxide. *(1 mark)*

   b) Carbon reduction of the zinc oxide produces zinc and carbon monoxide. Write the equation for the reaction. *(1 mark)*

   c) What would you add to zinc oxide to produce a solution of zinc sulfate? Write an equation for the reaction involved. *(2 marks)*

   d) At which electrode would the zinc be formed during the electrolytic extraction? Write the equation for the reaction occurring at that electrode. *(2 marks)*

   Total 6 marks

4. Underground salt deposits are an essential raw material in the chemical industry. The salt is extracted by solution mining, and the salt solution is electrolysed to produce three important chemicals.

   a) Name the three chemicals produced by the electrolysis of salt solution, and give a use for each of them. *(6 marks)*

   b) Which of the three is produced at the anode during the electrolysis? Write the equation for the reaction occurring at the anode. *(2 marks)*

   Total 8 marks

5. Ammonia is manufactured from hydrogen and nitrogen in the Haber process. The nitrogen and hydrogen are passed through a reaction vessel containing a catalyst. About 15% of the mixture is converted into ammonia gas. The ammonia is then separated from the unused nitrogen and hydrogen, which are recycled through the process.

   $$N_2(g) + 3H_2(g) \rightleftharpoons 2NH_3(g) \qquad \Delta H = -92\,kJ\,mol^{-1}$$

   a) State the source of: (i) the nitrogen, (ii) the hydrogen. *(2 marks)* *b)* Explain the meaning of the symbol ⇌ in the equation.

(1 mark)

c) State what a negative value for ΔH shows. *(1 mark)*

d) Name the catalyst for the reaction. *(1 mark)*

e) State: (i) the temperature, (ii) the pressure used in the process. *(2 marks)*

f) How is the ammonia separated from the unreacted nitrogen and hydrogen? *(1 mark)*

g) Give two uses for ammonia. *(2 marks)*

Total 10 marks

6. Sulfuric acid can be manufactured from sulfur using the sequence:
sulfur → sulfur dioxide → sulfur trioxide → sulfuric acid.

a) How is the sulfur converted into sulfur dioxide? *(1 mark)*

b) The key reaction in the overall process is the conversion of sulfur dioxide into sulfur trioxide. The equation for the reaction is:

$$2SO_2(g) + O_2(g) \rightleftharpoons 2SO_3(g) \qquad \Delta H = -196\,kJ\,mol^{-1}$$

(i) Name the catalyst for the reaction. *(1 mark)*

(ii) Use Le Chatelier's principle to explain whether the percentage yield of sulfur trioxide would be greater at a high or a low temperature. *(2 marks)*

(iii) The temperature used for the reaction is 450 °C. Explain the choice of this reaction temperature. *(2 marks)*

(iv) According to Le Chatelier, the yield of sulfur trioxide would be increased if you used a high pressure. In fact, the process is carried out at low pressures of about 1–2 atmospheres. Explain the reason for that choice. *(2 marks)*

c) Write two equations to show how the sulfur trioxide is converted into concentrated sulfuric acid. *(2 marks)*

d) State two large-scale uses for sulfuric acid. *(2 marks)*

Total 12 marks

Chapter 18: Introducing Organic Chemistry

When you start doing organic chemistry, you are suddenly faced with a whole lot of new compounds with strange names and unfamiliar ways of drawing them. It can be quite scary!

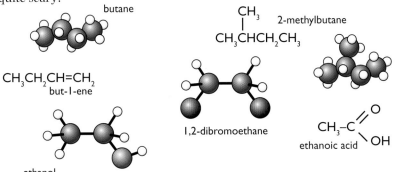

Figure 18.1 *Organic chemistry involves a lot of new compounds.*

There are literally millions of different organic compounds. They all contain carbon, and almost all contain hydrogen. Atoms such as oxygen or nitrogen or chlorine crop up quite commonly as well. This chapter introduces you to some of the important ideas that you need before you can start to make sense of organic chemistry.

The secret at the beginning is to spend a lot of time playing around with the subject – coding and decoding names, drawing structures and, above all, making models. If you are fortunate, your school will have models you can use. If you aren't so lucky, make your own out of children's modelling clay and matchsticks or small nails to use as bonds.

There is no point in going on to look at any detailed chemistry of the various compounds until you are confident that you can understand the names and how to draw the molecules on paper.

Types of formula for organic molecules

Molecular formulae

A molecular formula simply counts the numbers of each sort of atom present in the molecule, but tells you nothing about the way they are joined together. For example, the molecular formula of propane is C_3H_8, and the molecular formula of ethene is C_2H_4.

Molecular formulae are used very rarely in organic chemistry, because they don't give any useful information about the bonding in the molecule. You might use them in equations for the combustion of simple hydrocarbons where the structure of the molecule doesn't matter. For example:

$$C_3H_8(g) + 5O_2(g) \rightarrow 3CO_2(g) + 4H_2O(l)$$

In almost all other cases, you use a structural formula.

Structural formulae

A structural formula shows how the atoms are joined up. There are two ways of representing structural formulae – they can be drawn as a displayed formula, or they can be written out as, for example, $CH_3CH_2CH_3$. You need to be confident about doing it either way.

A structural formula such as $CH_3CH_2CH_3$ shows exactly how the molecule is joined up. A molecular formula, C_3H_8, doesn't give you the same sort of useful information about the molecule.

Displayed formulae

A displayed formula (sometimes called a fully displayed formula) shows all the bonds in the molecule as individual lines. You need to remember that each line represents a pair of shared electrons.

The diagram shows a model of butane, together with its displayed formula. Notice that the way the displayed formula is drawn bears no resemblance to the shape of the actual molecule. Displayed formulae are always drawn with the molecule straightened out and flattened. They do, however, show exactly how all the atoms are joined together.

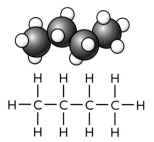

Figure 18.2 *Butane*

> If you are asked to draw the structure for a molecule in a GCSE exam, always draw it in the fully displayed form. You can't lose any marks by doing this, whereas you might if you use the simplified form. If, on the other hand, you are just writing a structure in an equation, for example, you can use whichever version you prefer.

The normal way to draw a structural formula

For anything other than the smallest molecules, drawing a fully displayed formula is very time-consuming. You can simplify the formula by writing, for example, CH_3 or CH_2 instead of showing all the carbon–hydrogen bonds.

Butane could be written quite quickly as $CH_3CH_2CH_2CH_3$ – and this shows all the necessary detail. But you have to be very careful. For example, all the structures in Figure 18.3 represent butane, even though they look different:

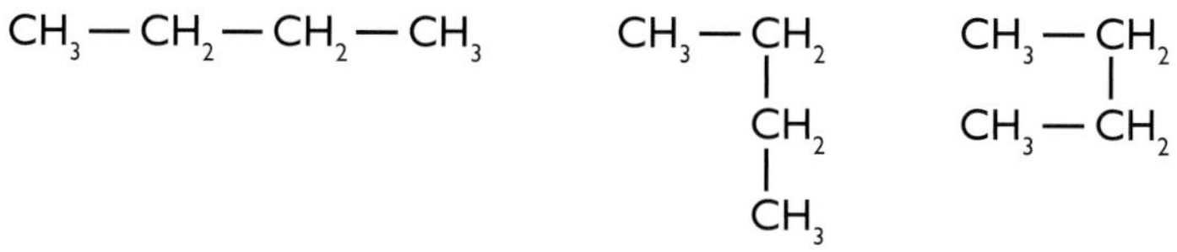

Figure 18.3 *All three structures represent butane.*

> The best way to understand this is to make some models. If you don't have access to atomic models, use blobs of modelling clay joined together with bits of matchstick or small nails to represent the bonds. You will find that you can change the shape of the model by rotating the bonds. That's what happens in real molecules.

Each structure shows four carbon atoms joined up in a chain, but the chain has simply twisted. This happens in real molecules as well.

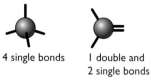

Figure 18.4 *All three molecules represent butane.*

Not one of the structural formulae accurately represents the shape of butane. The convention is to write it with all the carbon atoms in a straight line.

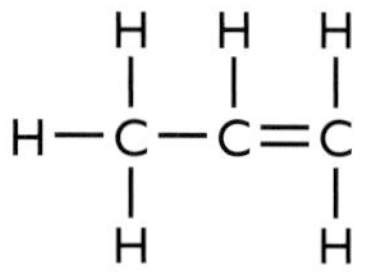

A molecule like propene, C_3H_6, has a carbon–carbon double bond. That is shown by drawing two lines between the carbon atoms to show the two pairs of shared electrons. You would normally write this in a simplified structural formula as $CH_3CH=CH_2$.

Making your own models

Make sure you have the bonds (the matchsticks or nails) pointing in the right directions. If there are four single bonds around a carbon atom, they are arranged as shown in Figure 18.6. If you tip the model over so that it is standing on three different 'legs', it should still look exactly the same.

If you have two single bonds and a double bond around a carbon atom, the arrangement in space is different. All the bonds lie in the same plane.

Figure 18.5 *Propene.*

4 single bonds   **1 double and 2 single bonds**

Figure 18.6 *Arrangement of bonds.*

Naming organic compounds

Names for organic compounds can appear quite complicated, but they are no more than a code that describes the molecule. Each part of a name tells you something specific about the molecule. One part of a name tells you how many carbon atoms there are in the longest chain, another part tells you whether there are any carbon–carbon double bonds, and so on.

Coding the chain length

Look for the code letters in the name – these are given in Table18.1.

Code letters	Number of carbons in chain
meth	1
eth	2
prop	3
but	4
pent	5

Table 18.1: *Coding the chain length.*

You have to learn these! The first four are the tricky ones because there isn't any pattern. 'pent' means five (as in **pent**agon), and following on from this are other logical ones. A six-carbon chain, for example, is coded as 'hex', meaning six (as in **hex**agon).

For example, **but**ane has a chain of four carbon atoms. **Prop**ane has a chain of three carbon atoms.

Coding for the type of compound

Alkanes

Alkanes are a family of similar hydrocarbons (compounds of carbon and hydrogen only) in which all the carbons are joined to each other with single covalent bonds. Compounds like this are coded with the ending '**ane**'. For example, eth**ane** is a two-carbon chain (because of 'eth') with a carbon–carbon single bond, CH_3CH_3.

Alkenes

Alkenes are a family of hydrocarbons which contain a carbon–carbon double bond. This is shown in their name by the ending '**ene**'. For example, eth**ene** is a two-carbon chain containing a carbon–carbon double bond, $CH_2=CH_2$. With longer chains, the position of the double bond could vary in the chain. This is shown by numbering the chain and noting which carbon atom the double bond *starts* from.

In more complicated molecules, the presence of the code '**an**' in the name again shows that the carbons are joined by single bonds. For example, you can tell that propan-1-ol contains three carbon atoms ('prop') joined together by carbon–carbon single bonds ('an'). The coding on the end gives you more information about the molecule. You will meet this later in the chapter.

Formula	Name	Description
$CH_2=CHCH_2CH_3$	but-1-ene	a four-carbon chain with a double bond starting on the first carbon
$CH_3CH=CHCH_3$	but-2-ene	a four-carbon chain with a double bond starting on the second carbon

Table 18.2: *Indicating the position of the double bond.*

How do you know which end of the chain to number from? The rule is that you number from the end which produces the smaller numbers in the name.

Don't worry too much about this. It isn't a big issue at GCSE, but it does arise from time to time later on in this chapter.

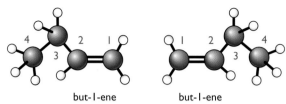

but-1-ene   but-1-ene

Figure 18.7 *But-1-ene.*

Both parts of Figure 18.7 show the same molecule, but in one case it has been flipped over so that what was originally on the left is now on the right, and *vice versa*. It would be silly to change the name every time the molecule moved! Both of them are called but-1-ene.

Coding for branched chains

Hydrocarbon chains can have side branches on them. You are only likely to come across two small side chains, shown in Table 18.3.

Side chain	Coded
CH_3-	methyl
CH_3CH_2-	ethyl

Table 18.3: *Coding for branched chains.*

The name of a molecule is always based on the longest chain you can find in it. The position of the side chain is shown by numbering, exactly as before.

The longest chain in the molecule in Figure 18.8 has four carbon atoms ('**but**') with no double bonds ('**ane**'). The name is based on butane. There is a **methyl** group branching off the **number 2** carbon. (Remember to number from the end that produces the smaller number.) The compound is called 2-methylbutane.

Where there is more than one side chain, you describe the position of each of them.

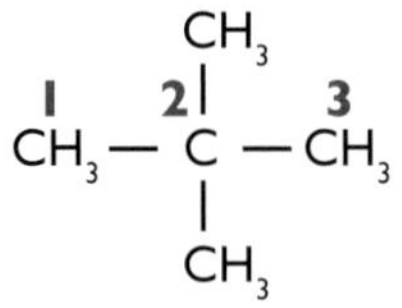

The longest chain in the molecule in Figure 18.9 has three carbon atoms and no double bonds. Therefore the name is based on propane.

There are two methyl groups attached to the second carbon. The compound is 2,2-dimethylpropane. The 'di' in the name shows the presence of the two methyl groups. '2,2-' shows that they are both on the second carbon atom.

You can reverse this process and draw a structural formula from a name. All you have to do is decode the name.

For example, what is the structural formula for **2,3-dimethylbut-2-ene**?

Start by looking for the code for the longest chain length. '**but**' shows a four-carbon chain. '**ene**' shows that it contains a carbon–carbon double bond starting on the second carbon atom ('**-2-ene**'). There are two methyl groups ('**dimethyl**') attached to the second and third carbon atom in the chain ('**2,3-**'). All you have to do now is to fit all this together into a structure.

Start by drawing the structure without any hydrogen atoms on the main chain. It doesn't matter whether you draw the CH_3 groups pointing up or down. Then add enough hydrogens so that each carbon atom is forming four bonds. Figure 18.10 shows how your thinking would work.

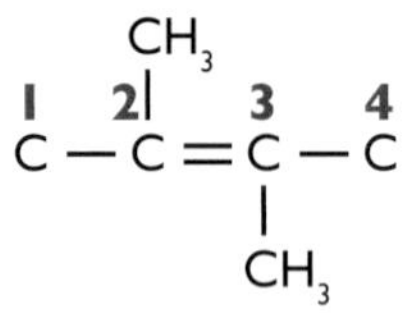

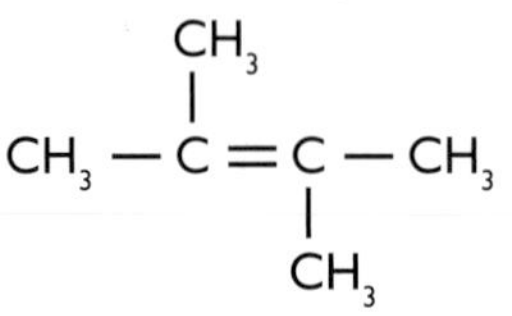

Notice that the count of the number of carbons in the side chain is coded exactly as before. 'meth' shows a one-carbon side chain. 'eth' shows two carbons. The 'yl' shows that the group is attached to something else.

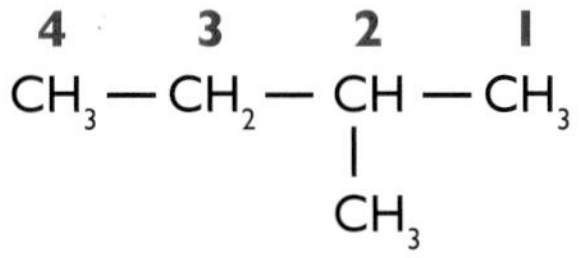

$$\overset{4}{CH_3} - \overset{3}{CH_2} - \overset{2}{CH} - \overset{1}{CH_3}$$
$$|$$
$$CH_3$$

Figure 18.8 *Number from the end that produces the smaller number.*

$$\begin{array}{c} CH_3 \\ | \\ \overset{1}{CH_3} - \overset{2}{C} - \overset{3}{CH_3} \\ | \\ CH_3 \end{array}$$

Figure 18.9 *Describe the position of each side chain.*

It is much more important to be able to decode names to give structures than the other way around. If you don't know what a teacher or an examiner is talking about, you are completely lost!

$$\begin{array}{c} CH_3 \\ | \\ \overset{1}{C} - \overset{2}{C} = \overset{3}{C} - \overset{4}{C} \\ | \\ CH_3 \end{array}$$

$$\begin{array}{c} CH_3 \\ | \\ CH_3 - C = C - CH_3 \\ | \\ CH_3 \end{array}$$

Figure 18.10 *First draw the structure, then add hydrogens.*

Structural isomerism

Structural isomers are molecules with the same molecular formula, but with different structural formulae. Examples will make this clear.

Structural isomerism in the alkanes

Isomers of butane, C_4H_{10}

If you had some atomic models and picked out four carbon atoms and 10 hydrogen atoms, you would find it was possible to fit them together in more than one way. The two different molecules formed are known as **isomers**. Both have the molecular formula C_4H_{10}, but they have different structures. **Structural isomerism** is the existence of two or more different structures with the same molecular formula.

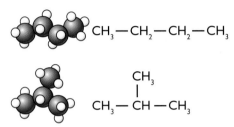

Figure 18.11 *Structural isomers.*

If you look carefully at the models in Figure 18.11, you can see that you couldn't change one into the other just by bending or twisting the molecule. You would have to take the model to pieces and rebuild it. That's a simple way of telling that you have isomers.

The 'straight chain' isomer is called butane. The branched chain has a three-carbon chain with no carbon–carbon double bond ('propane'), with a methyl group on the second carbon. The name is 2-methylpropane.

Isomers of pentane, C_5H_{12}

There are three isomers of pentane, shown in Figure 18.12.

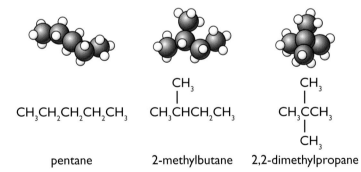

Figure 18.12 *The three isomers of pentane.*

Students frequently think they can find another isomer as well. If you look closely at this 'fourth' isomer (Figure 18.13), you will see that it is just 2-methylbutane rotated in space.

To avoid this sort of problem, always draw your isomers so that the longest carbon chain is drawn horizontally. Check each isomer after you have drawn it, to be sure you have done that.

A 'straight chain' is an unbranched chain.

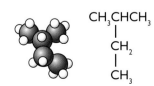

Figure 18.13 *There is no fourth isomer of pentane.*

Structural isomerism in the alkenes

Ethene and propene

Ethene, $CH_2=CH_2$, doesn't have any isomers. Propene, $CH_3CH=CH_2$, doesn't have a structural isomer that is still an alkene. (If you are interested, you can find a structural isomer of C_3H_6 that doesn't have a carbon–carbon double bond by joining the carbon atoms in a ring. It is called cyclopropane – which says 'a ring of three carbons with only single bonds between them'.)

You aren't going to be asked to name or draw cyclopropane in a GCSE exam, but it is interesting to see why it is called what it is!

Butene, C_4H_8

Butene has three structural isomers containing a carbon–carbon double bond.

If you aren't comfortable with the names, see pages 151–152 on organic names.

$$CH_3CH_2CH=CH_2 \qquad CH_3CH=CHCH_3 \qquad \underset{\underset{CH_3}{|}}{CH_3C}=CH_2$$

but-1-ene   but-2-ene   2-methylpropene

Figure 18.14 *The three structural isomers of butene.*

Notice the way that you can vary the position of the double bond as well as branching the chain.

A quick introductory look at the alcohols

Alcohols all contain an –OH group attached to a hydrocarbon chain. This is coded for in the name by the ending '-ol'.

Figure 18.15 shows four small alcohols.

Ethanol is what is commonly known just as 'alcohol'.

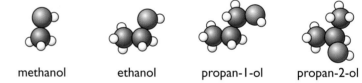

methanol   ethanol   propan-1-ol   propan-2-ol

Figure 18.15 *Four small alcohols.*

Notice the way the names work. Notice that they all end with '-ol', showing the –OH group. Notice the way the number of carbons in the chain is counted exactly as before with 'meth', 'eth' and 'prop'.

And notice the possibility of structural isomerism in the two different propanols. The –OH group can be attached to the end of the chain (in propan-1-ol) or to the second carbon in the chain (as in propan-2-ol). These are structural isomers because there is no way that you can bend or twist one of the molecules to make the other. A model would have to be taken to pieces to get from one to the other.

End of Chapter Checklist

You should now be able to:

✓ understand the difference between a molecular and a structural formula for an organic compound

✓ draw fully displayed structural formulae for simple compounds

✓ know that displayed formulae are often simplified by not showing all the bonds in groups such as CH_3 and CH_2

✓ know that organic names are just coded descriptions of the molecules

✓ use their names to draw structures for simple hydrocarbons containing either single or double carbon–carbon bonds limited to up to five (alkanes) or four (alkenes) carbon atoms

✓ work out the names of a similar range of compounds, given their structures

✓ recognise the presence of an –OH group in an alcohol by the ending '-ol' in its name

✓ understand what is meant by structural isomerism

✓ draw the structures of isomers in simple cases (molecules no bigger than those in this chapter).

Questions

Note: the questions below deliberately include some examples which are slightly beyond the level which you would expect to meet in a GCSE exam. None of them are difficult, though, if you have read the chapter.

1 a) Write down the names of the following hydrocarbons:

    (i) CH_4

    (ii) $CH_3CH_2CH_3$

    (iii) $CH_3CH_2CH_2CH_2CH_3$

    (iv) $CH_3CH=CH_2$

    (v) $CH_2=CH_2$

    (vi) $CH_2=CHCH_2CH_3$

b) Draw fully displayed formulae (showing all the bonds) for:

    (i)   butane

    (ii) ethane

    (iii) but-2-ene

    (iv) propane

    (v) methanol

    (vi) 2-methylpropane

    (vii) 2-methylpropene

    (viii) pent-1-ene

2 a) What do you understand by the term *structural isomerism*?

b) There are two structural isomers of C_4H_{10}. Draw their structures and name them.

c) There are five structural isomers of C_6H_{14}. Draw their structures and name them. (A six-carbon chain is coded as 'hex'.)

d) How many structural isomers can you find with a molecular formula C_4H_8? You don't need to restrict yourself to compounds with carbon–carbon double bonds. Draw their structures and name as many as you can.

3 a) Draw the structures for the following structural isomers of C_4H_9OH. (Note: this is beyond anything you will be asked to do at GCSE. The answer to the first one is shown to give you hints as to how to work out the others.)

    (i)   butan-1-ol (Answer: $CH_3CH_2CH_2CH_2OH$)

    (ii) butan-2-ol

    (iii) 2-methylpropan-1-ol

    (iv) 2-methylpropan-2-ol

b) (This question is even further beyond GCSE!) How many structural isomers of $C_5H_{11}OH$ can you find? Draw their structures, making sure that you always draw them with the longest carbon chain horizontal to avoid duplicate ones. Name as many as you can.

c) Can you find one or more structural isomers with the same molecular formula ($C_5H_{12}O$) which don't contain an –OH group? You won't be able to name any of these. Feel very pleased with yourself if you manage to find some!

Chapter 19: Alkanes, Alkenes and Alcohols

> *This chapter introduces three families of organic compounds, known technically as* **homologous series**. *It is assumed that you have already read Chapter 18 (Introducing Organic Chemistry).*

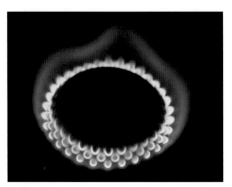

Figure 19.1 *The small alkanes are gases and are burnt as fuels.*

The alkanes

The alkanes are a family of simple **hydrocarbons**. Hydrocarbons are compounds that contain carbon and hydrogen only. The carbon atoms are joined only by carbon–carbon single bonds. Alkanes are described as **saturated** hydrocarbons in the sense that they contain the maximum possible number of hydrogen atoms for a given number of carbons.

The three smallest alkanes are shown in Figure 19.2.

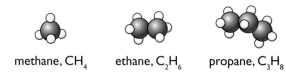

methane, CH_4 ethane, C_2H_6 propane, C_3H_8

Figure 19.2 *The three smallest alkanes.*

Methane is the major component of natural gas. Ethane and propane are also present in small quantities in natural gas, and are important constituents of the petroleum gases from crude oil distillation (discussed in Chapter 20).

Homologous series

A homologous series is a family of compounds with similar properties because they have similar bonding. The alkanes are the simplest homologous series.

Members of a homologous series have a general formula

In the case of the alkanes, if there are n carbons, there are $2n + 2$ hydrogens.

The general formula for the alkanes is C_nH_{2n+2}.

So, for example, if there are three carbons, there are $(2 \times 3) + 2 = 8$ hydrogens. The formula for propane is C_3H_8.

If you wanted the formula for an alkane with 15 carbons, you could easily work out that it was $C_{15}H_{32}$ – and so on.

Members of a homologous series have trends in physical properties

Figure 19.3 shows the boiling points of the first eight alkanes.

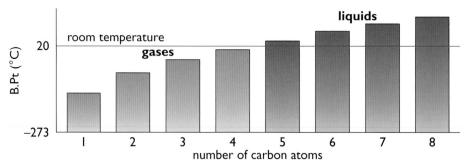

Figure 19.3 *Boiling points of the first eight alkanes.*

Notice that the first four alkanes are gases at room temperature. All the other ones you are likely to come across at GCSE are liquids. Solids start to appear at about $C_{17}H_{36}$.

The molecules of the members of a homologous series increase in size in a regular way. There is always a difference of CH_2 between one member and the next.

As the molecules get bigger, the intermolecular forces between them increase. This means that more energy has to be put in to break the attractions between one molecule and its neighbours. One effect of this is that the boiling points increase in a regular way.

Intermolecular forces are explained in Chapter 3, page 21.

Members of a homologous series have similar chemical properties

Chemical properties are dependent on bonding. Because alkanes only contain carbon–carbon single bonds and carbon–hydrogen bonds, they are all going to behave in the same way. These are strong bonds, and the alkanes don't have a lot of chemical reactions.

Two simple reactions of the alkanes

Combustion

All alkanes burn in air or oxygen. If there is enough oxygen, they burn completely to give carbon dioxide and water. For example:

$$CH_4(g) + 2O_2(g) \rightarrow CO_2(g) + 2H_2O(l)$$

$$2C_2H_6(g) + 7O_2(g) \rightarrow 4CO_2(g) + 6H_2O(l)$$

Don't try to learn these equations! Practise working them out for a wide range of different hydrocarbons. You will find guidance on how to work out the ethane equation in Chapter 5, page 38.

If there isn't enough oxygen, there is ***incomplete combustion*** of the hydrocarbon, and you get carbon monoxide or carbon (soot) produced instead of carbon dioxide.

The formation of carbon monoxide from the incomplete combustion of hydrocarbons is very dangerous. Carbon monoxide is colourless and odourless, and is very poisonous.

Carbon monoxide is poisonous because it combines with ***haemoglobin*** (the molecule that carries oxygen in the blood stream), preventing it from carrying the oxygen. You are made ill, or even die, because not enough oxygen gets to the cells in your body.

Reaction with bromine

Alkanes react with bromine in the presence of ultra-violet light (for example, from sunlight). A hydrogen atom in the alkane is replaced by a bromine atom. This is known as a ***substitution reaction***, because one atom has been substituted by a different one.

A mixture of methane and bromine gas is brown because of the presence of the bromine. If it is exposed to sunlight, it loses its colour, and a mixture of bromomethane and hydrogen bromide gases is formed.

$$CH_4(g) + Br_2(g) \rightarrow CH_3Br(g) + HBr(g)$$

An exactly similar reaction happens between methane and chlorine exposed to UV light. In that case, you would get a mixture of chloromethane and hydrogen chloride gases.

Figure 19.4 *As well as all the other poisonous or cancer-causing compounds, cigarette smoke contains carbon monoxide due to incomplete combustion.*

You don't need it for GCSE purposes, but this reaction actually goes on to substitute more of the hydrogens in the methane. What you end up with is a mixture of CH_3Br, CH_2Br_2, $CHBr_3$ and CBr_4 – and HBr, of course. You will find out more about this if you go on to do chemistry at a more advanced level.

You will also find information on alkenes in Chapter 20 (dealing with their production in the oil industry) and Chapter 21 (dealing with the formation of polymers such as polythene).

The alkenes

The alkenes are another family (homologous series) of hydrocarbons. They all contain a carbon–carbon double bond. Alkenes are **unsaturated** hydrocarbons. The presence of the double bond means that they don't contain as many hydrogen atoms as the corresponding alkane.

The general formula

Alkenes have a general formula C_nH_{2n}. There isn't an alkene with just one carbon atom. The two smallest alkenes are ethene and propene.

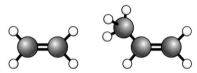

Figure 19.5 *Ethene (left) and propene (right).*

Physical properties

These are very similar to the alkanes. Remember that the small alkanes with up to four carbon atoms are gases. The same is true for the alkenes. They are gases up to C_4H_8, and the next dozen or so are liquids.

Chemical reactions of the alkenes

This isn't a reaction anybody would ever choose to do. Alkenes are much too useful to waste by burning them.

In common with all hydrocarbons, alkenes burn in air or oxygen to give carbon dioxide and water. For example:

$$C_2H_4(g) + 3O_2(g) \rightarrow 2CO_2(g) + 2H_2O(l)$$

The addition of bromine

More importantly, alkenes undergo **addition reactions**. Part of the double bond breaks and the electrons are used to join other atoms onto the two carbon atoms.

Bromine adds to alkenes without any need for heat or a catalyst. The reaction is often carried out using bromine solution ('bromine water'), as for example in Figure 19.6, with ethene.

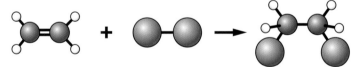

Figure 19.6 *An addition reaction: an alkene plus bromine.*

Decode the name, and make sure you can see how it works. 'eth' shows a two-carbon chain. 'ane' shows only carbon–carbon single bonds. The beginning of the name, '1,2-dibromo', shows two bromine atoms attached to the first and second carbon atoms.

The product is called 1,2-dibromoethane, and is a colourless liquid.

You can write this as an equation in two ways. The first is very close to the way the reaction is shown using the models (Figure 19.7).

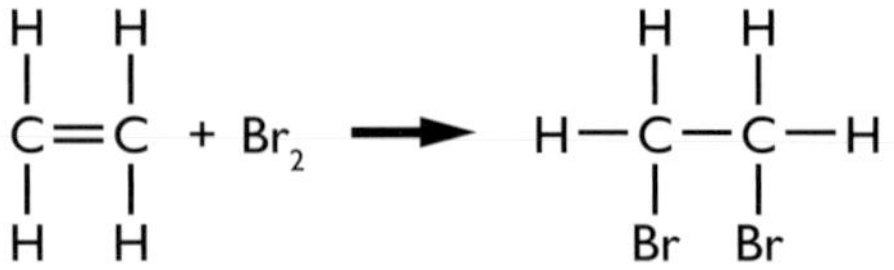

$$
\begin{array}{cccc}
\text{H} & \text{H} & & \text{H} \quad \text{H} \\
| & | & & | \quad\quad | \\
\text{C}=\text{C} & + \text{Br}_2 & \longrightarrow & \text{H}-\text{C}-\text{C}-\text{H} \\
| & | & & | \quad\quad | \\
\text{H} & \text{H} & & \text{Br} \quad \text{Br}
\end{array}
$$

Figure 19.7 *The equation using displayed formulae.*

The other method takes up rather less space:

$$CH_2=CH_2(g) + Br_2(aq) \rightarrow CH_2BrCH_2Br(l)$$

Any compound with a carbon–carbon double bond will react with bromine in a similar way. This is used to **test for a carbon–carbon double bond**.

If you shake an unknown organic compound with bromine water and the orange bromine water is decolorised, the compound contains a carbon–carbon double bond. If your unknown compound is a gas, you can simply bubble it through bromine water with the same effect.

The left-hand tube in Figure 19.8 shows the effect of shaking a liquid alkene with bromine water. The organic layer is on top. You can see that the bromine water has been completely decolorised – showing the presence of the carbon–carbon double bond.

The right-hand tube in Figure 19.8 shows what happens if you use a liquid alkane – which doesn't have a carbon–carbon double bond. The colour of the bromine is still there. Interestingly, most of the colour is now in the top organic layer. That is because the covalent bromine is more soluble in the organic compound than it is in water.

Alcohols

What everybody knows as 'alcohol' is just one member of a large family (homologous series) of similar compounds. Alcohols all contain an –OH group covalently bonded onto a carbon chain.

The familiar alcohol in drinks is C_2H_5OH (or, better, showing the structure, CH_3CH_2OH), and should properly be called **ethanol**.

The production of ethanol

Making ethanol by fermentation

Yeast is added to a sugar or starch solution and left in the warm (say, 30–40 °C) for several days in the absence of air (**anaerobic** conditions). **Enzymes** (biological catalysts) in the yeast convert the sugar into ethanol and carbon dioxide. The process is known as **fermentation**.

The biochemistry is very complicated. Assuming you are starting from ordinary sugar (sucrose), the sucrose is split into two smaller sugars, glucose and fructose. Glucose and fructose have the same molecular formulae, but different structures. They are isomers.

Enzymes in the yeast convert these sugars into ethanol and water in a multitude of small steps. All we normally write are the overall equations for the reactions.

$$C_{12}H_{22}O_{11}(aq) + H_2O(l) \rightarrow C_6H_{12}O_6(aq) + C_6H_{12}O_6(aq)$$
sucrose　　　　　　　　　　　glucose　　　　　fructose

$$C_6H_{12}O_6(aq) \rightarrow 2C_2H_5OH(aq) + 2CO_2(g)$$

Be sure you can see how these formulae relate to the full structures in the equation above.

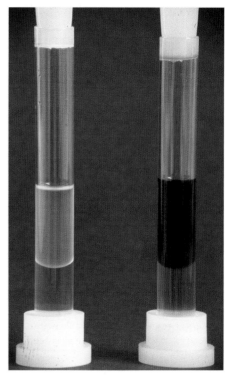

Figure 19.8 *The result of shaking a liquid alkene (left) or alkane (right) with bromine water.*

Figure 19.9 *Ethanol.*

Figure 19.10 *Sugar cane – one of the possible raw materials for making ethanol. Others include maize (called corn in the USA), wheat and other starchy materials.*

You will find a diagram and discussion for a lab-based fractional distillation of an ethanol/water mixture in Chapter 11, page 90.

The ethene comes from the oil industry. You can read about how it is made in Chapter 20, page 166.

Yeast is killed by more than about 15% of alcohol in the mixture, so it is impossible to make pure alcohol by fermentation. The alcohol is purified by fractional distillation. This takes advantage of the difference in boiling point between ethanol and water. Water boils at $100\,°C$ whereas ethanol boils at $78\,°C$.

The liquid distilling over at $78\,°C$ is 96% pure ethanol. The rest is water. It is impossible to remove this last 4% of water by simple distillation.

Making ethanol by the hydration of ethene

Ethanol is also made by reacting ethene with steam – a process known as **hydration**.

$$CH_2{=}CH_2(g) + H_2O(g) \rightarrow CH_3CH_2OH(g)$$

Starting materials: ethene and steam
Temperature: $300\,°C$
Pressure: 60–70 atmospheres
Catalyst: phosphoric acid

Only a small proportion of the ethene reacts. The ethanol produced is condensed as a liquid and the unreacted ethene is recycled through the process.

Comparing the two methods of producing ethanol

	Fermentation	Hydration of ethene
use of resources	uses renewable resources – sugar beet or sugar cane, corn and other starchy materials	uses finite resources – once all the oil has been used up there won't be any more
type of process	a batch process – everything is mixed together in a reaction vessel and then left for several days. That batch is then removed and a new reaction is set up – this is inefficient	a continuous flow process – a stream of reactants is constantly passed over the catalyst. This is more efficient than a batch process
rate of reaction	slow, taking several days for each batch	rapid
quality of product	produces very impure ethanol that needs further processing	produces much purer ethanol
reaction conditions	uses gentle temperatures and ordinary pressure	uses high temperatures and pressures, needing a high input of energy

Table 19.1: *Methods of producing ethanol*

At the moment, countries that have easy access to crude oil produce ethanol mainly from ethene, but one day the oil will run out. At that point, the production of ethanol from sugar and starch will provide an alternative route to many of the organic chemicals we need.

Some reactions of the alcohols

Alcohols burn

All alcohols burn to form carbon dioxide and water. For example, with ethanol:

$$C_2H_5OH(l) + 3O_2(g) \rightarrow 2CO_2(g) + 3H_2O(l)$$

Ethanol is a **biofuel** (a fuel made from biological sources, such as sugar cane or maize). Mixtures of petrol with ethanol are increasingly used in countries such as Brazil, which have little or no oil industry to produce their own petrol. On the other hand, they often have a climate which is good for growing sugar cane. Other countries are introducing biofuels such as ethanol to reduce dependence on fossil fuels such as oil and gas.

Dehydrating alcohols

Dehydration refers to the removal of water from a compound. The dehydration of ethanol produces ethene. Ethanol vapour is passed over hot aluminium oxide acting as a catalyst.

Figure 19.11 *Ethanol being used as a fuel in Brazil.*

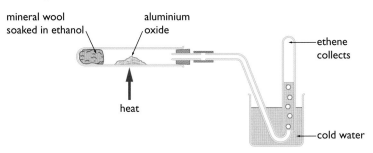

Figure 19.12 *Dehydration of ethanol to produce ethene.*

$$CH_3CH_2OH(g) \rightarrow CH_2=CH_2(g) + H_2O(l)$$

Notice that the –OH group is removed together with a hydrogen from the carbon atom next door.

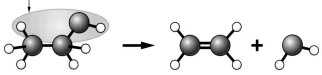

Figure 19.13 *Dehydration of ethanol – the –OH group and a hydrogen are removed.*

Other alcohols would dehydrate in a similar way. For example, the dehydration of propan-1-ol produces propene.

$$CH_3CH_2CH_2OH(g) \rightarrow CH_3CH=CH_2(g) + H_2O(l)$$

End of Chapter Checklist

You should now be able to:

✓ understand what is meant by a homologous series, and know the general formulae for alkanes and alkenes

✓ draw and name the alkanes (including isomers) with up to five carbon atoms (from Chapter 18)

✓ draw and name the alkenes (including isomers) with up to four carbon atoms (from Chapter 18)

✓ write equations for the complete combustion of alkanes

✓ understand what is meant by incomplete combustion, and explain why it is potentially dangerous

✓ know that alkenes undergo addition reactions with bromine, and that the reaction with bromine water is used to test for carbon–carbon double bonds

✓ describe the manufacture of ethanol by fermentation and by the hydration of ethene

✓ discuss the advantages and disadvantages of the two methods of manufacturing ethanol, including the availability of crude oil or suitable sources of sugar or starch

✓ describe the dehydration of ethanol to make ethene.

Questions

1 a) Alkanes are *saturated* hydrocarbons. What do you understand by the term saturated?

b) Undecane is an alkane with 11 carbon atoms.

(i) Write down the molecular formula for undecane.

(ii) What physical state (solid, liquid or gas) would you expect undecane to be in at room temperature?

(iii) Write an equation for the complete combustion of undecane.

2 A gaseous hydrocarbon, P, with three carbon atoms, decolorises bromine water.

a) What does the decolorisation of the bromine water test for?

b) Write the displayed formula for the hydrocarbon.

c) Write the equation for the reaction between the hydrocarbon and bromine, using fully displayed formulae for the hydrocarbon and the organic product.

d) The reaction between methane and bromine gas in the presence of UV light also causes the bromine to lose colour.

(i) Write an equation for this reaction.

(ii) This reaction is described as a substitution reaction, whereas the reaction between X and bromine is an addition reaction. Using the equations you have already written, explain the difference between addition and substitution.

3 a) State the conditions for the manufacture of ethanol by the hydration of ethene.

b) Give two advantages of this way of producing ethanol over the fermentation method.

c) Give two advantages of making ethanol by fermentation.

4 Ethene can be made from sucrose (sugar) in the lab using the following sequence:

sucrose → ethanol → ethene

Given about 25 g (a large spoonful) of sucrose, describe with the aid of diagrams how you would convert the sucrose into a few test tubes of ethene gas. You may use any apparatus commonly available in a student lab. In addition to your diagrams, you should name any other materials you need, and give any important conditions for the reactions involved.

5 During the first few years of the twenty-first century, there was serious worry about the effect of increasing carbon dioxide levels on global temperatures. One of the results of this was a drive to increase the amount of biofuels used (such as ethanol) in order to replace fuels based on oil or gas. By 2007–08, it became obvious that increased use of biofuels was having undesirable effects, such as increasing the world prices of some foods and, in some cases, even producing more carbon dioxide than they saved.

By doing an internet search (or otherwise), explain why the production of biofuels increased some world food prices and, in some cases, resulted in an increase in the amount of carbon dioxide in the atmosphere.

Section D: Organic Chemistry

Chapter 20: Useful Products from Crude Oil

Figure 20.1 *The oil industry is BIG business!*

The oil industry is at the very heart of modern life – providing fuels, plastics and the organic chemicals which go to make things as different as solvents, drugs, dyes and explosives. This chapter explores how an unappealing sticky black liquid is converted into useful things.

What is crude oil (petroleum)?

The origin of crude oil

Millions of years ago, plants and animals living in the sea died and fell to the bottom. Layers of sediment formed on top of them. Their shells and skeletons formed limestone. The soft tissue was gradually changed by high temperatures and pressures into crude oil. Crude oil is a **finite, non-renewable resource**. Once all the existing supplies have been used, they won't be replaced – or at least, not for many millions of years.

Crude oil contains hydrocarbons

Crude oil is a mixture of **hydrocarbons** – compounds containing carbon and hydrogen only. Hydrocarbons are **organic** molecules. The term 'organic' was originally used because it was believed that organic compounds could only come from living things. Now it is used for any carbon compound except for the very simplest (like carbon dioxide and the carbonates).

Hydrocarbons can exist as chains, branched chains, or rings of carbon atoms with hydrogens attached.

Figure 20.2 *This sticky black liquid underpins modern life.*

Hydrocarbons can occur as...

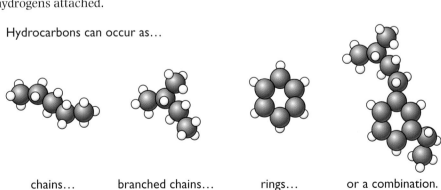

chains...   branched chains...   rings...   or a combination.

Figure 20.3 *Structures of hydrocarbons.*

How the properties of hydrocarbons change with molecule size

As the number of carbon atoms in the molecules increases, several properties of the compounds change in a regular pattern. Most of these changes are the result of increasing attractions between neighbouring molecules. As the molecules get bigger, these **intermolecular attractions** increase, and it gets more difficult to pull one molecule away from its neighbours.

As the molecules get bigger, the following changes occur.

- Boiling point increases – the larger the molecule, the higher the boiling point. This is because large molecules are attracted to each other more strongly than smaller ones. More heat is needed to break these stronger attractions to produce the widely separated molecules in the gas.

- The liquids become less volatile. The bigger the hydrocarbon, the more slowly it evaporates at room temperature. This is again because the bigger molecules are more strongly attracted to their neighbours and so don't turn to a gas so easily.

- The liquids flow less easily (they become more viscous). Liquids containing small hydrocarbon molecules are runny. Those containing large molecules are much stickier because of the greater attractions between their molecules.

- Bigger hydrocarbons do not burn as easily as smaller ones. This limits the use of the bigger ones as fuels.

Separating crude oil

Fractional distillation

Crude oil is heated and passed into a **fractionating column**, which is cooler at the top and hotter at the bottom. The crude oil is split into various **fractions**.

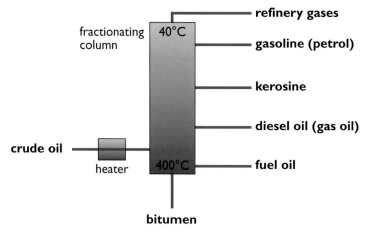

Figure 20.4 *Separation of crude oil.*

How far up the column a particular hydrocarbon gets depends on its boiling point. Suppose a hydrocarbon boils at 120 °C. At the bottom of the column, the temperature is much higher than 120 °C and so the hydrocarbon remains as a gas. As it travels up through the column, the temperature gets lower. When the temperature falls to 120 °C, that hydrocarbon will start to turn to a liquid. It condenses and can be tapped off.

Intermolecular attractions are explained in Chapter 3 (page 21).

We usually count a substance as being volatile if it turns to a vapour easily at room temperature. That means it will evaporate quickly at that temperature.

Warning! You will find a lot of disagreement, from various sources, about exactly what fractions are produced in this first distillation. Figure 20.4 matches the requirements of the Edexcel IGCSE specification (syllabus), but is a major simplification of what really goes on.

The hydrocarbons in the refinery gases have boiling points which are so low that the temperature of the column never falls low enough for them to condense to liquids.

The temperature of the column isn't hot enough to boil some of the large hydrocarbons found in the crude oil and they remain as a liquid, and are removed as a residue from the bottom of the column. **Bitumen**, which is used in road making, is made from this.

Uses of the fractions

All hydrocarbons burn in air (oxygen) to form carbon dioxide and water and release a lot of heat in the process. They can therefore be used as **fuels**.

For example, burning methane (the major constituent of natural gas):

$$CH_4(g) + 2O_2(g) \rightarrow CO_2(g) + 2H_2O(l)$$

. . . or burning octane (one of the hydrocarbons present in gasoline (petrol)):

$$2C_8H_{18}(l) + 25O_2(g) \rightarrow 16CO_2(g) + 18H_2O(l)$$

If there isn't enough air (or oxygen), you get **incomplete combustion**. This leads to the formation of carbon (soot) or carbon monoxide instead of carbon dioxide.

For example, if methane burns in a badly maintained gas appliance, there may not be enough oxygen available to produce carbon dioxide, and so you get dangerous carbon monoxide instead:

$$2CH_4(g) + 3O_2(g) \rightarrow 2CO(g) + 4H_2O(l)$$

Refinery gases

Refinery gases are a mixture of methane, ethane, propane and butane, which can be separated into individual gases if required. These gases are commonly used as LPG (liquefied petroleum gas) for domestic heating and cooking.

Gasoline (petrol)

As with all the other fractions, petrol is a mixture of hydrocarbons with similar boiling points. Its use is fairly obvious!

Kerosine

Kerosine is used as fuel for jet aircraft, as domestic heating oil and as 'paraffin' for small heaters and lamps.

Diesel oil (gas oil)

This is used for buses, lorries, some cars, and railway engines where the line hasn't been electrified. Some is also cracked to make other organic chemicals and produce more petrol.

Fuel oil

This is used for ships' boilers and for industrial heating.

> Don't try to learn these equations – there are too many possible hydrocarbons you could be asked about. Provided you know (or are told) the formula, they are easy to balance.

> The problem of incomplete combustion is described in more detail in Chapter 19, page 157.

Figure 20.5 *Kerosine is used as aviation fuel.*

Figure 20.6 *A train powered by diesel oil.*

Figure 20.7 *Ships' boilers burn fuel oil.*

Figure 20.8 *Bitumen is used in road construction.*

In Figure 20.9, the molecules have been drawn to show the various covalent bonds. They have also been 'straightened out'. The real molecules are much more 'worm-like'.

Bitumen

Bitumen is a thick, black material, which is melted and mixed with rock chippings to make the top surfaces of roads.

Cracking

Although the fractions from crude oil distillation are useful fuels, there are two problems.

● The amounts of each fraction you get will depend on the proportions of the various hydrocarbons in the original crude oil, not the amounts in which they are needed. Far more petrol is needed, for example, than is found in crude oil.

● Apart from burning, the hydrocarbons in crude oil are fairly unreactive. To make other organic chemicals from them, they must first be converted into something more reactive.

Cracking is a useful process in which large hydrocarbon molecules are broken into smaller ones. The big hydrocarbon molecules in gas oil, for example, can be broken down into the smaller ones needed for petrol.

The majority of the hydrocarbons found in crude oil have single bonds between the carbon atoms. During the cracking process, molecules are also formed that have double bonds between carbon atoms. These new molecules are much more reactive and can be used to make many other things.

How cracking works

The gas oil fraction is heated to give a gas and then passed over a catalyst of mixed silicon dioxide and aluminium oxide at about 600–700 °C. Cracking can also be carried out at higher temperatures without a catalyst.

Cracking is just an example of thermal decomposition – a big molecule splitting into smaller ones on heating. The molecules are broken up in a fairly random way. This is just one possibility:

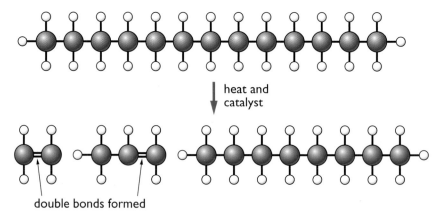

Figure 20.9 *How cracking works.*

As an equation, this would read:

$$C_{13}H_{28}(l) \rightarrow C_2H_4(g) + C_3H_6(g) + C_8H_{18}(l)$$

Cracking produces a mixture of alkanes and alkenes. In this case, two different alkenes are produced – ethene and propene. Octane, an alkane, is also formed. This particular cracking reaction has therefore produced two useful molecules for the chemical industry – ethene and propene are both used to make important polymers, as you will find in Chapter 21. And both are used in making other organic chemicals.

The reaction also produces octane, which is a component of petrol (gasoline).

The molecule might have split quite differently. All sorts of reactions are going on in a catalytic cracker. Two other possibilities might be:

$$C_{13}H_{28}(l) \rightarrow 2C_2H_4(g) + C_9H_{20}(l)$$
$$C_{13}H_{28}(l) \rightarrow 2C_2H_4(g) + C_3H_6(g) + C_6H_{14}(l)$$

Some reactions might even produce a small percentage of free hydrogen. For example:

$$C_{13}H_{28}(l) \rightarrow 2C_2H_4(g) + C_3H_6(g) + C_6H_{12}(l) + H_2(g)$$

In this case, all the hydrocarbons formed will have double bonds. They are all alkenes. C_6H_{12} is called hexene.

And there will also be very many other ways in which this particular molecule might have split up. Also, remember that the fraction being cracked contains a complex mixture of hydrocarbons, not just one. At the end of the cracking process, you will have an equally complex mixture of smaller hydrocarbons, both alkanes and alkenes.

This mixture will have to go through a lot of further processing (including further fractional distillation) to separate everything out into pure compounds.

Don't worry too much if you can't remember which are gases and which are liquids. State symbols are very commonly missed out in organic chemistry.

It is essential that you *don't* try to learn these equations. In an exam, you could be given one of a wide range of possible hydrocarbons to start with. You need to understand what is going on, so that you can be adaptable.

End of Chapter Checklist

You should now be able to:

✓ understand that crude oil is a mixture of hydrocarbons, and know how the simple properties of those hydrocarbons vary with molecular size

✓ know how crude oil is separated into fractions taking advantage of differences in boiling points

✓ know the uses of the main fractions from crude oil distillation

✓ understand what is meant by cracking, and why it is important

✓ give the conditions for catalytic cracking.

Questions

1 Six of the fractions which are obtained by the fractional distillation of crude oil are (in alphabetical order): bitumen, diesel oil (gas oil), fuel oil, gasoline, kerosine, refinery gases. Draw up a simple table listing these fractions in order of increasing boiling point. Give one use for each of the fractions.

2 Hydrocarbons burn in an excess of air or oxygen to give carbon dioxide and water.

 a) What do you understand by the term *hydrocarbon*?

 b) Write an equation for the complete combustion of the hydrocarbon heptane, $C_7H_{16}(l)$.

 c) The more volatile a hydrocarbon is, the more flammable it is. In a liquid, reaction with oxygen can only take place at the surface. In a gas, the oxygen molecules can mix easily with the hydrocarbon molecules.

  (i) What do you understand by the word *volatile*?

  (ii) Which is the more volatile hydrocarbon, $C_{15}H_{32}$ or C_8H_{18}? Explain your answer.

 d) Explain why the *incomplete combustion* of hydrocarbons causes safety problems.

3 Cracking is a process that splits larger hydrocarbons into smaller ones.

 a) Give two reasons why an oil company might want to crack a hydrocarbon.

 b) State the conditions under which cracking is carried out.

 c) A molecule of the hydrocarbon $C_{11}H_{24}$ was cracked to give two molecules of ethene, C_2H_4, and one other molecule. Write an equation for the reaction which took place. (You can omit the state symbols from your equation.)

 d) Write an equation for an alternative cracking reaction involving the same hydrocarbon, $C_{11}H_{24}$.

4 Imagine a world in which fossil fuels such as coal, natural gas and oil had never formed. This would have effects other than the immediately obvious ones. For example, the iron and steel industry depends on coke made from coal, although in the past (on a much smaller scale) it used charcoal made from wood. Choose one aspect of the modern world and explain, in no more than 300 words, how it would be different in the absence of fossil fuels. You could choose from: transport, use of materials, landscape, disease prevention, and power generation, for example, but you needn't restrict yourself to this list.

Try not to be too simplistic about this. Human beings are inventive! For example, it is possible to obtain organic chemicals from alcohol (from fermented sugar), and fuels from plant oils.

Chapter 21: Polymers

Addition polymerisation

The polymerisation of ethene

Ethene is one of the alkenes produced by cracking. It is the smallest hydrocarbon containing a carbon–carbon double bond. Figure 21.1 shows different ways of writing or drawing an ethene molecule.

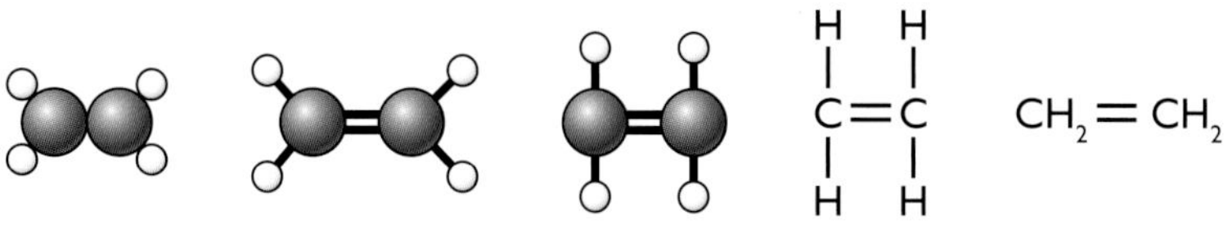

This chapter looks at two different ways that polymers can be made. Addition polymerisation for polymers such as polythene and PVC, and condensation polymerisation for polymers such as nylon.

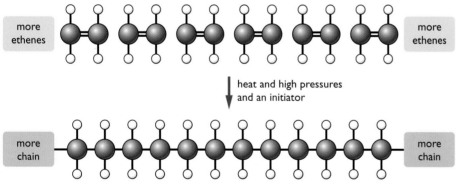

Figure 21.1 *Ethene.*

Under the right conditions, molecules containing carbon–carbon double bonds can join together to produce very long chains. Part of the double bond is broken, and the electrons in it are used to join to neighbouring molecules. This is called **addition polymerisation**.

Polymerisation is the joining up of lots of little molecules (the **monomers**) to make one big molecule (the **polymer**). In the case of ethene, lots of ethene molecules join together to make **poly(ethene)** – more usually called polythene.

more ethenes

heat and high pressures and an initiator

more chain

Figure 21.2 *The polymerisation of ethene.*

An **initiator** is used to get the process started. You mustn't call it a catalyst, because it gets used up in the reaction.
People occasionally wonder what happens at the ends of the chains. They don't end tidily! Bits of the initiator are bonded on at either end. You don't need to worry about that for GCSE.

The chain length can vary from about 4000 to 40,000 carbon atoms.

For normal purposes, this is written using displayed formulae. Remember that a displayed formula is rather like the models drawn here, but with symbols for the atoms rather than circles. For exam purposes, the acceptable form is the one shown in Figure 21.3.

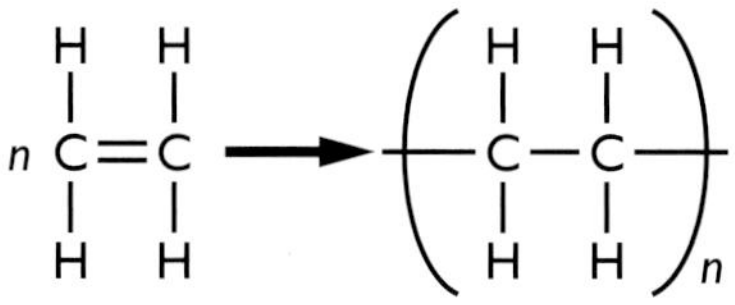

$$n \; \overset{\displaystyle H \quad H}{\underset{\displaystyle H \quad H}{C = C}} \longrightarrow \left(\overset{\displaystyle H \quad H}{\underset{\displaystyle H \quad H}{C - C}} \right)_n$$

In this structure for poly(ethene), *n* represents a large but variable number. It simply means that the structure in the brackets repeats itself many times in the molecule.

Figure 21.3 *Displayed formula for poly(ethene).*

Uses for poly(ethene)

Poly(ethene) comes in two types – low-density poly(ethene) (LDPE) and high-density poly(ethene) (HDPE). Low-density poly(ethene) is mainly used as a thin film to make polythene bags. It is very flexible and not very strong.

High-density poly(ethene) is used where rather greater strength and rigidity is needed – for example to make plastic bottles such as milk bottles. If you can find a recycling symbol with the letters HDPE next to it, then the bottle is made of high-density poly(ethene). If it has some other letters there, then it is a different polymer.

The polymerisation of propene

Propene is another alkene – this time with three carbon atoms in each molecule. Its formula is normally written as $CH_3CH=CH_2$. Think of it as a modified ethene molecule, with a CH_3 group attached in place of one of the hydrogen atoms.

> You will find that it is much easier to work out the structure of its polymer if you keep the CH_3 group tucked up out of the way when you draw it.

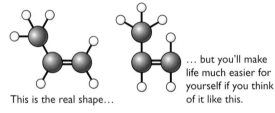

This is the real shape...

... but you'll make life much easier for yourself if you think of it like this.

Figure 21.4 *Propene.*

When propene is polymerised you get **poly(propene)**. This used to be called polypropylene.

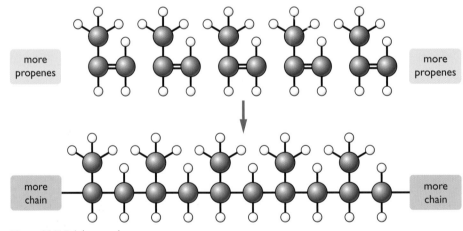

more propenes

more propenes

more chain

more chain

Figure 21.7 *Poly(propene)*

Write this as:

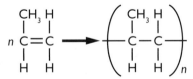

Figure 21.8 *Use this equation for exam purposes.*

Uses of poly(propene)

Poly(propene) is somewhat stronger than poly(ethene). It is used to make ropes and crates (among many other things). If an item has a recycling mark with PP inside it or near it, it is made of poly(propene).

Figure 21.5 *Poly(propene) is used to make crates . . .*

Figure 21.6 *. . . and ropes.*

The polymerisation of chloroethene

Chloroethene is an ethene molecule in which one of the hydrogen atoms is replaced by a chlorine. Its formula is $CH_2=CHCl$. It used to be called vinyl chloride. Polymerising chloroethene gives you poly(chloroethene). This is usually known by its old name, polyvinylchloride or PVC.

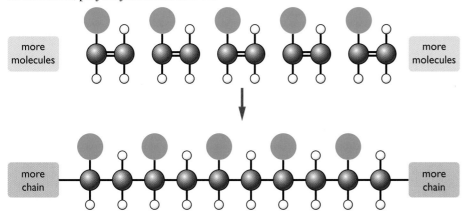

Figure 21.9 *Poly(chloroethene) (polyvinylchloride or PVC).*

Write this as:

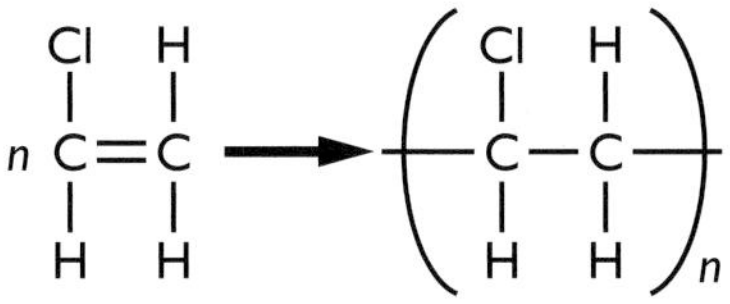

> It doesn't matter when you draw this whether you put the chlorine atom on the left-hand carbon atom or the right-hand one.

Figure 21.10 *Use this equation for exam purposes.*

Uses of poly(chloroethene)

Poly(chloroethene) – PVC – has a lot of uses. It is quite strong and rigid, and so can be used for drainpipes or replacement windows. It can also be made flexible by adding 'plasticisers'. That makes it useful for sheet floor coverings, and even clothing. These polymers don't conduct electricity, and PVC is used for electrical insulation.

Working out the monomer for a given addition polymer

In an exam, you may find that you are given the structure of a polymer and asked to work out what monomer it was made from. Figure 21.12 shows a part of the structure of a polystyrene molecule.

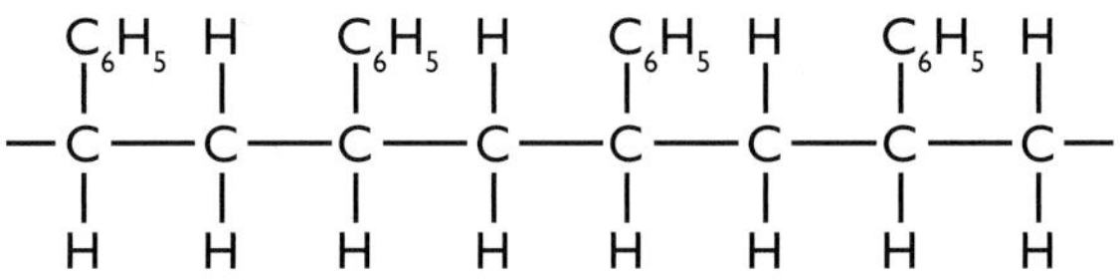

Figure 21.12 *Part of a polystyrene molecule.*

The C_6H_5 group is complicated, and we don't need to worry about that in writing the structure of the monomer – work from the structure you are given. First find the repeating unit, and then put back the original carbon–carbon double bond.

Figure 21.11 *PVC is used to insulate electric cables.*

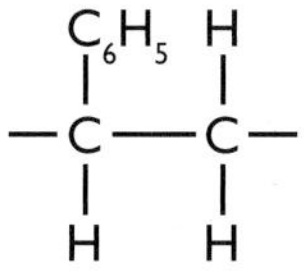

Figure 21.13 *Polystyrene – the repeating unit.*

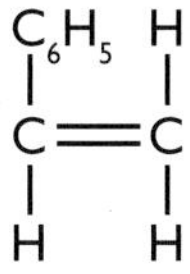

Figure 21.14 *Styrene – the monomer.*

There are several different types of nylon. The one we are going to talk about is called nylon-6,6 and has two monomers.

Warning! These are two of the most scary pages in the whole book. Take them very slowly. They throw a whole lot of new structures at you in a very short space of time. This is unavoidable – sorry! If you take it gently, step-by-step, it isn't actually very difficult.

Slightly confusingly, the family name is 'amine', but members of the group often have 'amino' in the name. This is probably just because a word like 'diaminohexane' sounds slightly better than 'diaminehexane'.

Condensation polymerisation

Making nylon

When a lot of ethene molecules combine to make a chain, the double bonds break and the monomer molecules just add on to each other to make a polymer. Nothing is lost. That is why it is called 'addition polymerisation'.

Making nylon is different. Instead of one monomer, you often have two, joining together alternately. And each time two monomers combine, a small molecule is lost. That is known as a **condensation reaction**.

The monomers

One of the monomers is a six-carbon organic acid with a –COOH group at each end, called hexanedioic acid. The –COOH group is known as a carboxylic acid group. It is present in familiar things such as ethanoic acid (CH_3COOH, previously called acetic acid) in vinegar, for example. The code 'di' in the name shows that there are two of these groups present. Hexanedioic acid is one of a family of compounds called **dicarboxylic acids**. Its formula is:

$$HOOCCH_2CH_2CH_2CH_2COOH$$

Notice that there are a total of six carbon atoms in the molecule. That's one of the sixes in nylon-6,6.

The other monomer is a **diamine** called 1,6-diaminohexane. The amino group is $-NH_2$, and there is one of these at each end of a six-carbon chain. That's the other six in nylon-6,6.

$$H_2NCH_2CH_2CH_2CH_2CH_2CH_2NH_2$$

Under the right conditions, these two molecules can join together with the loss of a molecule of water each time a new bond is formed.

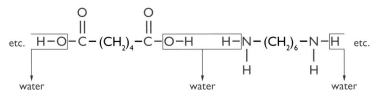

Figure 21.15 *Joining the monomers together. . .*

If you keep going with this over lots of pairs of monomers, you will get a chain as shown in Figure 21.16.

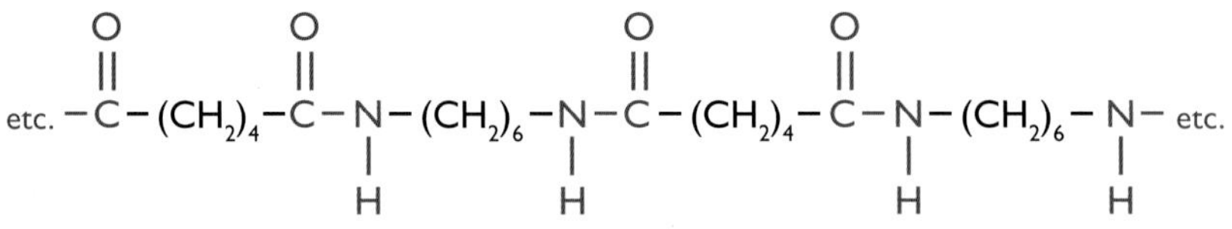

Figure 21.16 *. . . to make a chain.*

Now, this all looks pretty scary! So let's simplify it into what is known as a 'block diagram'. This just replaces the CH_2 groups by rectangles, and allows you to concentrate on the important bits.

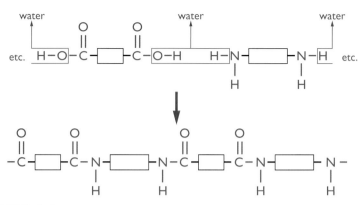

Figure 21.17 *Block diagram.*

This is how you set about learning this. Think of one of the monomers as being a rectangle with a –COOH group at either end. Think of the other one as being a rectangle with an –NH₂ group at either end. Draw those groups as displayed formulae. Then line them up so that you can remove water between them. Having removed the water, slot the rest of the molecules together as shown in these diagrams. It looks difficult because it is unfamiliar. Practise doing it a few times until it becomes familiar.

Industrially, this reaction is done at 350 °C, but with a small modification it can be done in the lab at room temperature. The modification replaces one of the monomers with a more reactive molecule. The –OH groups in the hexanedioic acid are replaced by chlorine atoms to give:

$$ClOCCH_2CH_2CH_2CH_2COCl$$

This time, the small molecule that gets lost during the condensation reaction is HCl.

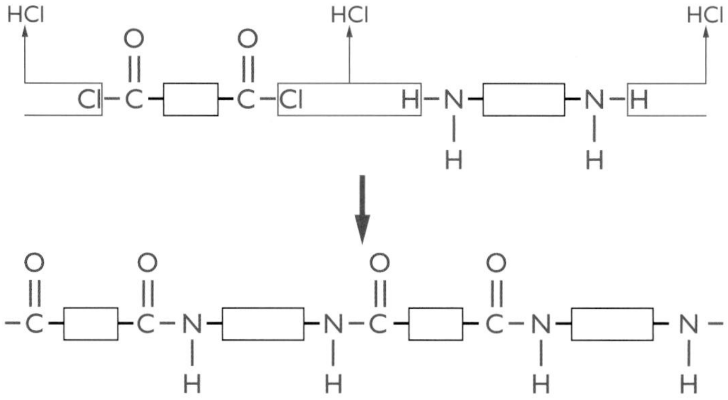

If you are interested, this is called hexanedioyl dichloride. Nobody is expecting you to remember that!

Comparing Figures 21.17 and 21.18, we see that nothing much has changed.

Figure 21.18 *HCl is lost during this condensation reaction.*

This reaction is the basis for a fascinating piece of practical work known as the **nylon rope trick**.

The hexanedioyl dichloride is dissolved in an organic solvent, which doesn't mix with water, and the 1,6-diaminohexane is dissolved in water. The two solutions are placed in a small beaker (or other container) so that one floats on top of the other, avoiding mixing as far as possible.

Nylon is formed at the boundary between the two layers. If this boundary layer is carefully caught with a pair of tweezers or tongs, you can pull out surprisingly long lengths of nylon. Messy, but fun!

Uses of nylon

Apart from obvious uses in textiles, the fibres are also used in ropes, and nylon can be cast into solid shapes for cogs and bearings in machines, for example.

Figure 21.19 *The nylon rope trick – at the time of writing, there were several excellent video clips of this experiment on YouTube. You can find links to these from the website accompanying this book.*

Figure 21.20 *The fabric for hot air balloons is based on either nylon or polyester. Like nylon, polyester is also a condensation polymer.*

End of Chapter Checklist

You should now be able to:

✓ understand what is meant by addition polymerisation as applied to poly(ethene), poly(propene) and poly(chloroethene)

✓ work out the structure of a monomer from the repeat unit of a polymer

✓ understand what is meant by condensation polymerisation as applied to nylon

✓ know the monomers used in the manufacture of nylon, and draw the structure of nylon using a block diagram.

Questions

1 Propene, C_3H_6, can be polymerised to make poly(propene).

a) What do you understand by the term *polymerisation*?

b) Draw a displayed formula (showing all the bonds) for propene.

c) Draw a diagram to show the structure of a poly(propene) chain. Restrict yourself to showing three repeating units.

d) The formation of poly(propene) is an example of *addition* polymerisation. Explain what is meant by the word *addition*.

e) Styrene has the formula $C_6H_5CH=CH_2$. Write an equation to show what happens when styrene is polymerised to make polystyrene. Your equation should clearly show the structure of the polystyrene. (Show the C_6H_5 group as a whole without worrying about its structure.)

f) A small part of a Perspex molecule looks like this:

Draw the structure of the monomer from which Perspex is made.

2 Nylon-6,6 is made by a condensation polymerisation of the monomers 1,6-diaminohexane and hexanedioic acid.

a) By drawing the two monomers in block format:

(i) explain what is meant by *condensation* polymerisation

(ii) draw a diagram to show the essential bonding in a chain of nylon-6,6.

b) Nylon-6,10 is made from 1,6-diaminohexane and a longer chain acid, decanedioic acid, containing a total of 10 carbon atoms:

$HOOCCH_2CH_2CH_2CH_2CH_2CH_2CH_2CH_2COOH$

(i) How will a chain of nylon-6,10 differ from one of nylon-6,6? Refer to the diagram you drew in (*a* ii).

(ii) In what way(s) will the two chains be the same? Again, refer to the diagram you drew in (*a* ii).

3 (This question contains new material, and is designed to look difficult. It is actually very easy as long as you understand about nylon.)

Polyesters such as Terylene (for clothes) or PET (commonly used to make drinks bottles) are made by condensation polymerisation from ethane-1,2-diol and terephthalic acid (properly known as benzene-1,4-dicarboxylic acid). The structures of these are:

Ethane-1,2-diol: $HO\text{-}CH_2CH_2\text{-}OH$

Terephthalic acid:

Draw the structure of a short length of polyester chain.

The structure of the C_6H_4 group is complicated, and you can write it simply as C_6H_4. You can draw this as a block diagram if you wish, but it is more satisfying (and no more difficult in this case) to draw the structure properly.

1. Crude oil (petroleum) is a complex mixture of **hydrocarbons**. The crude oil can be separated into simpler mixtures (called **fractions**) by taking advantage of differences in boiling points between the various hydrocarbons.

   a) What do you understand by the term 'hydrocarbon'?
   (2 marks)

   b) What is the relationship between the number of carbon atoms in a hydrocarbon and its boiling point? *(1 mark)*

   c) What name is given to the process of producing the simpler mixtures from the crude oil? *(1 mark)*

   d) One of the fractions produced from crude oil is called **kerosine**. Give one use for kerosine. *(1 mark)*

   e) One of the hydrocarbons present in kerosine is an alkane containing 10 carbon atoms, called decane. Write the molecular formula for decane. *(1 mark)*

   f) The hydrocarbon $C_{15}H_{32}$ (also present in kerosine) burns to form carbon dioxide and water. Write the equation for the reaction. *(2 marks)*

   g) How would you test the products when $C_{15}H_{32}$ burns to show that carbon dioxide had been formed? *(2 marks)*

   h) Liquefied petroleum gas (LPG), used for domestic heating and cooking, is propane (C_3H_8). Burning propane in badly maintained appliances or in poorly ventilated rooms can cause death. Explain why that is. *(4 marks)*

   Total 14 marks

2. Some of the gas oil fraction from crude oil is broken into smaller molecules by heating it in the presence of a catalyst. A mixture of **saturated** and **unsaturated** hydrocarbons is formed.

   a) Explain the difference between a saturated and an unsaturated hydrocarbon. *(2 marks)*

   b) What name is given to the process of breaking up the gas oil fraction in this way? *(1 mark)*

   c) When a molecule $C_{17}H_{36}$ was heated in the presence of a catalyst, it broke up to give two molecules of ethene, C_2H_4, one molecule of propene, C_3H_6, and another molecule, X.

   (i) Write a balanced equation for the reaction. *(2 marks)*

   (ii) Is molecule X an alkane or an alkene? *(1 mark)*

   d) How would you test to show the presence of a carbon–carbon double bond in ethene or propene? *(2 marks)*

   Total 8 marks

3. a) What do you understand by the term 'polymerisation'?
   (2 marks)

   b) Poly(chloroethene) (also called PVC) is a polymer produced from chloroethene, $CH_2\text{=}CHCl$. Draw a length of PVC chain showing at least three repeating units. *(2 marks)*

   c) The formation of nylon is an example of condensation polymerisation: that is, polymerisation happening via a **condensation reaction**. Explain what is meant by a 'condensation reaction'. *(1 mark)*

   d) The formation of nylon-6,6 involves two different monomers. Draw a block diagram to show a short length of nylon chain, including at least two of each monomer. *(3 marks)*

   Total 8 marks

4. This question is about **structural isomerism**.

   a) What are 'structural isomers'? *(2 marks)*

   b) Draw the structures of the three isomers of C_5H_{12}. *(3 marks)*

   c) Name the straight chain isomer. *(1 mark)*

   Total 6 marks

5. Ethanol, CH_3CH_2OH, can be made by **fermentation** followed by fractional distillation, or by the **hydration of ethene**.

   a) Describe briefly how an impure dilute solution of ethanol is made by fermentation. *(5 marks)*

   b) State the different boiling points of ethanol and water, which enable them to be separated by fractional distillation. *(2 marks)*

   c) Write an equation to show the hydration of ethene. *(1 mark)*

   d) State any two conditions used during the hydration reaction. *(2 marks)*

   e) Explain which of the two processes has the advantage in terms of:

   (i) the use of resources *(2 marks)*

   (ii) the conditions used *(2 marks)*

   (iii) the speed of production. *(2 marks)*

   Total 16 marks

Chapter 22: RAMs and Moles

This chapter introduces the ideas that you need in order to do some simple chemistry calculations. Don't worry – the level of maths involved is very low.

Figure 22.1 *Each gold bar contains almost 4×10^{25} gold atoms. That's 4 followed by 25 noughts!*

Remember that isotopes are atoms of the same element, but with different masses. Isotopes are explained in Chapter 2 (page 8).

This is a slight approximation. To be accurate, each of these hydrogen atoms has a mass of 1.008 on the carbon-12 scale. For GCSE purposes, we take it as being exactly 1.

You can make iron(II) sulfide by heating a mixture of iron and sulfur.

$$Fe(s) + S(l) \rightarrow FeS(s)$$

How do you know what proportions to mix them up in? You can't just mix equal masses of them, because iron and sulfur atoms don't weigh the same. Iron atoms contain more protons and neutrons than sulfur atoms, so an iron atom is one and three-quarters times heavier than a sulfur atom. In this or any other reaction, you can get the proportions right only if you know about the masses of the individual atoms taking part.

Relative atomic mass (RAM or A_r)

Defining relative atomic mass

Atoms are amazingly small. In order to get a gram of hydrogen, you would need to count out 602,204,500,000,000,000,000,000 atoms (to the nearest 100,000,000,000,000,000).

It would be silly to measure the masses of atoms in conventional mass units such as grams. Instead, their masses are compared with the mass of an atom of the carbon-12 isotope, taken as a standard. We call this the **carbon-12 scale**.

On this scale, one atom of the carbon-12 isotope weighs *exactly* 12 units.

An atom of the commonest isotope of magnesium weighs twice as much as this, and is therefore said to have a **relative isotopic mass** of 24.

An atom of the commonest isotope of hydrogen weighs only one-twelfth as much as a carbon-12 atom, and so has a relative isotopic mass of 1.

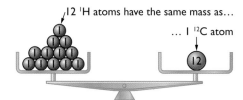

Figure 22.2 *The commonest hydrogen atom weighs one-twelfth as much as a ^{12}C atom.*

The basic unit on the carbon-12 scale is 1/12 of the mass of a ^{12}C atom – approximately the mass of the commonest hydrogen atom. For example, a fluorine-19 atom has a relative isotopic mass of 19 because its atoms have a mass 19 times that basic unit.

The **relative atomic mass (RAM)** of an element (as opposed to one of its isotopes) is given the symbol A_r and is defined like this:

> The relative atomic mass of an element is the weighted average mass of the isotopes of the element. It is measured on a scale on which a carbon-12 atom has a mass of exactly 12 units.

Explaining the term 'weighted average'

In any sample of chlorine, some atoms have a relative mass of 35, and others have a relative mass of 37. A simple average of 35 and 37 is, of course, 36 – but that isn't the relative atomic mass of chlorine. The problem is that there aren't equal numbers of ^{35}Cl and ^{37}Cl atoms.

Figure 22.3 *The masses of four typical chlorine atoms – the average of these isn't 36.*

A typical sample of chlorine has:	^{35}Cl	75%
	^{37}Cl	25%

If you had 100 typical atoms of chlorine, 75 would be ^{35}Cl, and 25 would be ^{37}Cl.

The total mass of the 100 atoms would be $\quad (75 \times 35) + (25 \times 37)$
$$= 3550$$

The average mass of one atom would be $\quad 3550/100$
$$= 35.5$$

The weighted average is closer to 35 than to 37, because there are more ^{35}Cl atoms than ^{37}Cl atoms. A weighted average allows for the unequal proportions.

35.5 is the relative atomic mass (RAM) of chlorine.

More examples of calculating relative atomic masses

Magnesium

The isotopes of magnesium and their percentage abundances are:

^{24}Mg $\quad$ 78.6%
^{25}Mg $\quad$ 10.1%
^{26}Mg $\quad$ 11.3%

Again, assume that you have 100 typical atoms.

The total mass would be $\quad (78.6 \times 24) + (10.1 \times 25) + (11.3 \times 26)$
$$= 2432.7$$

The RAM would be $\quad 2432.7/100$
$$= 24.3 \text{ (to three significant figures)}$$

The relative atomic mass of magnesium is 24.3.

The original percentages are quoted to only three significant figures. You mustn't quote your answer any more accurately. As a general guide at GCSE, if in doubt quote answers to three significant figures. You aren't likely to be penalised for doing that.

Lithium

The abundance data might be given in a different form. You might get a graph, with the most common isotope being given a relative abundance of 100 and the others quoted relative to that.

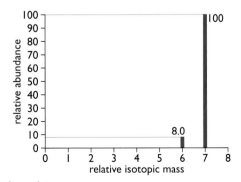

Figure 22.4 *Relative abundance data.*

In this case, there would be 8.0 atoms of ^{6}Li for every 100 of ^{7}Li.

The total mass of 108 atoms would be $\qquad (8.0 \times 6) + (100 \times 7)$

$\qquad\qquad\qquad\qquad\qquad\qquad\qquad = \ 748$

The average mass of one atom (the RAM) $\ = \ \dfrac{748}{108}$

$\qquad\qquad\qquad\qquad\qquad\qquad\qquad = \ 6.9$

The relative atomic mass of lithium is 6.9.

This time you can only quote your answer to two significant figures because one of the relative abundances is only given to two figures.

Relative formula mass (RFM or M_r)

You can measure the masses of compounds on the same carbon-12 scale. For example, it turns out that a water molecule, H_2O, has a mass of 18 on the ^{12}C scale. Where you are talking about compounds, you use the term **relative formula mass** (**RFM**). Relative formula mass is sometimes called relative molecular mass (RMM).

Relative formula mass is given the symbol M_r.

Avoid the term 'relative molecular mass' because it can only properly be applied to substances which are actually molecules – in other words, to covalent substances. You shouldn't use it for things like magnesium oxide or sodium chloride, which are ionic. RFM covers everything.

Working out some relative formula masses

To find the RFM of magnesium carbonate, $MgCO_3$

Relative atomic masses: C = 12; O = 16; Mg = 24

All you have to do is to add up the relative atomic masses to give you the relative formula mass of the whole compound. In this case, you need to add up the masses of $1 \times Mg$, $1 \times C$ and $3 \times O$.

You will never have to remember RAMs. They will always be given to you in an exam – either in the question, or on the Periodic Table. **If you use a Periodic Table, be sure to use the right number!** It will always be the larger of the two numbers given.

RFM $\qquad\qquad = 24 + 12 + (3 \times 16)$

$\qquad\qquad\qquad = 84$

To find the RFM of calcium hydroxide, $Ca(OH)_2$

Relative atomic masses: H = 1; O = 16; Ca = 40

RFM $\qquad\qquad = 40 + (16 + 1) \times 2$

$\qquad\qquad\qquad = 74$

To find the RFM of copper(II) sulfate crystals, $CuSO_4 \cdot 5H_2O$

Relative atomic masses: H = 1; O = 16; S = 32; Cu = 64

You will find the RAM of copper quoted variously as 64 or 63.5. In an exam, just use the value you are given.

RFM $\qquad\qquad = 64 + 32 + (4 \times 16) + 5 \times [(2 \times 1) + 16]$

$\qquad\qquad\qquad = 250$

Most people have no difficulty with RFM sums until they get to an example involving water of crystallisation (the $5H_2O$ in this example). $5H_2O$ means 5 molecules of water – so to get the total mass of this, work out the RFM of water (18) and then multiply it by 5. It is dangerous to do the hydrogens and oxygens separately. The common mistake is to work out 10 hydrogens (quite correctly!), but then only count 1 oxygen rather than 5.

Using relative formula mass to find percentage composition

Having found the relative formula mass of a compound, it is then easy to work out the percentage by mass of any part of it. Examples make this clear.

To find the percentage by mass of copper in copper(II) oxide, CuO

Relative atomic masses: O = 16; Cu = 64

RFM of CuO $\quad= 64 + 16$
$\quad\quad\quad\quad\quad= 80$

Of this, 64 is copper.

Percentage of copper $\quad= \dfrac{64}{80} \times 100$
$\quad\quad\quad\quad\quad\quad\quad= 80\%$

To find the percentage by mass of copper in malachite, $CuCO_3 \cdot Cu(OH)_2$

Relative atomic masses: H = 1; C = 12; O = 16; Cu = 64

RFM of $CuCO_3 \cdot Cu(OH)_2 = 64 + 12 + (3 \times 16) + 64 + 2 \times (16 + 1)$
$\quad\quad\quad\quad\quad\quad\quad\quad\quad = 222$

Of this, (2×64) is copper.

Percentage of copper $\quad= \dfrac{(2 \times 64)}{222} \times 100$
$\quad\quad\quad\quad\quad\quad\quad= 57.7\%$

Figure 22.5 *Malachite is a copper ore. You can think of it as behaving like a mixture of copper(II) carbonate and copper(II) hydroxide.*

To find the percentage of water in alabaster, $CaSO_4 \cdot 2H_2O$

Relative atomic masses: H = 1; O = 16; S = 32; Ca = 40

RFM of alabaster $\quad= 40 + 32 + (4 \times 16) + 2 \times [(2 \times 1) + 16]$
$\quad\quad\quad\quad\quad\quad= 172$

Of this, $2 \times [(2 \times 1) + 16]$ is water. That's 36.

Percentage of water $\quad= \dfrac{36}{172} \times 100$
$\quad\quad\quad\quad\quad\quad\quad= 20.9\%$

The mole

In Chemistry, the mole is a measure of **amount of substance**. A mole is a particular mass of that substance. You can use such expressions as:

- a mole of copper(II) sulfate crystals, $CuSO_4 \, 5H_2O$

- a mole of oxygen gas, O_2

- 0.1 mole of zinc oxide, ZnO

- 3 moles of magnesium, Mg

The abbreviation for mole is **mol**.

Figure 22.6 *Alabaster, $CaSO_4 \cdot 2H_2O$, is a soft mineral which is easily carved.*

You find the mass of 1 mol of a substance in the following way.

Work out the relative formula mass, and attach the units, grams.

Working out the masses of a mole of substance

1 mole of oxygen gas, O_2

Relative atomic mass: $O = 16$

RFM of oxygen, O_2 $= 2 \times 16$
$= 32$

1 mole of oxygen, O_2, weighs $32\,g$.

1 mole of calcium chloride, $CaCl_2$

Relative atomic masses: $Cl = 35.5$; $Ca = 40$

RFM of $CaCl_2$ $= 40 + (2 \times 35.5)$
$= 111$

1 mole of calcium chloride weighs $111\,g$.

1 mole of iron(II) sulfate crystals, $FeSO_4 \cdot 7H_2O$

Relative atomic masses: $H = 1$; $O = 16$; $S = 32$; $Fe = 56$

RFM of crystals $= 56 + 32 + (4 \times 16) + 7 \times [(2 \times 1) + 16]$
$= 278$

1 mole of iron(II) sulfate crystals weighs $278\,g$.

The importance of quoting the formula

Whenever you talk about a mole of something, you **must** quote its formula, otherwise there is the risk of confusion.

For example, if you talk about 1 mole of oxygen, this could mean:

● 1 mole of oxygen atoms, O, weighing $16\,g$

● 1 mole of oxygen molecules, O_2, weighing $32\,g$.

Or, if you were talking about 1 mole of copper(II) sulfate, this could mean:

● 1 mole of anhydrous copper(II) sulfate, $CuSO_4$ ($160\,g$)

● 1 mole of copper(II) sulfate crystals, $CuSO_4$ $5H_2O$ ($250\,g$)

Figure 22.7 *1 mole of copper(II) sulfate crystals, $CuSO_4 \cdot 5H_2O$.*

Simple calculations with moles

You need to be able to interconvert between a mass in grams and a number of moles for a given substance. There is a simple formula that you can learn:

$$\text{number of moles} = \frac{\text{mass (g)}}{\text{mass of 1 mole (g)}}$$

You can rearrange that to find whatever you want. If rearranging this expression causes you problems, you can learn a simple triangular arrangement, which does the whole thing for you.

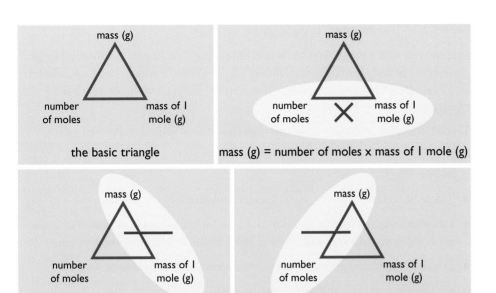

Figure 22.8 *Converting between mass in grams and number of moles.*

Look at this carefully, and make sure that you understand how you can use it to work out the three equations that you might need.

Finding the mass of 0.2 moles of calcium carbonate, $CaCO_3$

Relative atomic masses: C = 12; O = 16; Ca = 40

First find the relative formula mass of calcium carbonate.

$$\text{RFM of } CaCO_3 = 40 + 12 + (3 \times 16)$$
$$= 100$$

1 mol of $CaCO_3$ weighs 100 g.

$$\text{mass (g)} = \text{number of moles} \times \text{mass of 1 mole (g)}$$
$$= 0.2 \times 100\,\text{g}$$
$$= 20\,\text{g}$$

0.2 moles of $CaCO_3$ has a mass of 20 g.

Finding the number of moles in 54 g of water, H_2O

Relative atomic masses: H = 1; O = 16

1 mol of H_2O weighs 18 g.

$$\text{Number of moles} = \frac{\text{mass (g)}}{\text{mass of 1 mole (g)}}$$
$$= \frac{54}{18}$$
$$= 3\,\text{mol}$$

54 g of water is 3 moles.

> Don't get *too* reliant on learning formulae for working out simple calculations. If 1 mole weighs 100 g, it should be fairly obvious to you that 2 moles will weigh twice as much, 10 moles will weigh 10 times as much, and 0.2 moles will weigh 0.2 times as much.

> And here, if 1 mole weighs 18 g, then it seems fairly obvious that you need to find out how many times 18 goes into 54 to find out how many moles you have. On the other hand, if you feel safer using a formula, use it. All that matters is that you get the answer right.

Moles and the Avogadro constant

Suppose you had 1 mole of ^{12}C. It would have a mass of $12\,g$, and contain a huge number of carbon atoms – in fact, about 6×10^{23} carbon atoms – that's 6 followed by 23 noughts. This number of atoms in $12\,g$ of ^{12}C is called the **Avogadro constant**.

1 mole of anything else contains this same number of particles. For example:

- 1 mole of magnesium contains 6×10^{23} magnesium atoms, Mg, and has a mass of $24\,g$
- 1 mole of water contains 6×10^{23} water molecules, H_2O, and has a mass of $18\,g$
- 1 mole of sodium chloride contains 6×10^{23} formula units, NaCl, and has a mass of $58.5\,g$ (you can't say 'molecules of NaCl' because sodium chloride is ionic)
- 1 mole of oxide ions contains 6×10^{23} O_2^- ions and has a mass of $16\,g$
- 1 mole of electrons contains 6×10^{23} electrons.

Using moles to find formulae

Interpreting symbols in terms of moles

Assume that you know the formula for copper(II) oxide, for example. The formula is CuO.

When you are doing sums, it is often useful to interpret a symbol as meaning more than just 'an atom of copper' or 'an atom of oxygen'. For calculation purposes we take the symbol Cu to mean **1 mole of copper atoms**.

In a formula, 'Cu' means '$64\,g$ of copper'. 'O' means '$16\,g$ of oxygen' (RAMs: O = 16, Cu = 64). So in copper(II) oxide, the copper and oxygen are combined in the ratio of $64\,g$ of copper to $16\,g$ of oxygen.

You can read a formula like H_2O as meaning that 2 moles of hydrogen atoms are combined with 1 mole of oxygen atoms. In other words, $2\,g$ of hydrogen are combined with $16\,g$ of oxygen (RAMs: H = 1; O = 16).

Working out formulae

The formula for magnesium oxide

Suppose you did an experiment to find out how much magnesium and oxygen reacted together to form magnesium oxide. Suppose $2.4\,g$ of magnesium combined with $1.6\,g$ of oxygen. You can use these figures to find the formula of magnesium oxide (RAMs: O = 16; Mg = 24) – see Table 22.1.

Figure 22.9 1×10^{32} water molecules go over Niagara Falls every second during the summer. That's 100 million million million million million water molecules per second.

Remember: Number of moles is mass in grams divided by the mass of 1 mole in grams.

	Mg	O
combining masses (g)	2.4	1.6
number of moles of atoms	2.4/24	1.6/16
=	0.10	0.10
ratio of moles	1:1	
simplest formula	MgO	

Table 22.1: *Finding the formula of magnesium oxide.*

This simplest formula is called the **empirical formula**. The empirical formula just tells you the **ratio** of the various atoms. Without more information, it isn't possible to work out the 'true' or 'molecular' formula, which could be Mg_2O_2, Mg_3O_3, etc. For ionic substances, the formula quoted is *always* the empirical formula.

The formula for red copper oxide

You might get the data in a more complicated form. This example is about a less-common form of copper oxide. If hydrogen is passed over the hot oxide, it is reduced to metallic copper.

Mass of empty tube	= 52.2 g
Mass of tube + copper oxide (before experiment)	= 66.6 g
Mass of tube + copper (after experiment)	= 65.0 g

The tube loses mass because oxygen has been removed from the copper oxide, leaving metallic copper.

Mass of oxygen	= 66.6 – 65.0 = 1.6 g
Mass of copper	= 65.0 – 52.2 = 12.8 g

Figure 22.10 *Crystals of the copper-containing mineral cuprite, Cu_2O.*

Now you have all the information to find the empirical formula (RAMs: O = 16; Cu = 64) – see Table 22.2.

	Cu	**O**
combining masses (g)	12.8	1.6
number of moles of atoms	12.8/64	1.6/16
=	0.20	0.10
ratio of moles	2:1	
simplest formula	Cu_2O	

Table 22.2: *Finding the formula of red copper oxide.*

Working out formulae using percentage composition figures

Often, figures for the compound are given as percentages by mass. For example: Find the empirical formula of a compound containing 85.7% C, 14.3% H by mass (RAMs: H = 1; C = 12).

This isn't a problem! Those percentage figures apply to any amount of substance you choose – so choose 100 g. In which case, the percentages convert simply into masses. 85.7% of 100 g is 85.7 g (Table 22.3).

	C	**H**
given percentages (%)	85.7	14.3
combining masses in 100 g	85.7	14.3
number of moles of atoms	85.7/12	14.3/1
=	7.14	14.3
ratio of moles	1:2	
simplest (empirical) formula	CH_2	

Table 22.3: *Finding the ratio from percentage by mass.*

Usually the ratio will be fairly obvious, but if you can't spot it at once, divide everything by the smallest number and see if that helps. Sometimes, you may find that a ratio comes out as, for example, 1:1.5. In that case, all you have to do is double both numbers to give the true ratio of 2:3.

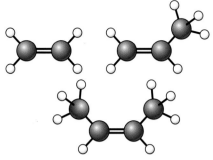

Figure 22.11 *All of these have an empirical formula CH_2.*

Even having got the molecular formula, you still don't know the structure. There are several isomers of C_4H_8. Isomerism is discussed in Chapter 18, pages 153–154.

Converting empirical formulae into molecular formulae

In the example we have just looked at, CH_2 can't possibly be the real formula of the hydrocarbon – the carbon would have spare unbonded electrons. The **molecular formula** (the true formula) would have to be some multiple of CH_2, like C_2H_4 or C_3H_6, or whatever – as long as the ratio is still 1 carbon to 2 hydrogens.

You could find the molecular formula if you knew the relative formula mass of the compound (or the mass of 1 mole – which is just the RFM expressed in grams).

In the previous example, suppose you knew that the relative formula mass of the compound was 56.

CH_2 has a relative formula mass of only 14 (RAMs: H = 1; C = 12).

All you need to find out is how many times 14 goes into 56.

$$\frac{56}{14} = 4$$

so you need four lots of CH_2
in other words, C_4H_8.
The molecular formula is C_4H_8.

Empirical formula calculations involving water of crystallisation

When some substances crystallise from solution, water becomes chemically bound up with the salt. This is called **water of crystallisation**. The salt is said to be **hydrated**. Examples include $CuSO_4 \cdot 5H_2O$ and $MgCl_2 \cdot 6H_2O$.

Finding the *n* in $BaCl_2 \cdot nH_2O$

When you heat a salt that contains water of crystallisation, the water is driven off, leaving the anhydrous salt behind. Hydrated barium chloride is a commonly used example, because the barium chloride itself doesn't decompose even on quite strong heating.

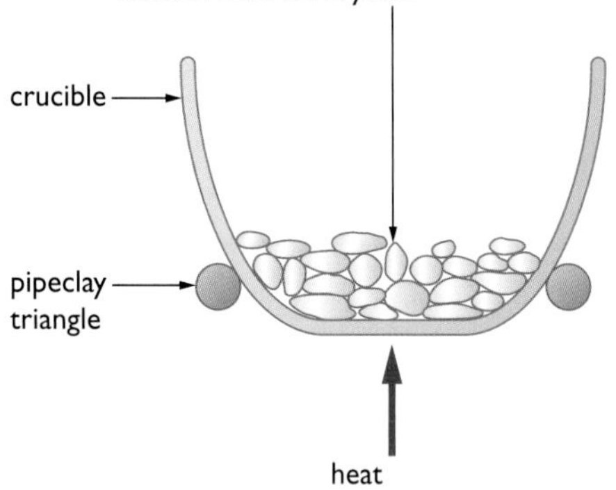

If you heated barium chloride crystals in a crucible you might end up with these results:

Mass of crucible	= 30.00 g
Mass of crucible + barium chloride crystals, $BaCl_2 \cdot nH_2O$	= 32.44 g
Mass of crucible + anhydrous barium chloride, $BaCl_2$	= 32.08 g

To find *n*, you need to find the ratio of the number of moles of $BaCl_2$ to the number of moles of water. It's just another empirical formula sum (RAMs: H = 1; O = 16; Cl = 35.5; Ba = 137).

Mass of $BaCl_2$ = 32.08 – 30.00 = 2.08 g
Mass of water = 32.44 – 32.08 = 0.36 g

barium chloride crystals

crucible

pipeclay triangle

heat

Figure 22.12 *Heating barium chloride crystals in a crucible.*

208 is the RFM of $BaCl_2$. 18 is the RFM of water. Check them if you aren't sure.

	$BaCl_2$	**H_2O**
combining masses (g)	2.08	0.36
number of moles	2.08/208	0.36/18
=	0.01	0.02
ratio of moles	1:2	
simplest (empirical) formula	$BaCl_2 \cdot 2H_2O$	

Table 22.4: *Finding the n in $BaCl_2 \cdot nH_2O$.*

You should now be able to:

✓ define relative atomic mass

✓ calculate the relative atomic mass of an element from information about the relative abundances of its isotopes

✓ calculate relative formula mass and use it to find percentage composition

✓ know how to work out the mass of a mole of a substance

✓ understand what is meant by the Avogadro constant

✓ convert from moles to mass and *vice versa*

✓ calculate empirical and molecular formulae

✓ calculate the *n* in a formula of the type 'salt·nH_2O'.

Questions

1 Calculate the relative atomic mass of gallium given the percentage abundances: ^{69}Ga 60.2%, ^{71}Ga 39.8%.

2 Calculate the relative atomic mass of silicon given:

Relative isotopic mass	Relative abundance
28	100
29	5.10
30	3.36

3 *a)* Define relative atomic mass.

  b) Calculate the relative atomic masses of copper and sulfur from the percentage abundances of their isotopes. Use your answers to find the relative formula mass of copper(II) sulfide, CuS.

    ^{63}Cu 69.1%; ^{65}Cu 30.9%.

    ^{32}S 95.0%; ^{33}S 0.76%; ^{34}S 4.22%; ^{35}S 0.020%.

4 Calculate the relative formula masses of the following compounds (RAMs: H = 1; C = 12; N = 14; O = 16; Na = 23; S = 32; Ca = 40; Cr = 52; Fe = 56).

  a) CO_2

  b) $(NH_4)_2SO_4$

  c) $Na_2CO_3·10H_2O$

  d) $Cr_2(SO_4)_3$

  e) $(NH_4)_2SO_4·FeSO_4·6H_2O$

5 Find the percentage by mass of the named substance in each of the following examples (RAMs: H = 1; C = 12; O = 16; Mg = 24; S = 32).

  a) Carbon in propane, C_3H_8

  b) Water in magnesium sulfate crystals, $MgSO_4·7H_2O$.

6 Work out the percentage of nitrogen in each of the following substances (all used as nitrogen fertilisers) (RAMs: H = 1; C = 12; N = 14; O = 16; S = 32; K = 39).

  a) urea, $CO(NH_2)_2$

  b) potassium nitrate, KNO_3

  c) ammonium nitrate, NH_4NO_3

  d) ammonium sulfate, $(NH_4)_2SO_4$

7 Work out the mass of the following (RAMs: H = 1; C = 12; N = 14; O = 16; Na = 23; Pb = 207):

  a) 1 mole of lead(II) nitrate, $Pb(NO_3)_2$

  b) 4.30 moles of methane, CH_4

  c) 0.24 moles of sodium carbonate crystals, $Na_2CO_3·10H_2O$

8 How many moles are represented by each of the following (RAMs: H = 1; O = 16; S = 32; Fe = 56; Cu = 64):

  a) 50 g of copper(II) sulfate crystals, $CuSO_4·5H_2O$

  b) 1 tonne of iron, Fe (1 tonne is 1000 kg)

  c) 0.032 g of sulfur dioxide, SO_2

9   Some more questions about converting between moles and grams of a substance (RAMs: H = 1; O = 16; Na = 23; Cl = 35.5; Ca = 40; Cu = 64).

   a) What is the mass of 4 mol of sodium chloride, NaCl?

   b) How many moles is 37 g of calcium hydroxide, $Ca(OH)_2$?

   c) How many moles is 1 kg (1000 g) of calcium, Ca?

   d) What is the mass of 0.125 mol of copper(II) oxide, CuO?

   e) 0.1 mol of a substance weighed 4 g. What is the mass of 1 mole?

   f) 0.004 mol of a substance weighed 1 g. What is the relative formula mass of the compound?

10 (RAMs: H = 1; C = 12; N = 14; O = 16; Na = 23; S = 32; K = 39; Br = 80.) Find the empirical formulae of the following compounds, which contained:

   a) 5.85 g K; 2.10 g N; 4.80 g O

   b) 3.22 g Na; 4.48 g S; 3.36 g O

   c) 22.0% C; 4.6% H; 73.4% Br (by mass).

11 1.24 g of phosphorus was burnt completely in oxygen to give 2.84 g of phosphorus oxide. Find (RAMs: O = 16; P = 31):

   a) the empirical formula of the oxide

   b) the molecular formula of the oxide given that 1 mole of the oxide weighs 284 g.

12 An organic compound contained C 66.7%, H 11.1%, O 22.2% by mass. Its relative formula mass was 72. Find (RAMs: H = 1; C = 12; O = 16):

   a) the empirical formula of the compound

   b) the molecular formula of the compound.

13 In an experiment to find the number of molecules of water of crystallisation in sodium sulfate crystals, $Na_2SO_4 \cdot nH_2O$, 3.22 g of sodium sulfate crystals were heated gently. When all the water of crystallisation had been driven off, 1.42 g of anhydrous sodium sulfate was left. Find the value for n in the formula (RAMs: H = 1; O = 16; Na = 23; S = 32).

14 Gypsum is hydrated calcium sulfate, $CaSO_4 \cdot nH_2O$. A sample of gypsum was heated in a crucible until all the water of crystallisation had been driven off. The following results were obtained:

mass of crucible	= 37.34 g
mass of crucible + gypsum, $CaSO_4 \cdot nH_2O$	= 45.94 g
mass of crucible + anhydrous calcium sulfate, $CaSO_4$	= 44.14 g

   Calculate the value of n in the formula $CaSO_4 \cdot nH_2O$ (RAMs: H = 1; O = 16; S = 32; Ca = 40).

15 How many water molecules, H_2O, are there in one drop of water? Assume one drop of water is 0.05 cm^3, and that the density of water is 1 g cm^{-3} (RAMs: H = 1; O = 16; Avogadro constant = 6 × 10^{23} mol^{-1}).

Chapter 23: Calculations from Equations

Calculations involving only masses

Typical calculations will give you a mass of starting material and ask you to calculate how much product you are likely to get. You will also meet examples done the other way around, where you are told the mass of the product and are asked to find out how much of the starting material you would need. In almost all the cases you will meet at GCSE, you will be given the equation for the reaction.

A problem involving heating limestone

When limestone, $CaCO_3$, is heated, calcium oxide is formed. Suppose you wanted to calculate the mass of calcium oxide produced by heating 25 g of limestone (relative atomic masses: C = 12; O = 16; Ca = 40).

The calculation

First write the equation:

$$CaCO_3(s) \rightarrow CaO(s) + CO_2(g)$$

Interpret the equation in terms of moles – remember that each formula represents 1 mole of that substance:

1 mol $CaCO_3$ produces 1 mol CaO (and 1 mol CO_2)

Substitute masses where relevant:

100 g (1 mol) $CaCO_3$ produces 56 g (1 mol) CaO

(Notice that we haven't calculated the mass of carbon dioxide. In this question you aren't interested in it, so working it out is just a waste of time – and potentially confusing.)

Do the simple proportion sum.

If: 100 g of calcium carbonate gives 56 g of calcium oxide

1 g of calcium carbonate gives $\frac{56}{100}$ g of calcium oxide = 0.56 g

25 g of calcium carbonate gives 25 × 0.56 g of calcium oxide

$$= 14 \text{ g of calcium oxide}$$

A problem involving the manufacture of lead

Lead is extracted from galena, PbS. The ore is roasted in air to produce lead(II) oxide, PbO.

$$2PbS(s) + 3O_2(g) \rightarrow 2PbO(s) + 2SO_2(g)$$

The lead(II) oxide is then reduced to lead by heating it with carbon in a blast furnace.

$$PbO(s) + C(s) \rightarrow Pb(l) + CO(g)$$

This chapter shows how you can use moles to work out the amounts of substances taking part in chemical reactions. Before you start, you must be confident about relative formula mass (RFM) and how to do simple sums with moles. If you aren't, first read pages 178–181 in Chapter 22.

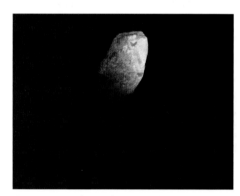

Figure 23.1 A glowing limestone chip.

The RFM of $CaCO_3$ is 100, and the RFM of CaO is 56. Work them out!

Your maths may be good enough that you don't need to take all these steps to get to the answer. If you can do it more quickly, that's fine. You must, however, still show all your working.

When you have finished a chemistry calculation, the impression should nearly always be that there are a lot of words with a few numbers scattered between them – not *vice versa*.

Figure 23.2 *Molten lead tapped from the bottom of a furnace.*

You could save yourself the bother of thinking about it by not simplifying this. That would cost you a little bit of extra arithmetic, because you would have to multiply everything by 2. Do it whichever way seems best to you.

If you need the practice, work out the RFMs for yourself.

The molten lead is tapped from the bottom of the furnace.

Calculate:

(a) the mass of sulfur dioxide produced when 1 tonne of galena is roasted

(b) the mass of lead that would eventually be produced from that 1 tonne of galena.

(Relative atomic masses: O = 16; S = 32; Pb = 207.)

Calculation part (a)

First write the equation:

$$2PbS(s) + 3O_2(g) \rightarrow 2PbO(s) + 2SO_2(g)$$

Interpret the equation in terms of moles:

2 mol PbS produces 2 mol SO_2 (the others aren't important for this calculation)

or, more simply:

1 mol PbS produces 1 mol SO_2

Substitute masses where relevant:

239 g PbS produces 64 g SO_2

Now there seems to be a problem. The question is asking about tonnes and not grams. You could work out how many grams there are in a tonne and then do hard sums with large numbers. However, it's much easier to think a bit, and realise that the ratio is always going to be the same whatever the units – so that . . .

if: 239 g PbS produces 64 g SO_2

then: 239 tonnes PbS produces 64 tonnes SO_2

Do the simple proportion sum:

if: 239 tonnes PbS produces 64 tonnes SO_2

then: 1 tonne PbS gives $\frac{64}{239}$ tonnes SO_2 = 0.268 tonnes SO_2

Calculation part (b)

First write the equation – this time there are two equations to think about:

$$2PbS(s) + 3O_2(g) \rightarrow 2PbO(s) + 2SO_2(g)$$
$$PbO(s) + C(s) \rightarrow Pb(l) + CO(g)$$

We've doubled the second equation so that we can trace what happens to all the 2PbO from the first one.

Interpret the equation in terms of moles – trace the lead through the equations:

2 mol PbS produces 2 mol PbO
2 mol PbO produces 2 mol Pb

In other words, every 2 mol of PbS produces 2 mol of lead.

Substitute masses where relevant – in this case, the relevant masses are only the PbS and the final lead.

$2 \times 239 \, g$ PbS produces $2 \times 207 \, g$ Pb

$478 \, g$ PbS produces $414 \, g$ Pb

So:

478 tonnes PbS produces 414 tonnes Pb

Do the simple proportion sum:

if: 478 tonnes PbS produces 414 tonnes Pb

then: 1 tonne PbS gives $\frac{417}{478}$ tonnes Pb = 0.866 tonnes

0.866 tonnes of lead is produced from 1 tonne of galena.

Calculations involving gas volumes

Units of volume

Volumes (of gases or liquids) are measured in: cubic centimetres (cm^3)

                or   cubic decimetres (dm^3)

                or   litres (l).

> 1 litre = 1 dm^3 = 1000 cm^3

Avogadro's law:

> **Equal volumes of gases at the same temperature and pressure contain equal numbers of molecules.**

This means that if you have $100 \, cm^3$ of hydrogen at some temperature and pressure, it contains exactly the same number of molecules as there are in $100 \, cm^3$ of carbon dioxide or any other gas under those conditions – irrespective of the size of the molecules.

A simple use of Avogadro's law is to show that the formula of water is H_2O.

If you electrolyse dilute sulfuric acid using carbon electrodes, hydrogen and oxygen are produced, with twice the volume of hydrogen as of oxygen. If you make several assumptions, you can show that this is consistent with an empirical formula for water of H_2O.

You have to assume that the sulfuric acid itself isn't changed by the electrolysis (in fact, it just gets more concentrated), and that hydrogen and oxygen are both diatomic molecules, H_2 and O_2.

If you have twice the volume of hydrogen, according to Avogadro, you have twice the number of molecules. Because both sorts of molecules are diatomic, you must have twice the number of hydrogen atoms as of oxygen atoms. In other words, the empirical formula of water must be H_2O. This doesn't, of course, prove anything about the molecular formula of the water, which could be H_2O, H_4O_2, H_6O_3 and so on.

Once again, you could well save a bit of time here by realising that if 2 mol PbS produces 2 mol Pb, that's exactly the same as 1 mol PbS producing 1 mol Pb. That would save you having to multiply two numbers by 2. On the other hand, you would have to think!

If you want to talk about 1000 cm^3, the cubic decimetre is the preferred unit rather than the litre, but it doesn't actually matter.

Figure 23.3 *Three identical flasks containing different gases at the same temperature and pressure all contain equal numbers of molecules.*

This isn't a very satisfactory experiment. Without also proving your assumptions, you can't *really* use it to show that water is H_2O. Proving that hydrogen and oxygen are both diatomic, and that electrolysing sulfuric acid doesn't change the acid, isn't easy. And unless you also show that the relative formula mass of water is 18, you can't prove the molecular formula anyway.

The molar volume of a gas

This is by far the most important consequence of Avogadro's law.

1 mole of any gas contains the same number of molecules and so occupies the same volume as 1 mole of any other gas at the same temperature and pressure.

The volume occupied by 1 mole of a gas is called the **molar volume**. At room temperature and pressure, the molar volume is approximately $24\,dm^3$ $(24,000\,cm^3)$.

The abbreviation **rtp** is commonly used for 'room temperature and pressure'.

> **1 mole of any gas occupies $24\,dm^3$ ($24,000\,cm^3$) at rtp.**

Simple calculations with the molar volume

Calculating the volume of a given mass of gas

Calculate the volume of 0.01 g of hydrogen at rtp (relative atomic mass: H = 1).

1 mol H_2 has a mass of 2 g.
0.01 g of hydrogen is $\frac{0.01}{2}$ mol = 0.005 mol
1 mol of hydrogen occupies $24,000\,cm^3$.
0.005 mol of hydrogen occupies $0.005 \times 24,000\,cm^3 = 120\,cm^3$

Calculating the mass of a given volume of gas

See Figure 9.8, page 73.

On 6 May 1937, the airship Hindenburg caught fire and 36 people died. Suppose an airship contained 180,000 cubic metres of hydrogen (a little bit less than the Hindenburg). We can calculate the mass of this hydrogen.

180,000 cubic metres is $180,000,000\,dm^3$. Assuming the gas was at room temperature and pressure, each $24\,dm^3$ represents one mole of hydrogen.

$$\text{Number of moles of } H_2 = \frac{180,000,000}{24}$$
$$= 7,500,000\,mol$$

Each mole of hydrogen, H_2, weighs 2 g (RAM: H = 1).
$$\text{Mass of hydrogen} = 7,500,000 \times 2\,g$$
$$= 15,000,000\,g$$

If you were to convert that into more reasonable units (you wouldn't do that in an exam!), the mass of hydrogen is 15 tonnes. That's a lot of hydrogen!

Using the molar volume in calculations from equations

Working out the volume of gas produced during a reaction

Calculate the volume of carbon dioxide produced at room temperature and pressure when an excess of dilute hydrochloric acid is added to 1.00 g of calcium carbonate. (You use an excess of acid to make sure that all the calcium carbonate reacts.) (RAMs: C = 12; O = 16; Ca = 40; molar volume = $24\,dm^3$ at rtp.)

First write the equation:

> $$CaCO_3(s) + 2HCl(aq) \rightarrow CaCl_2(aq) + CO_2(g) + H_2O(l)$$

Figure 23.4 *Shells of sea creatures such as limpets are made of calcium carbonate, $CaCO_3$. If they were 100% pure, 1 g of shells would react with hydrochloric acid to give $0.24\,dm^3$ of carbon dioxide.*

Interpret the equation in terms of moles:

1 mol $CaCO_3$ gives 1 mol CO_2

Substitute masses and volumes where appropriate.

100 g $CaCO_3$ gives 24 dm³ CO_2 at rtp.

Do the simple proportion sum:

if: 100 g $CaCO_3$ gives 24 dm³ CO_2 at rtp

then: 1 g $CaCO_3$ gives $\frac{1}{100} \times 24$ dm³

$$= 0.24 \text{ dm}^3$$

So 1 g of calcium carbonate gives 0.24 dm³ of carbon dioxide.

A problem involving making hydrogen

What is the maximum mass of aluminium that you could add to an excess of dilute hydrochloric acid so that you produced no more than 100 cm³ of hydrogen at room temperature and pressure? (RAM: Al = 27; molar volume = 24,000 cm³ at rtp.)

What you are being asked is what mass of aluminium will give 100 cm³ of hydrogen at rtp.

First write the equation:

$$2Al(s) + 6HCl(aq) \rightarrow 2AlCl_3(aq) + 3H_2(g)$$

Interpret the equation in terms of moles:

2 mol Al gives 3 mol H_2

Substitute masses and volumes where appropriate:

2 × 27 g Al gives 3 × 24,000 cm³ H_2

54 g Al gives 72,000 cm³ H_2

Do the simple proportion sum:

if: 72,000 cm³ H_2 comes from 54 g Al

then: 1 cm³ H_2 comes from $\frac{54}{72,000}$ g Al   = 0.000 75 g

and: 100 cm³ H_2 comes from 100 × 0.000 75 g Al   = 0.075 g Al

To get 100 cm³ of hydrogen, you would need 0.075 g of aluminium.

Important: The commonest mistake in a sum of this kind is to work out the **mass** of 1 mole of CO_2. Once you have that figure of 44 g, you feel you have to do something with it, and will probably work out the mass of CO_2 produced instead of the volume.

You would almost certainly be given this equation in an exam.

Figure 23.5 *The flue gas desulfurisation plant at Drax power station uses limestone to remove sulfur dioxide from the waste gases.*

If you don't like this, there is no reason why you can't do the sum with 2 moles of everything!

Unfortunately, this time you can't work directly in tonnes – you have to work in grams. 1 tonne is a million grams. 10,000 tonnes is 10,000,000,000 grams.
It would be much more sensible to do this in scientific notation! 10,000 tonnes is 1×10^{10} g.
The volume of SO_2 then turns out to be 2.4×10^9 dm^3.

An industrial example

Coal contains sulfur compounds. When these burn, sulfur dioxide is produced. To remove it from the waste gases from power stations, the sulfur dioxide is reacted with limestone (calcium carbonate) and air.

$$2CaCO_3(s) + 2SO_2(g) + O_2(g) \rightarrow 2CaSO_4(s) + 2CO_2(g)$$

The calcium sulfate produced can be used to make plasterboard for building.

The Drax power station uses 10,000 tonnes of crushed limestone every week. We are going to calculate what mass of calcium sulfate is produced, and what volume of sulfur dioxide the limestone removes from the flue gases (assuming the sulfur dioxide is at rtp). (RAMs: C = 12; O = 16; S = 32; Ca = 40; molar volume = 24 dm^3 at rtp.)

First write the equation:

$$2CaCO_3(s) + 2SO_2(g) + O_2(g) \rightarrow 2CaSO_4(s) + 2CO_2(g)$$

Interpret the equation in terms of moles:

2 mol $CaCO_3$ reacts with 2 mol SO_2 and produces 2 mol $CaSO_4$.

That's exactly the same as saying that:

1 mol $CaCO_3$ reacts with 1 mol SO_2 and produces 1 mol $CaSO_4$.

Substitute masses and volumes where appropriate:

100 g $CaCO_3$ reacts with 24 dm^3 SO_2 and produces 136 g $CaSO_4$.

Do the simple proportion sum for the calcium sulfate:

if: 100 g $CaCO_3$ produces 136 g $CaSO_4$

then: 100 tonnes $CaCO_3$ produces 136 tonnes $CaSO_4$

and: 1 tonne $CaCO_3$ produces 1.36 tonnes $CaSO_4$

so: 10,000 tonnes $CaCO_3$ produces $10,000 \times 1.36$ tonnes $CaSO_4$

$= 13,600$ tonnes.

10,000 tonnes of calcium carbonate produces 13,600 tonnes of $CaSO_4$.

Do the simple proportion sum for the SO_2:

if: 100 g $CaCO_3$ reacts with 24 dm^3 SO_2

then: 1 g $CaCO_3$ reacts with 0.24 dm^3 SO_2

and: 10,000,000,000 g $CaCO_3$ reacts with $10,000,000,000 \times 0.24$ dm^3 SO_2

$= 2,400,000,000$ dm^3 SO_2

10,000 tonnes of calcium carbonate reacts with 2,400,000,000 dm^3 SO_2.

Calculating percentage yields

What is a percentage yield?

If you calculate how much of a product you might get during a reaction, in real life you rarely get as much as you expected. If you expected to get 100 g, but only got 80 g, your percentage yield is only 80%. The rest of it has been lost in some way. This could be due to spillages, or losses when you transfer a liquid from one container to another. Or it may be that there are all sorts of side reactions going on, so that some of your starting materials are changed into unwanted products. That happens a lot during reactions in organic chemistry.

Figure 23.6 *Experiments done by students to make and purify organic compounds rarely give a high percentage yield.*

Calculating how much you would expect to get

You would do the sort of calculations that we have looked at in this chapter, but you have to think carefully what you base your calculation on. When you make something in the lab, you rarely mix things together in exactly the right proportions. Usually, something is in excess, and you get rid of the excess (by filtering it off, for example) when the reaction is complete.

The amount of product you get is governed by the amount of the substance you started with which *isn't* in excess – and that's the one you base your calculation on.

Suppose you mix together 10 g of substance A and an excess of substance B. The actual amount of B is irrelevant because it is in excess. You would work out your expected mass of product from the mass of A.

Calculating the percentage yield

Suppose you work out that 10 g of A would give 12.5 g of product, but you only get 11.2 g.

The percentage yield is $\frac{11.2}{12.5} \times 100 = 89.6\%$

End of Chapter Checklist

You should now be able to:

✓ calculate masses of reactants or products from given equations

✓ understand what is meant by the molar volume

✓ use the molar volume to convert between volume and mass for a particular gas

✓ carry out calculations from equations involving masses of solids and volumes of gases

✓ calculate the percentage yield during a reaction.

Questions

1 Titanium is manufactured by heating titanium(IV) chloride with sodium.

$TiCl_4(g) + 4Na(l) \rightarrow Ti(s) + 4NaCl(s)$

What mass of sodium is required to produce 1 tonne of titanium? (RAMs: Na = 23; Ti = 48).

2 2.67 g of aluminium chloride was dissolved in water and an excess of silver nitrate solution was added to give a precipitate of silver chloride.

$AlCl_3(aq) + 3AgNO_3(aq) \rightarrow Al(NO_3)_3(aq) + 3AgCl(s)$

What mass of silver chloride precipitate would be formed? (RAMs: Al = 27, Cl = 35.5, Ag = 108).

3 Calcium hydroxide is manufactured by heating calcium carbonate strongly to produce calcium oxide, and then adding a controlled amount of water to produce calcium hydroxide.

$CaCO_3(s) \rightarrow CaO(s) + CO_2(g)$
$CaO(s) + H_2O(l) \rightarrow Ca(OH)_2(s)$

a) What mass of calcium oxide would you produce from 1 tonne of calcium carbonate?

b) What mass of water would you need to add to that calcium oxide?

c) What mass of calcium hydroxide would you eventually produce?
(RAMs: H = 1, C = 12, O = 16, Ca = 40.)

4 Copper(II) sulfate crystals, $CuSO_4 \cdot 5H_2O$, can be made by heating copper(II) oxide with dilute sulfuric acid and then crystallising the solution formed.

a) Calculate the maximum mass of crystals that could be made from 4.00 g of copper(II) oxide using an excess of sulfuric acid.

$CuO(s) + H_2SO_4(aq) \rightarrow CuSO_4(aq) + H_2O(l)$
$CuSO_4(aq) + 5H_2O(l) \rightarrow CuSO_4 \cdot 5H_2O(s)$

b) If the actual mass of copper(II) sulfate collected at the end of the experiment was 11.25 g, calculate the percentage yield (RAMs: H = 1; O = 16; S = 32; Cu = 64).

5 Chromium is manufactured by heating a mixture of chromium(III) oxide with aluminium powder.

$Cr_2O_3(s) + 2Al(s) \rightarrow 2Cr(s) + Al_2O_3(s)$

a) Calculate the mass of aluminium needed to react with 1 tonne of chromium(III) oxide.

b) Calculate the mass of chromium produced from 1 tonne of chromium(III) oxide.
(RAMs: O = 16; Al = 27; Cr = 52.)

6 If the mineral pyrite, FeS_2, is heated strongly in air, iron(III) oxide and sulfur dioxide are produced. What mass of **a)** iron(III) oxide, and **b)** sulfur dioxide could be made by heating 1 tonne of an ore which contained 50% by mass of pyrite? (RAMs: O = 16; S = 32; Fe = 56).

$4FeS_2(s) + 11O_2(g) \rightarrow 2Fe_2O_3(s) + 8SO_2(g)$

7 Take the molar volume to be 24 dm³ (24,000 cm³) at rtp.

a) Calculate the mass of 200 cm³ of chlorine gas (Cl_2) at rtp (RAM: Cl = 35.5).

b) Calculate the volume occupied by 0.16 g of oxygen (O_2) at rtp (RAM: O = 16).

c) If 1 dm³ of a gas at rtp weighs 1.42 g, calculate the mass of 1 mole of the gas.

8 Calculate the volume of hydrogen (measured at room temperature and pressure) which can be obtained by reacting 0.240 g of magnesium with an excess of dilute sulfuric acid. (RAM: Mg = 24; molar volume = 24,000 cm³ at rtp).

$Mg(s) + H_2SO_4(aq) \rightarrow MgSO_4(aq) + H_2(g)$

9 What mass of potassium nitrate would you have to heat in order to produce $1.00\,dm^3$ of oxygen at rtp? (RAMs: N = 14, O = 16, K = 39; molar volume = $24\,dm^3$ at rtp).

$$2KNO_3(s) \rightarrow 2KNO_2(s) + O_2(g)$$

10 Chlorine can be prepared by heating manganese(IV) oxide with an excess of concentrated hydrochloric acid. What is the maximum volume of chlorine (measured at room temperature and pressure) that could be obtained from $2.00\,g$ of manganese(IV) oxide? (RAMs: O = 16, Mn = 55; molar volume = $24,000\,cm^3$ at rtp).

$$MnO_2(s) + 4HCl(aq) \rightarrow MnCl_2(aq) + Cl_2(g) + 2H_2O(l)$$

11 (This question looks quite difficult when you first read through it. There is a confusing amount of information. The secret with a question like this is just to skim quickly through everything until you get to the actual questions. Look at part **(a)** and then read the information above it to just work out this part. Then go on to part **(b)** and do the same thing. By concentrating on just those bits of the information you actually need at the time, you will find that the question becomes much easier.)

Sodium sulfite, Na_2SO_3, oxidises very slowly in the air to form sodium sulfate, Na_2SO_4. $1.000\,g$ of an old sample of sodium sulfite was analysed to find out how much had been oxidised to sodium sulfate.

The entire sample was dissolved in water and acidified with dilute hydrochloric acid. The remaining sodium sulfite reacts to form sodium chloride and takes no further part in the reaction.

$$Na_2SO_3(s) + 2HCl(aq) \rightarrow 2NaCl(aq) + SO_2(g) + H_2O(l)$$

An excess of barium chloride solution was added to the resulting solution. A white precipitate of barium sulfate was produced.

$$Na_2SO_4(aq) + BaCl_2(aq) \rightarrow BaSO_4(s) + 2NaCl(aq)$$

This was separated, dried and weighed. It was found to have a mass of $0.328\,g$ (RAMs: O = 16; Na = 23; S = 32; Ba = 137).

a) Calculate the number of moles of barium sulfate formed.

b) How many moles of sodium sulfate were there in the mixture of sodium sulfate and sodium sulfite?

c) Calculate the mass of sodium sulfate present in the mixture.

d) What percentage by mass of sodium sulfite was left in the mixture?

Chapter 24: Electrolysis Calculations

The calculations in this chapter are similar to those in Chapter 23, but with an added twist because of the electrons involved in electrolysis equations. It is important that you are confident about ordinary calculations from equations before you go on.

How to interpret electrode equations

Moles of electrons

Magnesium is manufactured by electrolysing molten magnesium chloride. Magnesium is produced at the cathode (the negative electrode) and chlorine at the anode (the positive electrode). The electrode equations are:

$$Mg^{2+}(l) + 2e^- \rightarrow Mg(l)$$
$$2Cl^-(l) \rightarrow Cl_2(g) + 2e^-$$

In terms of moles, you can say:

- 1 mole of Mg^{2+} ions gains 2 moles of electrons and produces 1 mole of magnesium, Mg

- 2 moles of Cl^- ions form 1 mole of chlorine, Cl_2, and release 2 moles of electrons.

When you are doing calculations, you just read e^- as '**1 mole of electrons**'.

Quantities of electricity

The **coulomb** is a measure of quantity of electricity. 1 coulomb is the quantity of electricity which passes if 1 ampere (amp) flows for 1 second.

Number of coulombs = current in amps × time in seconds

You may find this written in symbols using Q for the quantity of electricity, I for the current in amps, and t for the time in seconds:
$Q = I \times t$

So, if 2 amps flows for 20 minutes, you can calculate the quantity of electricity (not forgetting to convert the time into seconds) as:

Quantity of electricity $= 2 \times 20 \times 60$ coulombs

$= 2400$ coulombs

The Faraday constant

A flow of electricity is a flow of electrons. **1 faraday** is the quantity of electricity which represents 1 mole of electrons passing a particular point in the circuit – in other words approximately 6×10^{23} electrons.

1 faraday = 96,000 coulombs

1 faraday is more accurately quoted as 96,500 coulombs. Use whichever value you are given in a question.

Interpreting electrode equations

In electrolysis calculations, you are usually only interested in the quantity of electricity and the mass or volume of the product. For example:

$$Na^+(l) + e^- \rightarrow Na(l)$$

1 mole of sodium, Na, is produced by the flow of 1 mole of electrons (= 1 faraday).

$$Cu^{2+}(aq) + 2e^- \rightarrow Cu(s)$$

1 mole of copper, Cu, is produced by the flow of 2 moles of electrons (= 2 faradays).

It takes twice as much electricity to produce a mole of copper as it does a mole of sodium. That's because the Cu^{2+} ion carries twice the charge, and needs twice as many electrons to neutralise it.

$$2Cl^-(l) \rightarrow Cl_2(g) + 2e^-$$

1 mole of chlorine, Cl_2, is produced when 2 moles of electrons (= 2 faradays) flow around the circuit.

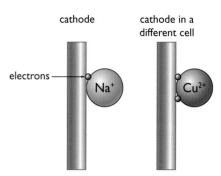

Figure 24.1 *Each sodium ion needs one electron from the cathode to neutralise its charge; each copper ion needs twice that number.*

Some sample calculations

Electrolysing copper(II) sulfate solution

What mass of copper is deposited on the cathode during the electrolysis of copper(II) sulfate solution if 0.15 amps flows for 10 minutes?

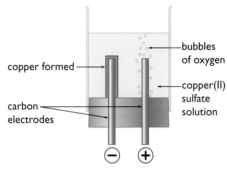

Figure 24.2 *Electrolysing copper(II) sulfate solution.*

The electrode equation is:

$$Cu^{2+}(aq) + 2e^- \rightarrow Cu(s)$$

(RAM: Cu = 64. 1 faraday = 96,000 coulombs.)

Start by working out the number of coulombs:

$$\begin{aligned}
\text{number of coulombs} &= \text{amps} \times \text{time in seconds} \\
&= 0.15 \times 10 \times 60 \\
&= 90
\end{aligned}$$

The 60 converts minutes into seconds.

Now work from the equation:

$$Cu^{2+}(aq) + 2e^- \rightarrow Cu(s)$$

2 moles of electrons give 1 mole of copper, Cu

2 × 96,000 coulombs give 64 g of copper

192,000 coulombs give 64 g of copper

90 coulombs give $\dfrac{90}{192,000} \times 64 = 0.03$ g

If you aren't happy with the last line, work out what 1 coulomb produces by dividing 64 by 192,000, and then multiply by 90.

A calculation involving gases

During the electrolysis of dilute sulfuric acid using platinum electrodes, hydrogen is released at the cathode and oxygen at the anode. Calculate the volumes of hydrogen and oxygen produced (measured at room temperature and pressure) if 1.0 amp flows for 20 minutes.

The electrode equations are:

2H⁺(aq) + 2e⁻ → H₂(g)
4OH⁻(aq) → 2H₂O(l) + O₂(g) + 4e⁻

(The molar volume of a gas = 24,000 cm³ at rtp; 1 faraday = 96,000 coulombs.)

Again, start by working out the number of coulombs:

$$\text{number of coulombs} = \text{amps} \times \text{time in seconds}$$
$$= 1.0 \times 20 \times 60$$
$$= 1200$$

Calculating the volume of hydrogen

2H⁺(aq) + 2e⁻ → H₂(g)

2 moles of electrons give 1 mole of hydrogen, H₂
2 × 96,000 coulombs give 24,000 cm³ of hydrogen at rtp.
192,000 coulombs give 24,000 cm³ of hydrogen at rtp.
1200 coulombs give $\frac{1200}{192,000} \times 24,000 = 150\,cm^3$

Calculating the volume of oxygen

4OH⁻(aq) → 2H₂O(l) + O₂(g) + 4e⁻

A flow of 4 moles of electrons produces 1 mole of oxygen, O₂
4 × 96,000 coulombs produces 24,000 cm³ of oxygen
384,000 coulombs produces 24,000 cm³ of oxygen
1200 coulombs produces $\frac{1200}{384,000} \times 24,000 = 75\,cm^3$
Therefore, 150 cm³ of hydrogen and 75 cm³ of oxygen are produced.

A reversed calculation

How long would it take to deposit 0.500 g of silver on the cathode during the electrolysis of silver(I) nitrate solution using a current of 0.250 amp? The cathode equation is:

Ag⁺(aq) + e⁻ → Ag(s)

(RAM: Ag = 108; 1 faraday = 96,000 coulombs.)

1 mole of electrons give 1 mole of silver, Ag.

96,000 coulombs give 108 g of silver.

To produce 0.500 g of silver you would need $\frac{0.500}{108} \times 96,000 = 444.4$ coulombs.

$$\text{number of coulombs} = \text{amps} \times \text{time in seconds}$$
$$444.4 = 0.250 \times t$$
$$t = \frac{444.4}{0.250}$$
$$= 1780\,s$$

The time needed to deposit 0.500 g of silver is 1780 seconds.

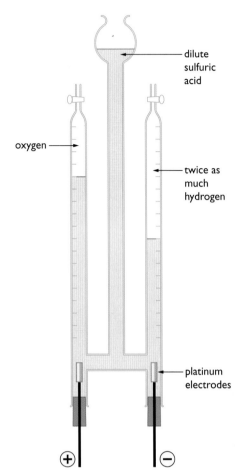

Figure 24.3 *Apparatus for electrolysing dilute sulfuric acid and measuring the volume of gases produced.*

oxygen — twice as much hydrogen — dilute sulfuric acid — platinum electrodes

If you need help: divide 96,000 by 108 to find out how many coulombs you need for 1 g of silver. Then multiply by 0.5 to find how many you need for 0.5 g.

Electrolysing more than one solution

Suppose you have two solutions connected together in series, so that the same quantity of electricity flows through both.

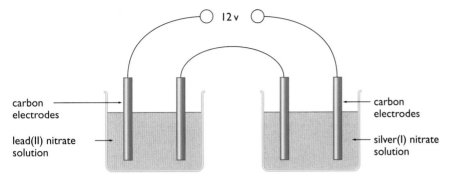

Figure 24.4 *Electrolysing more than one solution.*

At the end of the electrolysis, it was found that 2.07 g of lead had been deposited on the cathode in the left-hand beaker.

(a) Calculate the quantity of electricity that passed during the experiment.

(b) Calculate the mass of silver that was deposited on the cathode in the right-hand beaker. (RAMs: Pb = 207; Ag = 108; 1 faraday = 96,000 coulombs.)

(a)

$$Pb^{2+}(aq) + 2e^- \rightarrow Pb(s)$$

2 moles of electrons give 1 mole of lead, Pb

2 × 96,000 coulombs give 207 g of lead

if: 192,000 coulombs give 207 g of lead

then: 1920 coulombs give 2.07 g of lead.

The quantity of electricity that passed = 1920 coulombs.

(b) If 1920 coulombs passed through the beaker containing the lead(II) nitrate solution, then exactly the same amount passed through the rest of the circuit.

$$Ag^+(aq) + e^- \rightarrow Ag(s)$$

1 mole of electrons give 1 mole of silver, Ag

96,000 coulombs give 108 g of silver

1920 coulombs give $\dfrac{1920}{96,000} \times 108 = 2.16$ g

The mass of silver deposited is 2.16 g

An alternative way of solving part (b)

If you weren't asked to find the quantity of electricity in part (a), you could do part (b) much more easily without knowing anything at all about the Faraday constant or even about coulombs.

How do you know which method to use? In an exam, look at the information you are given. If you are given a value for the Faraday constant (96,000 coulombs), then you would be expected to use it. If you aren't given it, there must be another way of solving the problem.

Look again at the equations:

$$Pb^{2+}(aq) + 2e^- \rightarrow Pb(s)$$
$$Ag^+(aq) + e^- \rightarrow Ag(s)$$

If 2 moles of electrons flow, you will get 1 mole of lead and 2 moles of silver. However many electrons flow, you will always get twice as many moles of silver as of lead.

In this calculation, 2.07 g of lead were formed, which is 0.01 mol.

You will therefore get 0.02 mol of silver = $0.02 \times 108 = 2.16$ g.

A similar example involving just one solution

During the electrolysis of concentrated copper(II) chloride solution, 3.2 g of copper was deposited at the cathode. What volume of chlorine (measured at rtp) would be formed at the anode? (RAM: Cu = 64; molar volume = 24,000 cm^3 at rtp).

The electrode equations are:

This time, you aren't given the Faraday constant. There must be another way!

$$Cu^{2+}(aq) + 2e^- \rightarrow Cu(s)$$
$$2Cl^-(aq) \rightarrow Cl_2(g) + 2e^-$$

Notice that for every 2 moles of electrons that flow, you will get 1 mole of Cu and 1 mole of chlorine, Cl_2. You are bound to get the same number of moles of each.

In this case, 3.2 g of copper is $\frac{3.2}{64}$ mol = 0.05 mol.

So you will also get 0.05 mol of chlorine which is $0.05 \times 24{,}000$ cm^3 at rtp.

The volume of chlorine produced is 1200 cm^3.

You should now be able to:

✓ calculate the quantity of electricity in coulombs, given the current and time

✓ understand that 1 mole of electrons is represented by 96,000 coulombs, which is called the Faraday constant

✓ perform calculations for electrolysis reactions involving the masses (or volumes) of products, the current and the time

✓ calculate the mass (or volume) of one product of electrolysis given the mass (or volume) of another one.

Questions

1 During the electrolysis of copper(II) sulfate solution using carbon electrodes, copper is deposited on the cathode according to the equation:

$Cu^{2+}(aq) + 2e^- \rightarrow Cu(s)$

Calculate the gain in mass at the cathode if a current of 0.50 amps flows for 1 hour (RAM: Cu = 64; 1 faraday = 96,000 coulombs).

2 During the electrolysis of lead(II) nitrate solution, lead is deposited at the cathode and oxygen is released from the anode. If a current of 0.350 amps flows for 1000 s, calculate *a)* the mass of lead deposited; *b)* the volume of oxygen (measured at room temperature and pressure) produced (RAM: Pb = 207; the molar volume of a gas is 24,000 cm³ at rtp; 1 faraday = 96,000 coulombs).

$Pb^{2+}(aq) + 2e^- \rightarrow Pb(s)$
$4OH^-(aq) \rightarrow 2H_2O(l) + O_2(g) + 4e^-$

3 Some copper(II) sulfate solution was electrolysed using a pure copper cathode and an impure copper anode. Copper is lost from the anode and deposited on the cathode. Insoluble impurities in the anode form a sludge underneath the anode.

Cathode equation:

$Cu^{2+}(aq) + 2e^- \rightarrow Cu(s)$

Anode equation:

$Cu(s) \rightarrow Cu^{2+}(aq) + 2e^-$

a) What mass of copper will be deposited on the cathode if 0.40 amps flows for 75 minutes? (RAM: Cu = 64; 1 faraday = 96,000 coulombs).

b) If the anode was found to have lost 0.80 g during the experiment, calculate the percentage purity of the impure copper anode, assuming that only insoluble impurities were present.

4 Aluminium is manufactured by electrolysing a solution of aluminium oxide, Al_2O_3, in molten cryolite. The electrode equation is:

$Al^{3+}(l) + 3e^- \rightarrow Al(l)$

A typical cell produces 1 tonne (1000 kg) of aluminium every 24 hours. What current (in amps) is needed to produce this amount of aluminium? (RAM: Al = 27; 1 faraday = 96,000 coulombs).

5 Two solutions were electrolysed in series using the apparatus on page 199. One beaker contained chromium(III) sulfate solution, and the other cobalt(II) sulfate solution. 0.295 g of cobalt was deposited on the cathode in the beaker containing cobalt(II) sulfate. The electrode equations are:

$Cr^{3+}(aq) + 3e^- \rightarrow Cr(s)$
$Co^{2+}(aq) + 2e^- \rightarrow Co(s)$

Calculate:

a) the quantity of electricity that flowed during the experiment

b) the mass of chromium deposited on the cathode in the other beaker

(RAMs: Cr = 52; Co = 59; 1 faraday = 96,000 coulombs).

6 Copper(II) sulfate solution and lead(II) nitrate solution were electrolysed in two beakers connected in series. If 0.64 g of copper was deposited at the cathode in one beaker, calculate the mass of lead deposited in the other one (RAMs: Cu = 64; Pb = 207).

$Cu^{2+}(aq) + 2e^- \rightarrow Cu(s)$
$Pb^{2+}(aq) + 2e^- \rightarrow Pb(s)$

Chapter 25: Energy Calculations

This chapter looks at how energy changes during reactions can be calculated in simple cases, or measured by experiments. It would be helpful to re-read page 123 in Chapter 14 before you go on.

Bond energies are measured in kilojoules per mole. For example, if you see '$Cl_2(g)$' written in an equation, it will take 346 kJ to break all the bonds in that one mole of chlorine gas. If you see '$2HCl(g)$', it will take 2×432 kJ to break all the bonds in the two moles of hydrogen chloride gas. Bond energies apply only to gaseous compounds.

Calculations involving bond energies

Bond energies (bond strengths)

It needs energy to break chemical bonds. The stronger the bond is, the more energy is needed to break it. Bond energy measures the amount of energy needed to break a particular bond.

bond	C–H	C–Cl	C–I	Cl–Cl	I–I	H–Cl	H–I
bond energy (kJ mol⁻¹)	+413	+346	+234	+243	+151	+432	+298

Table 25.1: *The energy needed to break these bonds.*

You can see that some bonds are much stronger than others – for example, the bond between iodine and hydrogen is about twice as strong as the bond between two iodine atoms.

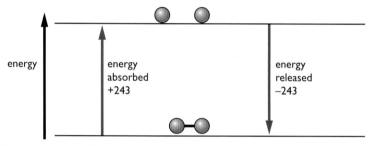

Figure 25.1 *Breaking and making bonds between chlorine atoms.*

Figure 25.1 shows that it needs an input of 243 kJ per mole to break chlorine molecules into atoms. If the atoms recombine into their original molecules, then obviously exactly the same amount of energy will be released again. When bonds are made, energy is given out.

● Breaking bonds needs energy.

● Making bonds releases energy.

Bond energies can be used to work out how much heat will be absorbed or released during reactions involving covalent compounds. If a reaction involves ionic compounds, different energy terms have to be used, which are beyond GCSE.

Calculating the heat released or absorbed during a reaction

You can estimate the heat released or absorbed by working out how much energy would be needed to break the substances up into individual atoms, and then how much would be given out when those atoms recombine into new arrangements. For example:

Bond energy calculations only ever give *estimates* of the amount of heat evolved or absorbed. They never give exact values. The strength of a bond varies slightly depending on what is around it in the molecule. Quoted bond energies are usually average values, which give fairly good, but not perfect, answers.

if:	heat needed to break all the bonds	=	+1000 kJ
and:	heat released when new bonds are made	=	−1200 kJ
then:	overall change	=	− 200 kJ

The reaction between methane and chlorine

$$CH_4(g) + Cl_2(g) \rightarrow CH_3Cl(g) + HCl(g)$$

Methane reacts with chlorine in the presence of ultra-violet light to produce chloromethane and hydrogen chloride. You can picture all the bonds being broken in the methane and chlorine and then being reformed in new ways in the products.

You can work out the heat needed to break all the bonds, and the heat given out as new ones are made.

Bonds that need to be broken:

4 C–H bonds	$= 4 \times (+413)$	$= +1652\,kJ$
1 Cl–Cl bond	$= 1 \times (+243)$	$= +243\,kJ$
Total		$= +1895\,kJ$

New bonds made:

3 C–H bonds	$= 3 \times (-413)$	$= -1239\,kJ$
1 C–Cl bond	$= 1 \times (-346)$	$= -346\,kJ$
1 H–Cl bond	$= 1 \times (-432)$	$= -432\,kJ$
Total		$= -2017\,kJ$

The overall energy change is $+1895 + (-2017)\,kJ = -122\,kJ$

The negative sign of the answer shows that, overall, heat is given out as the bonds rearrange. More energy is released when the new bonds were made than is used to break the old ones.

The excess heat given out means that the reaction is exothermic.

You can show all this happening on an energy diagram, as in Figure 25.2.

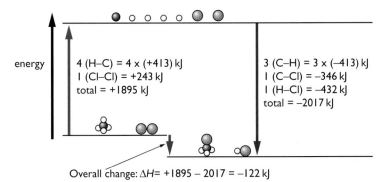

Overall change: $\Delta H = +1895 - 2017 = -122\,kJ$

Figure 25.2 *Methane reacts with chlorine to produce chloromethane and hydrogen chloride.*

The reaction between hydrogen and fluorine

Calculate the heat released or absorbed when this reaction occurs:

$$H_2(g) + F_2(g) \rightarrow 2HF(g)$$

The bond energies (in $kJ\,mol^{-1}$) are: H–H 436, F–F 158, H–F 568.

Important! The real reaction doesn't happen by all the bonds being broken in this way. That doesn't matter. The *overall* amount of heat released or absorbed is the same, however you do the reaction – even if one of the ways you use to work it out is entirely imaginary! This is summarised in an important law called Hess's law, which you will meet if you do Chemistry at a higher level.

Remember that when heat is given out, you show this by putting a negative sign in front of the value.

Bonds that need to be broken:

1 H–H bond	= 1 × (+436)	=	+436 kJ
1 F–F bond	= 1 × (+158)	=	+158 kJ
Total		=	+594 kJ

New bonds made:

2 H–F bonds	= 2 × (568)	=	–1136 kJ

The overall energy change is +594 +(–1136) = –542 kJ

Because the answer is negative, the reaction is exothermic.

Experimental work

It is easy to measure the amount of heat absorbed or given out during two different kinds of reaction. One involves solutions, and the other involves burning liquids.

Measuring energy changes involving solutions

Measuring the heat evolved when magnesium reacts with an acid

When magnesium reacts with dilute sulfuric acid, the mixture gets very warm. The reaction is:

$$Mg(s) + H_2SO_4(aq) \rightarrow MgSO_4(aq) + H_2(g)$$

$50\,cm^3$ of dilute sulfuric acid (a huge excess) is run into a polystyrene cup using a pipette or burette, and the temperature of the acid is measured. A small amount of magnesium powder is placed in a weighing bottle, and the mass of the bottle plus magnesium is recorded.

The magnesium is then tipped into the acid, and the maximum temperature reached is measured on the thermometer.

The mass of the empty weighing bottle is found, and then the experiment is repeated to check the reliability of the result.

Table 25.2 gives some results.

Volume of acid used = $50.0\,cm^3$

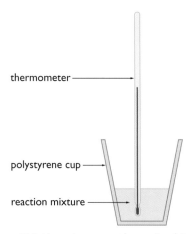

thermometer

polystyrene cup

reaction mixture

Figure 25.3 *Measuring energy changes involving solutions.*

These are real results produced by the author as part of a sample piece of coursework for an earlier GCSE book.

	Experiment 1	Experiment 2
mass of weighing bottle + Mg (g)	10.810	10.800
mass of weighing bottle afterwards (g)	10.687	10.685
mass of Mg used (g)	0.123	0.115
initial temperature (°C)	17.4	17.3
maximum temperature (°C)	27.5	26.7
temperature rise (°C)	10.1	9.4

Table 25.2: *Results for the reaction of magnesium with an acid.*

We will use the figures in Table 25.2 to work out how much heat is given out when 1 mole of magnesium reacts with 1 mole of sulfuric acid, according to the equation above.

If you do a reaction using a known mass of solution and measure the temperature rise, the amount of heat given out during the reaction is given by:

heat given out = mass × specific heat × temperature rise

The specific heat is the amount of heat needed to raise the temperature of 1 gram of a substance by 1 °C.

For water, the value is $4.18 \, J \, g^{-1} \, °C^{-1}$ (joules per gram per degree Celsius).

You can normally assume that dilute solutions have the same specific heat ($4.18 \, J \, g^{-1} \, °C^{-1}$) and density ($1 \, g \, cm^{-3}$; 1 gram per cubic centimetre) as water. You can also assume that negligibly small amounts of heat are used to warm up the cup and the thermometer.

In this case, we will take the mass of the solution as 50 g. The mass of the magnesium is so small that it can be ignored. There are other major sources of error in the experiment which will make much more difference to the results.

Calculations for Experiment 1:

Heat evolved when 0.123 g Mg reacts

$$= 50 × 4.18 × 10.1 \, J$$
$$= 2111 \, J$$

Refer back to Table 25.2 where necessary so that you can be sure where the numbers come from.

Energy changes in reactions are always quoted in kJ. Dividing by 1000 gives 2.111 kJ evolved when 0.123 g of Mg react.

Now we need to calculate how much heat is evolved when 24.3 g of Mg react. 24.3 is an accurate value for the relative atomic mass of magnesium.

If: 0.123 g Mg produce   2.111 kJ

then: 24.3 g Mg produce $\frac{24.3}{0.123} × 2.111 \, kJ = 417 \, kJ$

The amount of heat given out by the reaction is therefore:

$$Mg(s) + H_2SO_4(aq) \rightarrow MgSO_4(aq) + H_2(g) \qquad \Delta H = -417 \, kJ \, mol^{-1}$$

Remember: the negative sign shows that heat is evolved.

Calculations for Experiment 2:

Repeat this calculation yourself to be sure that you get the same answer.

If you repeat this for Experiment 2, you will get a value of $-415 \, kJ \, mol^{-1}$. That is in remarkable agreement with the first result. Unfortunately, it is quite wide of the accepted value for this reaction, which is $-466.9 \, kJ \, mol^{-1}$. The measured temperature rise isn't as high as it should be.

There are several reasons for this. We aren't allowing for the heat absorbed by the cup or the thermometer, but, more importantly, we aren't allowing for the heat lost from the surface of the liquid, in the spray that the reaction produces, and in the escaping hydrogen gas.

Other reactions you could use this method for

You could use this for neutralisation reactions (e.g. sodium hydroxide solution and dilute hydrochloric acid), displacement reactions (e.g. zinc and copper(II) sulfate solution), or for the heat evolved or absorbed in making solutions (e.g. dissolving sodium chloride in water).

Measuring the heat evolved in burning liquids

The most common use of this at GCSE is to measure the amount of heat given off when a number of small alcohols are burnt. You might perhaps use methanol, ethanol, propan-1-ol and butan-1-ol.

The alcohols are burnt in a small spirit burner, and the heat produced is used to warm up some water in a flask or other container.

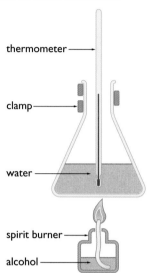

Figure 25.4 *Measuring the heat evolved in burning liquids.*

$100\,cm^3$ of cold water is put in a conical flask (or other container), and its temperature is recorded. The spirit burner is filled with the alcohol and weighed. Ideally, the burner will have a small cap to fit over the wick. If so, that is weighed as well. The apparatus is shielded as far as possible to prevent draughts.

Now the burner is placed under the flask (minus the cap), and lit. The water is stirred constantly with the thermometer until the temperature rises by, say, $40\,°C$. The flame is extinguished, and the cap immediately put over the wick. This stops any hot alcohol in the wick from evaporating. The maximum temperature reached is recorded.

Finally, the spirit burner plus remaining alcohol are reweighed.

The experiment can be repeated with the same alcohol to check the reliability, and then carried out again with whatever other alcohols are available.

Specimen results and calculation for ethanol

Volume of water	$= 100\,cm^3$
Mass of burner + ethanol before experiment	$= 37.355\,g$
Mass of burner + ethanol after experiment	$= 36.575\,g$
Original temperature of water	$= 21.5\,°C$
Final temperature of water	$= 62.8\,°C$
Mass of ethanol burnt	$= 0.780\,g$
Water temperature increase	$= 41.3\,°C$
Mass of water being heated	$= 100\,g$
Heat gained by water	$= 100 \times 4.18 \times 41.3\,J$
	$= 17260\,J$
	$= 17.26\,kJ$

Burning $0.780\,g$ of ethanol produces $17.26\,kJ$.

You may come across other versions of this experiment recommending a different temperature rise, or suggesting that you heat it for a fixed number of minutes. There's no ideal answer to this. The higher the temperature the water reaches, the greater the heat losses during the experiment. On the other hand, if you just increase the temperature of the water by a small amount, errors in reading the thermometer or finding the mass of the alcohol become important. Don't worry too much about this. This experiment is incapable of producing good results whatever you do!

You will find that results for these experiments are frequently quoted in terms of the amount of heat evolved per gram of alcohol. In this case . . .

Amount of heat produced when 1 g of ethanol burns $= \frac{17.26}{0.780}$ kJ

$= 22.1$ kJ

We are going to quote the final answer to three significant figures. In that case, you round intermediate answers to four significant figures.

However, it is much more useful to work out the amount of heat produced per mole of ethanol, CH_3CH_2OH. The mass of 1 mole of ethanol is 46 g.

The amount of heat produced from 1 mole of ethanol $= \frac{17.26}{0.780} \times 46$ kJ

$= 1020$ kJ

How accurate is this figure? The accepted value for ethanol is that 1370 kJ (to three significant figures) of heat are evolved when 1 mole of ethanol burns. The figure produced in this particular experiment is far too low. Why?

There are many sources of error – in particular, large amounts of heat losses. There is heat lost from the warming water; there is heat lost from the flame, which goes straight into the air rather than into the water. There is heat being used to raise the temperature of the flask and of the thermometer. Other errors of measurement (reading temperatures, weighing, etc.) are completely negligible compared with these.

That doesn't mean you can't use this experiment to make useful comparisons. If you repeat it with other alcohols, under as similar conditions as possible, you can find how the heat evolved changes as the alcohol gets bigger. The figures used in the following graphs are accurate ones, but inaccurate ones from school experiments would show the same trends.

Bar charts of heat evolved as the size of the alcohol increases

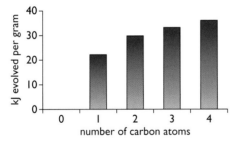

Figure 25.5 *Heat evolved per* **gram** *of alcohol against alcohol size.*

In Figure 25.5, notice that the amount of heat evolved gets greater as the alcohol gets bigger – but it isn't a regular increase. The change from one alcohol to the next gets smaller as the alcohol gets bigger. You may sometimes see this plotted as a smooth graph, but that is technically wrong. A smooth curve should only be used for a continuous variable – one which can take any value. There is no such thing as an alcohol with 0.5 or 1.64 carbon atoms! The number of carbon atoms is a non-continuous variable, because it can only take whole number values.

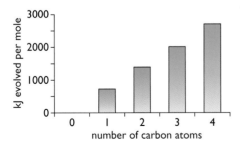

Figure 25.6 *Heat evolved per* **mole** *of alcohol against alcohol size.*

Notice that if you plot the heat evolved per mole, the increase becomes regular. Working it out *per mole* means that you are working from the same number of molecules each time. The difference between one alcohol and the next is always an extra CH_2, and so the number of extra bonds broken and made increases is a regular way. That means that the heat evolved will also increase in a regular way.

End of Chapter Checklist

You should now be able to:

✓ understand what is meant by bond energies (bond strengths), and know that energy is needed to break bonds and is released when bonds are made

✓ use bond energies to estimate the heat released or absorbed in simple reactions

✓ describe simple experiments to measure temperature changes during reactions involving solutions or burning liquids

✓ use the results from these experiments to calculate the heat energy changes in terms of kJ per gram or kJ per mole of reactant.

Questions

1 Use the bond energies in the table to estimate the amount of heat released or absorbed when the following reactions take place. In each case, say whether the change is exothermic or endothermic.

Bond	Bond energy (kJ mol⁻¹)
C–H	+413
C–Br	+290
Br–Br	+193
H–Br	+366
H–H	+436
Cl–Cl	+243
H–Cl	+432
O=O	+498
O–H	+464

a) $CH_4(g) + Br_2(g) \rightarrow CH_3Br(g) + HBr(g)$

(The structure of CH_3Br is the same as that of CH_3Cl; see Figure 25.2.)

b) $H_2(g) + Cl_2(g) \rightarrow 2HCl(g)$

c) $2H_2(g) + O_2(g) \rightarrow 2H_2O(g)$

2 A student investigated the amount of heat given out when hexane, C_6H_{14}, burns using the apparatus in Figure 25.4. Hexane is a highly flammable liquid which is one of the components of petrol (gasoline).

In each case, she calculated the amount of heat evolved per mole of hexane. Her first two experiments produced answers of 3200 and 3900 kJ mol⁻¹ of heat evolved. She then decided to do a third experiment. Her results were as follows:

volume of water in flask	$= 100\,cm^3$
mass of burner + hexane before experiment	$= 35.62\,g$
mass of burner + hexane after experiment	$= 35.23\,g$
original temperature of water	$= 19.0\,°C$
final temperature of water	$= 55.0\,°C$

a) Suggest a reason why the student decided to do a third experiment.

b) Apart from the obvious need to wear eye protection in all experimental work, suggest two other safety hazards that might arise during the experiment.

c) Use the results table to calculate the amount of heat in kJ evolved by the burning hexane during the experiment. (Specific heat of water = $4.18\,J\,g^{-1}\,°C^{-1}$; density of water = $1\,g\,cm^{-3}$.)

d) Calculate the amount of heat evolved per gram of hexane.

e) Calculate the amount of heat evolved per mole of hexane (RAMs: H = 1; C = 12).

f) To calculate the average value of the heat evolved per mole when hexane burns, the student took an average of her results. She decided not to use the figure of 3900 in calculating the average, because it was so different from the other two. Suggest any two reasons why it might have been higher than the others.

g) A data book gave a figure of 4194 kJ of heat evolved when 1 mole of hexane burns. Why are all the results in the student's experiment so much lower than this?

Chapter 26: Titration Calculations

Working with solution concentrations

Concentrations of solutions

Concentrations can be measured in either

- $g\,dm^{-3}$
- $mol\,dm^{-3}$

These are exactly the same as writing g/dm^3 and mol/dm^3. You read them as 'grams per cubic decimetre' and 'moles per cubic decimetre'. 1 cubic decimetre is the same as 1 litre.

You have to be able to convert between $g\,dm^{-3}$ and $mol\,dm^{-3}$. This is no different from converting moles into grams and *vice versa*. When you are doing the conversions in concentration sums, the amount of substance you are talking about happens to be dissolved in $1\,dm^3$ of solution. That doesn't affect the sum in any way.

$$\text{Number of moles} = \frac{\text{mass(g)}}{\text{mass of 1 mole (g)}}$$

A sample of sea water had a concentration of sodium chloride of $35.1\,g\,dm^{-3}$. Find its concentration in $mol\,dm^{-3}$ (RAMs: Na = 23; Cl = 35.5).

1 mol NaCl weighs $58.5\,g$

$35.1\,g$ is $\frac{35.1}{58.5}mol = 0.600\,mol$

The concentration of the NaCl is $0.600\,mol\,dm^{-3}$.

Converting from $mol\,dm^{-3}$ to $g\,dm^{-3}$

What is the concentration of a $0.050\,mol\,dm^{-3}$ solution of sodium carbonate, Na_2CO_3, in $g\,dm^{-3}$? (RAMs: C = 12; O = 16; Na = 23).

1 mol Na_2CO_3 weighs $106\,g$

$0.050\,mol$ weighs $0.050 \times 106\,g = 5.3\,g$

$0.050\,mol\,dm^{-3}$ is therefore $5.3\,g\,dm^{-3}$.

Making it as tricky as possible!

What is the concentration in $mol\,dm^{-3}$ of a solution containing $2.1\,g$ of sodium hydrogencarbonate, $NaHCO_3$, in $250\,cm^3$ of solution? (RAMs: H = 1; C = 12; O = 16; Na = 23).

The problem here is that the volume is wrong. The solid is dissolved in $250\,cm^3$ instead of $1000\,cm^3$ ($1\,dm^3$).

$250\,cm^3$ is $\frac{1}{4}$ of $1000\,cm^3$ ($1\,dm^3$).

Therefore a solution containing $2.1\,g$ in $250\,cm^3$ has the same concentration as one containing $4 \times 2.1\,g$ in $1000\,cm^3$.

In previous chapters we have looked at calculations from equations involving masses of solids and volumes of gases. Many reactions are done in solution, and this chapter looks at how you handle problems involving concentrations of solutions.

You may also find the symbol M used. For example, dilute hydrochloric acid might have a concentration quoted as 2 M. 'M' means '$mol\,dm^{-3}$' and is described as the **molarity** of the solution. You can also read '2 M' as '2 molar'. This is all unnecessarily confusing, and won't be used in this book.

Figure 26.1 *Sea water contains about 0.6 moles of NaCl per cubic decimetre.*

$4 \times 2.1\,g$ is $8.4\,g$.

1 mol $NaHCO_3$ weighs $84\,g$.

$8.4\,g$ is $\frac{8.4}{84}$ mol $= 0.10$ mol.

The concentration is therefore $0.10\,mol\,dm^{-3}$.

Calculations from equations involving solutions

A calculation involving hard water

A sample of hard water contained $0.002\,mol\,dm^{-3}$ of calcium hydrogencarbonate, $Ca(HCO_3)_2$. When this is heated, it decomposes to make calcium carbonate. This forms as a white precipitate known as limescale. Calculate the mass of calcium carbonate which could be formed when $100\,dm^3$ (100 litres) of the hard water is heated (RAMs: C = 12; O = 16; Ca = 40).

$$Ca(HCO_3)_2(aq) \rightarrow CaCO_3(s) + CO_2(g) + H_2O(l)$$

$1\,dm^3$ of hard water contains 0.002 mol of $Ca(HCO_3)_2$.

$100\,dm^3$ contains 100×0.002 mol $= 0.2$ mol.

The equation says that 1 mol of $Ca(HCO_3)_2$ gives 1 mol of $CaCO_3$.

That means that 0.2 mol of $Ca(HCO_3)_2$ gives 0.2 mol of $CaCO_3$.

1 mol $CaCO_3$ weighs $100\,g$.

0.2 mol weighs $0.2 \times 100\,g = 20\,g$.

$20\,g$ of calcium carbonate would be formed.

Another calculation involving hard water

Limescale can be removed from, for example, electric kettles by reacting it with a dilute acid such as the ethanoic acid present in vinegar.

$$CaCO_3(s) + 2CH_3COOH(aq) \rightarrow (CH_3COO)_2Ca(aq) + CO_2(g) + H_2O(l)$$

What mass of calcium carbonate can be removed by $50\,cm^3$ of a solution containing $2\,mol\,dm^{-3}$ of ethanoic acid? (RAMs: C = 12; O = 16; Ca = 40).

In any question of this sort, it is always a good policy to start by working out the number of moles of any substance where you know both the volume and the concentration. In this case, we know both of those for the ethanoic acid.

Number of moles of ethanoic acid $= \frac{50}{1000} \times 2 = 0.1$ mol

Now look at the equation, which says that 1 mol $CaCO_3$ reacts with 2 mol ethanoic acid.

That means that however many moles of ethanoic acid there are in the reaction, there will only be half as many moles of calcium carbonate.

Number of moles of $CaCO_3 = \frac{0.1}{2} = 0.05$ mol.

1 mol $CaCO_3$ weighs $100\,g$.

0.05 mol weighs $0.05 \times 100\,g = 5\,g$.

The ethanoic acid would react with $5\,g$ of calcium carbonate.

Figure 26.2 *Water becomes hard when carbon dioxide in rainwater reacts with limestone.*

Don't be scared that some of this is unfamiliar! As long as you realise that CH_3COOH is ethanoic acid, that's all you need worry about for this calculation.

If you aren't happy with this, put in an extra step. If there are 2 moles in $1000\,cm^3$ (because it is $2\,mol\,dm^{-3}$), work out how many there are in $1\,cm^3$ by dividing by 1000. That gives 0.002 mol. Multiply that by 50 to find out how many moles there are in $50\,cm^3$.

Calculations from titrations

A reminder about acid–alkali titrations

A solution of the alkali is measured into a conical flask using a pipette. The acid is run in from the burette – swirling the flask constantly. Towards the end, the acid is run in a drop at a time until the indicator just changes colour.

Figure 26.3 shows the end point of a titration using methyl orange as indicator. If the indicator changes to red (its acidic colour), you have added too much acid.

Figure 26.3 *The end point colour for methyl orange – the flask on the left shows the colour before the end point.*

The standard calculation

A simple titration problem will look like this:

$25.0\,cm^3$ of $0.100\,mol\,dm^{-3}$ sodium hydroxide solution required $23.5\,cm^3$ of dilute hydrochloric acid for neutralisation. Calculate the concentration of the hydrochloric acid.

$$NaOH(aq) + HCl(aq) \rightarrow NaCl(aq) + H_2O(l)$$

You do a titration to find the concentration of one solution, knowing the concentration of the other one.

Planning a route through the calculation

- Start with what you know most about. In this case, you know both the volume and the concentration of the sodium hydroxide solution. Work out how many moles of this you have got.

- Look at the equation to work out how many moles of hydrochloric acid that amount of sodium hydroxide reacts with.

- Work out the concentration of the hydrochloric acid.

Doing the calculation

The experiment used $25.0\,cm^3$ of $0.100\,mol\,dm^{-3}$ NaOH solution.

Number of moles of NaOH $= \frac{25.0}{1000} \times 0.100\,mol = 0.00250\,mol$.

The equation says that 1 mol NaOH reacts with 1 mol HCl.
Therefore $0.00250\,mol$ NaOH reacts with $0.00250\,mol$ HCl.

That $0.00250\,mol$ HCl must have been in the $23.5\,cm^3$ of hydrochloric acid that was added during the titration – otherwise neutralisation wouldn't have occurred.

All you need to do now is to find out how many moles there would be in $1000\,cm^3$ ($1\,dm^3$) of this solution.

If $23.5\,cm^3$ contain $0.00250\,mol$ HCl,
$1000\,cm^3$ contain $\frac{1000}{23.5} \times 0.00250\,mol$ HCl $= 0.106\,mol$.

The concentration is therefore $0.106\,mol\,dm^{-3}$.

Put in an extra step if you need to. Work out how many moles there are in $1\,cm^3$ by dividing 0.100 by 1000. (The concentration is $0.100\,mol$ in $1000\,cm^3$.) Then multiply by 25 to find out how many there are in $25\,cm^3$.

Again, insert an extra step if you need to. Work out the number of moles in $1\,cm^3$ by dividing by 23.5, and then multiply by 1000 to find out how many moles there are in $1000\,cm^3$.

A very slightly harder calculation

25 cm³ of sodium hydroxide solution of unknown concentration was titrated with dilute sulfuric acid of concentration 0.050 mol dm⁻³. 20.0 cm³ of the acid was required to neutralise the alkali. Find the concentration of the sodium hydroxide solution in mol dm⁻³.

$$2NaOH(aq) + H_2SO_4(aq) \rightarrow Na_2SO_4(aq) + 2H_2O(l)$$

This time, you know everything about the sulfuric acid.

The experiment used 20.0 cm³ of 0.050 mol dm⁻³ H_2SO_4.

Number of moles of sulfuric acid used $= \frac{20.0}{1000} \times 0.050$ mol

$= 0.0010$ mol.

> Use more steps for this, and for similar future problems, it you need to.

The equation proportions aren't 1:1 this time. That's what makes the calculation slightly different from the last one. The equation says that each mole of sulfuric acid reacts with 2 moles of sodium hydroxide.

Number of moles of sodium hydroxide $= 2 \times 0.0010$ mol

$= 0.0020$ mol

That 0.0020 mol must have been in the 25 cm³ of sodium hydroxide solution.

Concentration $= \frac{1000}{25} \times 0.0020$ mol dm⁻³

$= 0.080$ mol dm⁻³

A straightforward titration sum with a sting in the tail

Washing soda crystals have the formula $Na_2CO_3 \cdot nH_2O$. The object of this calculation is to find the number of molecules of water of crystallisation, n.

28.6 g of washing soda crystals were dissolved in pure water. More pure water was added to make the total volume of the solution up to 1000 cm³.

A 25.0 cm³ sample of this solution was neutralised by 40.0 cm³ of 0.125 mol dm⁻³ hydrochloric acid using methyl orange as indicator.

Figure 26.4 *Washing soda crystals.*

$$Na_2CO_3(aq) + 2HCl(aq) \rightarrow 2NaCl(aq) + CO_2(g) + H_2O(l)$$

(a) Calculate the concentration of the sodium carbonate solution in moles of sodium carbonate (Na_2CO_3) per cubic decimetre.

(b) Calculate the mass of Na_2CO_3 and mass of water in the washing soda crystals, and use those results to find a value for n in the formula $Na_2CO_3 \cdot nH_2O$ (RAMs: H = 1; C = 12; O = 16; Na = 23).

Part (a) is the straightforward titration calculation. Part (b) is an extra bit.

Part (a) – the titration calculation

You know the volume and concentration of the hydrochloric acid.

Number of moles of HCl $= \frac{40.0}{1000} \times 0.125$ mol

$= 0.00500$ mol.

From the equation, you can see that you only need half that number of moles of sodium carbonate.

Number of moles of Na_2CO_3 $= \frac{0.00500}{2}$ mol

$= 0.00250$ mol.

The sodium carbonate solution contained 0.00250 mol in $25.0\,cm^3$.

Concentration of Na_2CO_3 $= \frac{1000}{25.0} \times 0.00250$ mol dm^{-3}

$= 0.100$ mol dm^{-3}.

Part (b)

First calculate the mass of Na_2CO_3 in the total $1000\,cm^3$ ($1\,dm^3$) of solution. Remember that you have just worked out that the solution is 0.100 mol dm^{-3}.

1 mol Na_2CO_3 weighs $106\,g$.

0.100 mol Na_2CO_3 weighs $0.100 \times 106\,g = 10.6\,g$.

Now for the mass of water in the crystals:

The original mass of the crystals dissolved in the water was $28.6\,g$. Of this, we have worked out that $10.6\,g$ is Na_2CO_3.

Mass of water $= 28.6 - 10.6 = 18.0\,g$.

But 1 mol H_2O weighs $18\,g$.

There is therefore 1 mol of H_2O in the crystals together with the 0.100 mol of Na_2CO_3.

Since there are ten times as many moles of H_2O as of Na_2CO_3, the formula is $Na_2CO_3 \cdot 10H_2O$.

Reversing the calculations

Instead of working out the concentration of a solution using titration results, you may be asked to work out what volume of a solution is needed to neutralise something else. Here are two examples.

Example 1

Calculate the volume of 0.100 mol dm^{-3} sodium hydrogencarbonate solution needed to neutralise $20.0\,cm^3$ of 0.125 mol dm^{-3} hydrochloric acid.

$$NaHCO_3(aq) + HCl(aq) \rightarrow NaCl(aq) + CO_2(g) + H_2O(l)$$

As before, start from what you know most about – in this case the hydrochloric acid.

No of moles of HCl $= \frac{20.0}{1000} \times 0.125$ mol $= 0.00250$ mol

The equation shows that you will need the same number of moles of sodium hydrogencarbonate. At this point, you need to think about the concentration of the sodium hydrogencarbonate solution slightly differently from before.

Notice that we've only just got around to using the figure of $28.6\,g$, despite the fact that it was the very first number in the question. That is quite common in titration sums. You always start from the volume and concentration of the substance you know most about. In a GCSE exam, you would almost certainly be guided through a calculation as complicated as this.

A concentration of 0.100 mol dm^{-3} means that $1000\,cm^3$ contains 0.100 mol. That's obviously exactly the same as saying that 0.100 mol is contained in $1000\,cm^3$.

Students often feel uncomfortable with the step in the 'then' statement, because they aren't happy about dividing by the 0.100 value. The first part of the expression is calculating the volume which contains 1 mole, and then you multiply that by 0.00250 to find out what volume contains 0.00250 mol.

In a case like this, imagine you had an easy number, like 2, and work out what you would do with that. Suppose, for example, the concentration of the sodium hydrogencarbonate was 2 mol dm^{-3}. In that case, 2 mol would be contained in 1000 cm^3. To find the volume which contains 1 mol, you would divide by 2. You are going to do the same sort of thing whatever your number is. So if you would divide by a simple number like 2, you will also divide by a more complicated one like 0.100.

If: 0.100 mol of $NaHCO_3$ is contained in 1000 cm^3 (1 dm^3)

then: 0.00250 mol of $NaHCO_3$ is contained in $\frac{1000}{0.100} \times 0.00250 \text{ cm}^3$

$$= 25.0 \text{ cm}^3$$

You will need 25.0 cm^3 of the sodium hydrogencarbonate solution to neutralise the hydrochloric acid.

Example 2

It is possible to learn a fairly simple formula for doing these calculations in straightforward cases, but this is dangerous. If you get dependent on using a formula without understanding what you are doing, you are going to be totally lost if the example won't easily fit the formula. This example is deliberately designed to upset anyone using the commonest formula – because it won't work! However, if you have understood Example 1, the following question shouldn't be a problem to you.

A student was making up a solution of sodium hydroxide by dissolving 8.0 g of sodium hydroxide in water. Unfortunately, the beaker broke and the solution spilled onto the bench. All he had to hand to neutralise it was some 0.50 mol dm^{-3} sulfuric acid. What is the minimum volume of acid that he would have to use? (RAMs: $H = 1$; $O = 16$; $Na = 23$).

$$2NaOH(aq) + H_2SO_4(aq) \rightarrow Na_2SO_4(aq) + 2H_2O(l)$$

In the first example, we started by calculating the number of moles of the sodium hydrogencarbonate. This time, we've got all the information we need to calculate the number of moles of the sodium hydroxide, but it is in a different form.

1 mol NaOH weighs 40 g

8.0 g of NaOH is therefore $\frac{8.0}{40} \text{ mol} = 0.20 \text{ mol}$.

The equation shows that you only need half the number of moles of sulfuric acid to neutralise the sodium hydroxide.

Number of moles of H_2SO_4 needed $= \frac{0.20}{2} \text{ mol} = 0.10 \text{ mol}$.

If: 0.50 mol of H_2SO_4 is contained in 1000 cm^3 (1 dm^3)

then: 0.10 mol of H_2SO_4 is contained in $\frac{1000}{0.50} \times 0.10 \text{ cm}^3 = 200 \text{ cm}^3$.

You would need a minimum of 200 cm^3 of 0.50 mol dm^{-3} sulfuric acid to neutralise the sodium hydroxide spilt.

You should now be able to:

- ✓ convert concentrations from $g\,dm^{-3}$ to $mol\,dm^{-3}$ and *vice versa*
- ✓ calculate the number of moles of substance given a volume of solution and a concentration in $mol\,dm^{-3}$
- ✓ carry out simple calculations involving volumes and concentrations of solutions
- ✓ work out unknown concentrations from titration results
- ✓ use results from titrations to calculate other things, given guidance on method.

Questions

1 Some dilute sulfuric acid, H_2SO_4, had a concentration of $4.90\,g\,dm^{-3}$. What is its concentration in $mol\,dm^{-3}$? (RAMs: H = 1; O = 16; S = 32).

2 What is the concentration in $g\,dm^{-3}$ of some potassium hydroxide, KOH, solution with a concentration of $0.200\,mol\,dm^{-3}$? (RAMs: H = 1; O = 16; K = 39).

3 What mass of sodium carbonate, Na_2CO_3, would be dissolved in $100\,cm^3$ of solution in order to get a concentration of $0.100\,mol\,dm^{-3}$? (RAMs: C = 12; O = 16; Na = 23).

4 What mass of barium sulfate would be produced by adding excess barium chloride solution to $20.0\,cm^3$ of copper(II) sulfate solution of concentration $0.100\,mol\,dm^{-3}$? (RAMs: O = 16; S = 32; Ba = 137).

$BaCl_2(aq) + CuSO_4(aq) \rightarrow BaSO_4(s) + CuCl_2(aq)$

5 What is the maximum mass of calcium carbonate which will react with $25.0\,cm^3$ of $2.00\,mol\,dm^{-3}$ hydrochloric acid? (RAMs: C = 12; O = 16; Ca = 40).

$CaCO_3(s) + 2HCl(aq) \rightarrow CaCl_2(aq) + H_2O(l) + CO_2(g)$

6 Copper(II) sulfate crystals, $CuSO_4·5H_2O$, are made by adding an excess of copper(II) oxide to hot sulfuric acid, filtering the mixture and then crystallising the solution. What is the maximum mass of crystals that could be obtained by adding an excess of copper(II) oxide to $25\,cm^3$ of $1.0\,mol\,dm^{-3}$ sulfuric acid? (RAMs: H = 1; O = 16; S = 32; Cu = 64).

$CuO(s) + H_2SO_4(aq) \rightarrow CuSO_4(aq) + H_2O(l)$
$CuSO_4(aq) + 5H_2O(l) \rightarrow CuSO_4·5H_2O(s)$

7 **a)** Calculate the volume of $0.200\,mol\,dm^{-3}$ sulfuric acid needed to neutralise $25.0\,cm^3$ of $0.400\,mol\,dm^{-3}$ sodium hydroxide solution.

$2NaOH(aq) + H_2SO_4(aq) \rightarrow Na_2SO_4(aq) + 2H_2O(l)$

b) Calculate the minimum volume of $2.00\,mol\,dm^{-3}$ hydrochloric acid needed to react with $10.0\,g$ of calcium carbonate (RAMs: C = 12; O = 16; Ca = 40).

$CaCO_3(s) + 2HCl(aq) \rightarrow CaCl_2(aq) + H_2O(l) + CO_2(g)$

8 In each of these questions concerning simple titrations, calculate the unknown concentration in $mol\,dm^{-3}$.

a) $25.0\,cm^3$ of $0.100\,mol\,dm^{-3}$ sodium hydroxide was neutralised by $20.0\,cm^3$ of dilute nitric acid of unknown concentration.

$NaOH(aq) + HNO_3(aq) \rightarrow NaNO_3(aq) + H_2O(l)$

b) $25.0\,cm^3$ of sodium carbonate solution of unknown concentration was neutralised by $30.0\,cm^3$ of $0.100\,mol\,dm^{-3}$ nitric acid.

$Na_2CO_3(aq) + 2HNO_3(aq) \rightarrow 2NaNO_3(aq) + CO_2(g) + H_2O(l)$

c) $25.0\,cm^3$ of $0.250\,mol\,dm^{-3}$ potassium carbonate solution was neutralised by $12.5\,cm^3$ of ethanoic acid of unknown concentration.

$2CH_3COOH(aq) + K_2CO_3(aq) \rightarrow 2CH_3COOK(aq) + CO_2(g) + H_2O(l)$

9 Lime water is calcium hydroxide solution. In an experiment to find the concentration of calcium hydroxide in lime water, $25.0\,cm^3$ of lime water needed $18.8\,cm^3$ of $0.0400\,mol\,dm^{-3}$ hydrochloric acid to neutralise it.

$Ca(OH)_2(aq) + 2HCl(aq) \rightarrow CaCl_2(aq) + 2H_2O(l)$

Calculate the concentration of the calcium hydroxide in

a) $mol\,dm^{-3}$

b) $g\,dm^{-3}$

(RAMs: H = 1; O = 16; Ca = 40).

1. a) What do you understand by the term 'relative atomic mass' of an element? *(2 marks)*

   b) Show that the relative atomic mass of chlorine is 35.5, given that an average sample of chlorine contains 75% ^{35}Cl and 25% ^{37}Cl. *(2 marks)*

   c) Chlorine gas was bubbled through a solution containing 4.15 g of potassium iodide until no further reaction occurred. Calculate the mass of iodine produced by the reaction:

   $Cl_2(g) + 2KI(aq) \rightarrow 2KCl(aq) + I_2(s)$
   (relative atomic masses: K = 39; I = 127) *(4 marks)*

   d) Calculate the density of chlorine gas at room temperature and pressure in $g\,dm^{-3}$.

   (Volume of 1 mole of a gas at room temperature and pressure = $24.0\,dm^3$) *(2 marks)*

   Total 10 marks

2. In an experiment to find the empirical formula of some lead oxide, a small porcelain dish was weighed, filled with lead oxide, and weighed again. The dish was placed in a tube, and was heated in a stream of hydrogen. The hydrogen reduced the lead oxide to a bead of metallic lead. When the apparatus was cool, the dish with its bead of lead was weighed.

   Mass of porcelain dish = 17.95 g
   Mass of porcelain dish + lead oxide = 24.80 g
   Mass of porcelain dish + lead = 24.16 g
   (relative atomic masses: O = 16; Pb = 207)

   a) Calculate the mass of lead in the lead oxide. *(1 mark)*

   b) Calculate the mass of oxygen in the lead oxide. *(1 mark)*

   c) There are three different oxides of lead: PbO, PbO_2 and Pb_3O_4. Use your results from (a) and (b) to find the empirical formula of the oxide used in the experiment. *(3 marks)*

   d) Calculate the percentage by mass of lead in the oxide PbO_2. *(2 marks)*

   Total 7 marks

3. In an experiment to find the percentage of calcium carbonate in sand from a beach, 1.86 g of sand reacted with an excess of dilute hydrochloric acid to give 0.55 g of carbon dioxide.

   $CaCO_3(s) + 2HCl(aq) \rightarrow CaCl_2(aq) + H_2O(l) + CO_2(g)$

   a) Calculate the number of moles of carbon dioxide present in 0.55 g of CO_2 (relative atomic masses: C = 12; O = 16). *(2 marks)*

   b) How many moles of calcium carbonate must have been present in the sand to produce this amount of carbon dioxide? *(1 mark)*

   c) Calculate the mass of calcium carbonate present in the sand (relative atomic masses: C = 12; O = 16; Ca = 40). *(2 marks)*

   d) Calculate the percentage of calcium carbonate in the sand. *(1 mark)*

   Total 6 marks

4. a) Chalcopyrite is a copper-containing mineral with the formula $CuFeS_2$.

   (i) Calculate the percentage by mass of copper in pure chalcopyrite (relative atomic masses: S = 32; Fe = 56; Cu = 64). *(2 marks)*

   (ii) Analysis of a copper ore showed that it contained 50% chalcopyrite by mass. Assuming that all the copper can be extracted, what mass of copper could be obtained from 1 tonne (1000 kg) of the copper ore? *(2 marks)*

   b) Copper reacts with concentrated nitric acid to give copper(II) nitrate solution and nitrogen dioxide gas.

   $Cu(s) + 4HNO_3(aq) \rightarrow Cu(NO_3)_2(aq) + 2NO_2(g) + 2H_2O(l)$

   (i) Calculate the maximum mass of copper(II) nitrate, $Cu(NO_3)_2$, which could be obtained from 8.00 g of copper (relative atomic masses: N = 14; O = 16; Cu = 64). *(3 marks)*

   (ii) Calculate the volume of nitrogen dioxide produced at room temperature and pressure using 8.00 g of copper (volume of 1 mole of a gas at room temperature and pressure = $24.0\,dm^3$). *(2 marks)*

   Total 9 marks

5. If pyrite (FeS_2) is heated strongly in air, it reacts according to the equation:

   $4FeS_2(s) + 11O_2(g) \rightarrow 2Fe_2O_3(s) + 8SO_2(g)$

   Iron can be extracted from the iron(III) oxide produced, and the sulfur dioxide can be converted into sulfuric acid.

   a) Calculate the mass of iron(III) oxide that can be obtained from 480 kg of pure pyrite (relative atomic masses: O = 16; S = 32; Fe = 56). *(2 marks)*

   b) What mass of iron could be obtained by the reduction of the iron(III) oxide formed from 480 kg of pyrite? *(2 marks)*

   c) Calculate the volume of sulfur dioxide (measured at room temperature and pressure) produced from 480 kg of pyrite (volume of 1 mole of a gas at room temperature and pressure = $24.0\,dm^3$). *(3 marks)*

   d) The next stage of the manufacture of sulfuric acid is to convert the sulfur dioxide into sulfur trioxide.

   $2SO_2(g) + O_2(g) \rightarrow 2SO_3(g)$

   Calculate the volume of oxygen (measured at room temperature and pressure) needed for the complete conversion of the sulfur dioxide produced in (c) into sulfur trioxide. *(1 mark)*

   Total 8 marks

6. Strontium hydroxide, $Sr(OH)_2$, is only sparingly soluble in water at room temperature. In an experiment to measure its solubility, a student made a saturated solution of strontium hydroxide. She pipetted 25.0 cm³ of this solution into a conical flask, added a few drops of methyl orange indicator, and then titrated it with 0.100 mol dm⁻³ hydrochloric acid from a burette. She needed to add 32.8 cm³ of the acid to neutralise the strontium hydroxide.

$$Sr(OH)_2(aq) + 2HCl(aq) \rightarrow SrCl_2(aq) + 2H_2O(l)$$

a) Calculate the number of moles of HCl in 32.8 cm³ of 0.100 mol dm⁻³ hydrochloric acid. *(1 mark)*

b) How many moles of strontium hydroxide does that react with? *(1 mark)*

c) Calculate the concentration of the strontium hydroxide in mol dm⁻³. *(2 marks)*

d) Calculate the concentration of the strontium hydroxide solution in g dm⁻³ (relative atomic masses: H = 1; O = 16; Sr = 88). *(2 marks)*

Total 6 marks

7. a) What mass of sodium hydroxide (NaOH) must be dissolved to make 250 cm³ of solution with a concentration of 0.100 mol dm⁻³? (relative atomic masses: H = 1; O = 16; Na = 23). *(2 marks)*

b) 25.0 cm³ of this 0.100 mol dm⁻³ sodium hydroxide solution was neutralised by 20.0 cm³ of dilute sulfuric acid. Calculate the concentration of the sulfuric acid in mol dm⁻³.

$$2NaOH(aq) + H_2SO_4(aq) \rightarrow Na_2SO_4(aq) + 2H_2O(l)$$
(4 marks)

c) 1.00 dm³ of this same sulfuric acid was reacted with magnesium.

$$Mg(s) + H_2SO_4(aq) \rightarrow MgSO_4(aq) + H_2(g)$$

(i) What is the maximum mass of magnesium which would react with the acid? (relative atomic mass: Mg = 24). *(2 marks)*

(ii) What volume of hydrogen gas would be produced at room temperature and pressure? (volume of 1 mole of a gas at room temperature and pressure = 24.0 dm³). *(2 marks)*

Total 10 marks

8. a) During the electrolysis of concentrated copper(II) chloride solution using carbon electrodes, 0.64 g of copper was deposited on the cathode. Calculate the volume of chlorine (measured at room temperature and pressure) produced at the anode.

Cathode equation: $\qquad Cu^{2+}(aq) + 2e^- \rightarrow Cu(s)$

Anode equation: $\qquad 2Cl^-(aq) \rightarrow Cl_2(g) + 2e^-$

(relative atomic mass: Cu = 64; volume of 1 mole of a gas at room temperature and pressure = 24.0 dm³). *(2 marks)*

b) Magnesium is manufactured by electrolysing molten magnesium chloride ($MgCl_2$) in electrolytic cells operating at 250,000 amps.

Cathode equation: $\qquad Mg^{2+}(l) + 2e^- \rightarrow Mg(l)$
(relative atomic mass: Mg = 24; 1 faraday = 96,000 coulombs).

(i) Calculate the number of moles of electrons required to produce 1.20 tonnes of magnesium (1 tonne = 1000 kg). *(2 marks)*

(ii) Calculate the number of coulombs needed to produce this much magnesium. *(1 mark)*

(iii) How long (in hours) would it take to produce 1.20 tonnes of magnesium in a cell operating at 250,000 amps? *(2 marks)*

Total 7 marks

This Appendix is designed to help you answer the practically based questions you will find in the Edexcel IGCSE Chemistry papers.

Why is this appendix so important?

Chemistry is a practical subject. If you are lucky enough to be taught in a well equipped school, you will probably have done a lot of practical work, and most of this Appendix will already be familiar to you. However, not everybody is so fortunate.

Of the possible marks in your Chemistry exams, 20% will be given to questions designed to find out whether you have some important laboratory skills. If you have done a lot of practical work, that shouldn't be a problem. If you haven't, this Appendix is here to help you.

Safety

As part of a question, you might be asked to comment on what safety precautions are needed during a particular experiment.

The obvious precaution is to **wear eye protection**. That's true of **all** practical work in chemistry. However, you might be asked a question that says 'Apart from wearing eye protection, explain a safety precaution that you would need to take in doing this experiment. (*2 marks*)'.

Notice the word 'explain' in the last sentence. 'Explain' means that, as well as giving a precaution, you have to give a reason for it. Look at the number of marks available. If there is more than 1 mark, you have to give more than one piece of information.

Presence of:	**Precaution and reason** (marks)
poisonous gas, e.g. chlorine.	Do the experiment in a fume cupboard (1), because chlorine is poisonous (1).
corrosive liquid, e.g. acid or sodium hydroxide solution.	Clear up spills with a lot of water (1), because the acid (or whatever) is corrosive (1).
flammable liquid, e.g. ethanol.	Keep away from naked flames (1), because the ethanol might catch fire (1).
any hot liquid or apparatus.	Take care not to touch (1), in case you burn yourself (for solids) or scald yourself (for liquids) (1).
any especially fragile apparatus, e.g. pipette or thermometer.	Be careful not to break the fragile pipette (1), because you might cut yourself (1).

Table A1: *Other possible precautions.*

This is all fairly obvious when it is pointed out to you, but if your practical experience is limited, you might not think of it under exam conditions.

Choosing and using measuring equipment

If you want to measure the mass of something, you would use a balance. If you want to measure a temperature, you would use a thermometer. That's obvious. It isn't quite so obvious, though, when it comes to volumes. In this case, you have a number of choices, and it is important to pick the right one.

Choices include: measuring cylinders of various sizes, burettes, pipettes and gas syringes.

Measuring volumes of liquid

Measuring cylinders

Measuring cylinders are fine for approximate volumes. Choose the smallest measuring cylinder that will take the volume you need. Trying to measure, say, $8\,cm^3$ in a $100\,cm^3$ measuring cylinder is going to be fairly inaccurate. Use a $10\,cm^3$ cylinder instead.

Pipettes

Pipettes will measure the volume printed on them very accurately (typically to within $0.05\,cm^3$). Common pipettes have volumes of 25 or $10\,cm^3$, but you may also come across other sizes, such as 5, 20 or $50\,cm^3$.

Burettes

The most common size of burette will measure variable volumes up to $50\,cm^3$, and you can take measurements to the nearest $0.05\,cm^3$.

Measuring volumes of gas

To measure the volume of a gas you are collecting, you can either use a gas syringe, or collect it into an inverted measuring cylinder over water. You will find diagrams for both methods on page 47. A gas syringe is more accurate, and has to be used if the gas is soluble in water.

Taking readings

You take your measurement from the bottom of the meniscus (if you have a liquid) – ignoring any liquid that has 'curled up' at the sides. Edexcel examiners expect you to read a scale to an accuracy of half the smallest divisions marked on whatever piece of apparatus you are using. If the smallest division is $0.1\,cm^3$, you are expected to estimate the volume to the nearest $0.05\,cm^3$ if the meniscus falls between two marks.

The diagram shows a burette reading of $5.85\,cm^3$. Be very careful to look closely at which way the scale runs. Many students would make the mistake of reading this as $6.15\,cm^3$, because they don't notice that the meniscus is somewhere between 5 and 6 on the scale. Don't just read from the nearest number – think about what you are doing!

If you are reading a thermometer, the process is the same – unless it is a mercury thermometer. In that case, the surface of the mercury curls the other way, and you would read from the top of the meniscus. Don't worry too much about this. In an exam, it is usually fairly obvious what you should be reading. Just take care in using the scale.

Recording readings

The number you write down should show the degree of accuracy used. For example, if a burette reading happened to fall exactly on the $11\,cm^3$ line, you should record it as $11.00\,cm^3$, because it was possible to read it to $0.05\,cm^3$ – and your answer wasn't 11.05 or $10.95\,cm^3$. Recording it as $11\,cm^3$ implies that you couldn't read it more accurately than to the nearest $1\,cm^3$.

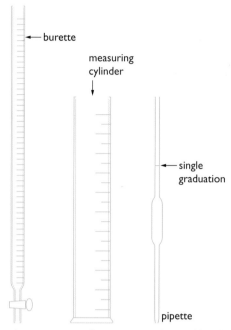

Figure A1 *Devices for measuring volumes of liquid.*

Figure A2 *Measuring from the bottom of the meniscus.*

Tables of results

Drawing up a table

Table A2 contains some real measurements that the author took during a piece of practical work to measure the heat evolved when magnesium reacted with dilute hydrochloric acid. Ignore the bottom row for the moment.

Volume of acid used = $50\,cm^3$

Notice that the figure for volume of acid shows how accurately it was measured.

Notice the figure of 11.0 °C in the third column of Table A2. That shows that the temperature was measured accurate to 0.1 of a degree.

	Experiment		
	1	2	3
Mass of weighing bottle plus Mg (g)	10.807	10.806	10.820
Mass of weighing bottle afterwards (g)	10.684	10.689	10.687
Mass of Mg used (g)	0.123	0.117	0.133
Initial temperature (°C)	17.4	17.5	17.4
Maximum temperature (°C)	27.5	27.4	28.4
Temperature rise (°C)	10.1	9.9	11.0
Accuracy check – temperature rise per gram of Mg (°C/g)	82.1	(84.6)	82.7

Table A2: *Results from an experiment to measure the heat evolved when magnesium reacts with dilute hydrochloric acid.*

Notice that Table A2 contains both measured and calculated results (the mass of Mg used, and the temperature rise). Notice that every row and column is properly labelled – including units, wherever appropriate. Column or row headings for things such as mass, temperature, volume and time are useless unless the units are included, and you will lose marks for leaving them out.

If you have measured something like time in a variety of units while you were doing the experiment, you must change them to one consistent unit before you draw up your table. For example, if you have measured times of 15 s, 30 s, 45 s, 1 min, 1 min 30 s, 2 min, 5 min, you must convert them all to seconds before you can make use of them.

Reliability of results

If you just produce one set of results, you can't be sure that you haven't made a mistake somewhere. Experiments have to be repeated to check their reliability. **Reliable results are those that are in close agreement – but not necessarily the same**. All practical work has built-in errors, which you can't avoid. If you have two results exactly the same, that's just luck!

If you are asked how you would improve the reliability of a set of results, say that you would repeat the experiment (possibly more than once), and check the new results for consistency with the old ones. If two sets of results agree closely and a third doesn't, then you discard the third set of results.

How can you tell whether your results are consistent and reliable? In Table A2, the last row calculates the temperature rise per gram of magnesium used. In this experiment, that result should be consistent if your experiment is reliable.

Notice that two values are in close agreement, but the other one is slightly different. When you were doing calculations from these results, you would omit the results from experiment 2, because they aren't likely to be quite as reliable as the others.

Processing the results

Graphs

Drawing good graphs

It may sound obvious, but the most important tool you need is a **very** sharp pencil. You can't draw a good graph with a pen – and, of course, it is impossible to rub out a mistake.

In an exam, you are likely to be given a graph grid, probably with at least one axis unlabelled. Choose a scale that uses as much of the graph paper as possible, but without making it really difficult to plot the points. Label each axis clearly (in ink), and don't forget the units. Plot the points carefully and, if any don't seem to be following the general pattern (towards a straight line or a smooth curve), double-check them.

Anomalous results

Edexcel examiners may include one result that is clearly wrong, because it falls well away from the pattern of the others. They call this an **anomalous result**, and will usually ask you to draw a circle around it. They may also ask you to explain what might have caused it. When you are drawing your straight line or curve, you ignore the anomalous point completely.

Your explanation should be as precise as you can make it. Decide whether the point is too high or too low on the graph, then try to think of an experimental reason why that might have happened. It isn't enough to say simply that 'wrong measurements were taken' – you have to be much more precise. For example, 'Too much calcium carbonate was added by mistake, and that produced too much carbon dioxide'.

The best (in fact, the only) way of being sure what the examiners want in this sort of case is to look at mark schemes and Examiners' Reports from past papers. You will find more about this at the end of this Appendix.

Straight line graphs

Most (but not all) straight line graphs that you will get at GCSE will go through the origin (0,0). Does your graph look as if it is going to go through the origin? If so, is it **reasonable** that it should go through the origin?

For example, if you were plotting results from a reaction between calcium carbonate and hydrochloric acid, it would be reasonable that if you didn't use any calcium carbonate, you wouldn't get any carbon dioxide. On the other hand, if you were plotting rates of reaction against temperature, it isn't reasonable to assume that a reaction rate would be zero if the temperature was $0\,°C$. If it does go through the origin, that's really helpful, because it gives you one absolutely certain point.

Suppose you were plotting a graph from an experiment reacting small amounts of calcium carbonate with dilute hydrochloric acid (Table A3). You are trying to find the relationship between the volume of carbon dioxide produced and the mass of calcium carbonate used.

Mass $CaCO_3$ (g)	0.020	0.040	0.060	0.080	0.100	0.120
Vol CO_2 (cm³)	3	10	13	13	24	31

Table A3: *Volume of carbon dioxide produced and mass of calcium carbonate used when reacting calcium carbonate with dilute hydrochloric acid.*

The graph must also go through (0,0) as explained above.

Figure A3 is just a sketch graph of these figures. You would need to draw this yourself on graph paper to see exactly how the points should lie.

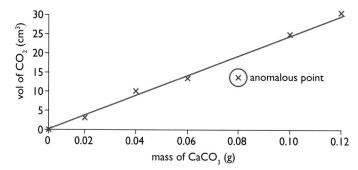

Figure A3 *Volume of carbon dioxide produced versus mass of calcium carbonate used.*

This is a best fit line, and the anomalous point hasn't been included. **It mustn't be – it is obviously wrong!** When you draw a best fit line, make sure that you have an even spread of points each side of the line you have drawn. Don't worry if it only goes through one or two of your points. In this case, the only point you are certain about is (0,0) – your line **must** go through (0,0) in this particular experiment.

Straight lines must be drawn with a ruler. If you draw a straight line freehand, you will lose marks.

Curved graphs

Exactly the same principles apply, except that it is more difficult to draw a smooth curve than a straight line. The line should still be a 'best fit' curve and, again, you shouldn't include any anomalous point(s) when you draw it. Don't assume that the curve must go through the origin. In Figure A4, it won't.

Figure A4 shows how the rate at which oxygen was given off during a reaction varied with temperature. These are imaginary results just to illustrate a point. They don't relate to any real experiment.

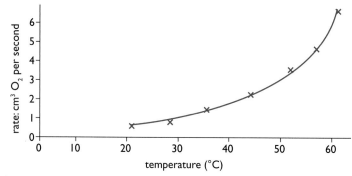

Figure A4 *The rate of an imaginary reaction against temperature.*

In a case like this, you might be asked how you would modify the experiment to obtain more results between 0 and 20 °C. The obvious thing to do would be to cool the substances you are going to react together, before you mix them, by surrounding them with ice. More than once in the past, examiners have commented that students often suggested moving the experiment to a colder climate. You won't get credit for that!

If you are going to be drawing a lot of graphs in the future (because you are going to do maths or science subjects at a higher level, for example), it is really worth buying a flexible rubber ruler designed for the job. Do an internet search for **flexible ruler**. Don't confuse the chunky rubber rulers for drawing graphs, which stay in whatever shape you put them, with plastic rulers that will bend, but return to their original shape when you let them go. Those are very difficult to use to draw curves without an extra pair of hands!

This is an excellent example of why it is essential to look at mark schemes for past papers and read Examiners' Reports. They point out the sort of answers they **won't** accept. If you have read it, you won't make the same mistake yourself, and so won't waste marks. If you were unlucky, one mark lost for a silly reason could be the difference between an A* and an A, or a C and a D, or whatever else might be important to you.

Graphs with unusual shapes

Occasionally, you might be given results that increase for a bit, and then decrease again. The final graph might be two intersecting straight lines, or a curve, as shown in Figure A5.

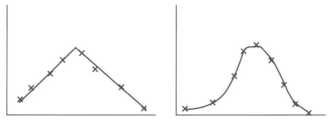

Figure A5 *Plotting unusual curves.*

You need to look carefully at how the points fall to see which of these you need to draw. You may well find a clue in the question – for example, the use of the word 'curve' at some point.

As a follow-on from graphs of this kind, you might be asked how you could improve their accuracy. The answer is to take more readings around what is known as the 'turning point' of the graph. With either of these graphs (but especially the curve), what you draw would be more accurate if you had more points around the peak in each case.

Bar charts

Bar charts are easy to draw. Don't forget to label them.

Describing the relationships shown by a graph

Look back at the straight line graph in Figure A3. What does it show? The correct expression is that 'the volume of carbon dioxide is **directly proportional to** the mass of calcium carbonate used'. If you just say that 'as the mass of calcium carbonate increases, the volume of carbon dioxide increases', that isn't precise enough, and you probably won't get the mark. That faulty statement could equally well describe a curve.

The graph in Figure A4 is more difficult to describe. You can start by saying that as the temperature increases, the rate gets faster, but you have to make the point that the line is curved. The examiners commented on a similar question by saying that they were looking for words like 'non-linear' or 'exponential'. You could say something like 'The rate increases exponentially with temperature'. That suggests a strong upward curve.

Technically, the term 'exponential increase' has a precise mathematical meaning, which won't necessarily apply to all curves that look like this. However, if in the past an Examiners' Report recommends you to use the term, they can hardly turn around later and say that it is wrong!

Calculating results

You will find that the calculations involved with these questions are usually easy, often with a simple formula that you have to slot numbers into. Two things need a comment.

Calculating averages

This is a simple thing to do, but if you are calculating an average from a number of results that include one or more inconsistent ones, you would normally just take the average of the consistent ones, and ignore the others.

For example, with good titration technique you should get results that are consistent to within $0.10\,cm^3$. Suppose your actual results were

21.20   21.45 $21.30\,cm^3$

You have two consistent results (21.20 and 21.30), and one that is outside the usual limits of consistency for a titration. Take the average of the two consistent ones ($21.25\,cm^3$) and ignore the other one.

Significant figures

You shouldn't quote an answer to more significant figures than the least accurate piece of information you are using in the calculation.

For example, if you are measuring a volume of gas as, say, $28\,cm^3$, and a mass of solid of, say, $1.325\,g$, and use both those figures in your calculation, you can't quote your answer to more than two significant figures, because that's all the least accurate number (the volume) is quoted to.

And be careful when you round numbers to the correct number of significant figures. Remember that you are rounding them – not just chopping off the unwanted figures from your number. So, for example:

12.382651 on your calculator rounds to 12.4 to three sig figs – **not** 12.3.

Remember that you round a 5 or greater upwards; anything less than 5, you round down. For example:

2.465 rounds to 2.47 to three sig figs;

2.464 rounds to 2.46 to three sig figs.

Modifying experiments

Suppose you were given a question involving rates of reaction – for example, the decomposition of hydrogen peroxide in the presence of manganese(IV) oxide as a catalyst. The results you are given are designed to show how the temperature of the reaction affects the rate. At the end of the question, you might then be asked to suggest how you would find out how changing the concentration of the hydrogen peroxide affects the rate, or how changing the quantity of catalyst affects it.

What you are asked to do has got to be fairly simple, because the number of marks available isn't going to be more than about 3–5. In an IGCSE Chemistry exam, you are working at the rate of about 1 mark per minute – and that includes thinking time. There are two things you must keep in mind in answering a question like this.

Be precise about what you are talking about

Don't use vague expressions like 'I would change the amount of hydrogen peroxide.' Avoid the word 'amount' entirely. If you are talking about a solution, say whether you are intending to change the volume of the solution, or its concentration. If you are talking about a solid, say whether you are talking about changing its mass, or how many moles of it you have got, or its surface area. You must be precise in order to get the mark

Make sure you are describing a fair test

Whatever it is that you are changing, **that must be the only thing which changes from one experiment to the next**. If you are changing the concentration of one solution, the concentration of every other solution involved must stay the same as before. The total volume must stay the same. The temperature must stay the same. The mass of any solid must stay the same, and so must its state of division (powder, small lumps, big lumps, and so on), so that its surface area stays the same.

The only way to be sure that you know what sort of things the examiners want is to look carefully at similar questions they have asked in the past, together with the mark schemes and the examiners' comments.

Maximising your success

The very best way of revising for the exam at the end of your course is to work through past papers set by your examiners – looking especially at the most recent ones. You need to check your answers against the published mark schemes and against the comments in the Examiners' Reports. The Examiners' Reports are particularly useful for these practically based questions, where what they are looking for isn't always obvious.

This book was written for the new Edexcel IGCSE Chemistry specification (syllabus) to be examined for the first time in 2011, so in the early stages there will be a shortage of past papers tied directly to the new specification. In that case, you will have to look instead at the questions set in similar exams in the past.

In the new specification, practically based questions are mixed up with more theoretical ones in the same exam papers. Previously, there was a separate paper in which all the practical questions were found.

On the website accompanying this book, you will find advice about how to get hold of past papers, mark schemes and reports for the new specification as soon as they become available after May 2011 (the first exam for the new specification).

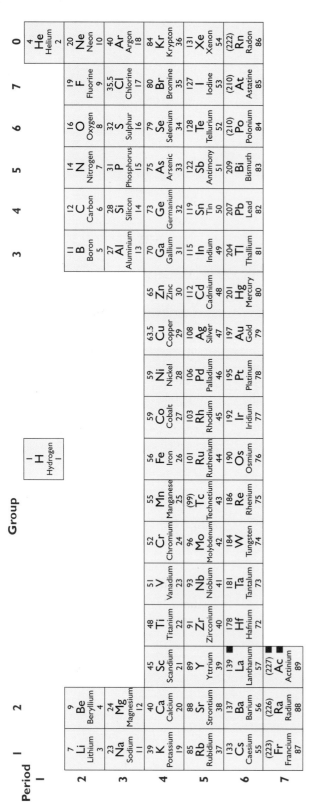

Group

Period	1	2		3	4	5	6	7	0
1									4 He Helium 2
			1 H Hydrogen 1						
2	7 Li Lithium 3	9 Be Beryllium 4		11 B Boron 5	12 C Carbon 6	14 N Nitrogen 7	16 O Oxygen 8	19 F Fluorine 9	20 Ne Neon 10
3	23 Na Sodium 11	24 Mg Magnesium 12		27 Al Aluminium 13	28 Si Silicon 14	31 P Phosphorus 15	32 S Sulphur 16	35.5 Cl Chlorine 17	40 Ar Argon 18

Transition elements:

Period	3	4	5	6	7	8	9	10	11	12
4	45 Sc Scandium 21	48 Ti Titanium 22	51 V Vanadium 23	52 Cr Chromium 24	55 Mn Manganese 25	56 Fe Iron 26	59 Co Cobalt 27	59 Ni Nickel 28	63.5 Cu Copper 29	65 Zn Zinc 30
5	89 Y Yttrium 39	91 Zr Zirconium 40	93 Nb Niobium 41	96 Mo Molybdenum 42	(99) Tc Technetium 43	101 Ru Ruthenium 44	103 Rh Rhodium 45	106 Pd Palladium 46	108 Ag Silver 47	112 Cd Cadmium 48
6	139 La Lanthanum 57 ◼	178 Hf Hafnium 72	181 Ta Tantalum 73	184 W Tungsten 74	186 Re Rhenium 75	190 Os Osmium 76	192 Ir Iridium 77	195 Pt Platinum 78	197 Au Gold 79	201 Hg Mercury 80
7	(227) Ac Actinium 89 ◼									

Period 4 group 3–7/0: 70 Ga Gallium 31, 73 Ge Germanium 32, 75 As Arsenic 33, 79 Se Selenium 34, 80 Br Bromine 35, 84 Kr Krypton 36

Period 5 group 3–7/0: 115 In Indium 49, 119 Sn Tin 50, 122 Sb Antimony 51, 128 Te Tellurium 52, 127 I Iodine 53, 131 Xe Xenon 54

Period 6 group 3–7/0: 204 Tl Thallium 81, 207 Pb Lead 82, 209 Bi Bismuth 83, (210) Po Polonium 84, (210) At Astatine 85, (222) Rn Radon 86

Period 6 group 1–2: 133 Cs Caesium 55, 137 Ba Barium 56

Period 7 group 1–2: (223) Fr Francium 87, (226) Ra Radium 88

Lanthanide series:

140 Ce Cerium 58	141 Pr Praseodymium 59	144 Nd Neodymium 60	(147) Pm Promethium 61	150 Sm Samarium 62	152 Eu Europium 63	157 Gd Gadolinium 64	159 Tb Terbium 65	163 Dy Dysprosium 66	165 Ho Holmium 67	167 Er Erbium 68	169 Tm Thulium 69	173 Yb Ytterbium 70	175 Lu Lutetium 71

Actinide series:

232 Th Thorium 90	(231) Pa Protoactinium 91	238 U Uranium 92	(237) Np Neptunium 93	(242) Pu Plutonium 94	(243) Am Americium 95	(247) Cm Curium 96	(247) Bk Berkelium 97	(251) Cf Californium 98	(254) Es Einsteinium 99	(253) Fm Fermium 100	(256) Md Mendelevium 101	(254) No Nobelium 102	(257) Lr Lawrencium 103

Key:

a = relative atomic mass
X = atomic symbol
b = atomic number

a
X
Name
b

(Masses in brackets are the mass numbers
of the most stable isotope)

Index